SHORT STORIES FOR DISCUSSION

SHORT STORIES for DISCUSSION

EDITED BY

ALBERT K. RIDOUT

Head of the English Department

Pelham Memorial High School Pelham, New York

JESSE STUART

Poet, Novelist and Short Story Writer

Greenup, Kentucky

CHARLES SCRIBNER'S SONS

New York

A–4.65[V]

PRINTED IN THE UNITED STATES OF AMERICA
LIBRARY OF CONGRESS CATALOG CARD NUMBER 65-16698

5-8197

Acknowledgments

The authors are indebted to the following authors, publishers, and other holders of copyright for permission to use copyrighted materials.

Heywood Hale Broun and Constance M. Broun for "The Fifty-First Dragon," copyright 1921, 1941 by Heywood Hale Broun.

J. M. Dent & Sons Limited, acting on behalf of the Trustees of the Joseph Conrad Estate, for "The Tale."

Devin-Adair Company for "The Wild Duck's Nest" from *The Game Cock* by Michael McLaverty, published in 1947.

Doubleday & Company, Inc. for "Jamesie" copyright 1947 by J. F. Powers, from the book, *Prince of Darkness and Other Stories* by J. F. Powers.

E. P. Dutton & Co., Inc. for "The Lion-Tamer" from the book *The Lion Tamer and Other Stories* by Bryan MacMahon. Copyright, 1949, by Bryan MacMahon. Dutton Paperback Series.

Esquire, Inc. and Jesse Stuart for "Rain on Tanyard Hollow," first published in *Esquire Magazine*, © 1941 by Esquire, Inc.

Farrar, Straus & Giroux, Inc. for "The First Seven Years" reprinted from *The Magic Barrel* by Bernard Malamud. Copyright © 1950, 1958 by Bernard Malamud.

Harcourt, Brace & World, Inc. for "Learn to Say Good-by" copyright, 1951, by Jessamyn West. Reprinted from her volume *Love, Death, and*

ACKNOWLEDGMENTS (continued)

The Ladies' Drill Team. First published in *The New Yorker.* For "Livvie Is Back" copyright, 1942, by Eudora Welty. Reprinted from her volume *The Wide Net and Other Stories.* For "Mr. Kaplan's Hobo" from *The Education of Hyman Kaplan* by Leonard Q. Ross, copyright, 1937, by Harcourt, Brace & World, Inc. First published in *The New Yorker.*

Alfred A. Knopf, Inc. for "The Bride Comes to Yellow Sky." Reprinted by permission from *Stephen Crane: An Omnibus,* edited by Robert Wooster Stallman. Published 1952 by Alfred A. Knopf, Inc. For "The Garden Party" copyright, 1922, by Alfred A. Knopf, Inc. Renewed, 1950 by J. Middleton Murry. Reprinted from *The Short Stories of Katherine Mansfield* by permission of the publisher.

Emily Lewis (Mrs. Hiram Norcross) and the American Book Company for "Little Boy Blue."

J. B. Lippincott Company for "The Quiet Man," from *Take Your Choice* by Maurice Walsh. Copyright 1933, 1961, by Curtis Publishing Co. Published by J. B. Lippincott Co.

Harold Ober Associates Incorporated for "The Egg," copyright © 1920, 1948 by Eleanor Anderson. Published originally in *The Dial* Magazine, 1920 and also in *The Triumph of The Egg* (B. W. Huebsch).

Frank O'Connor and A. D. Peters & Co., London, for "The Idealist" originally published in *The New Yorker*, February 18, 1950.

Random House, Inc. for "The Tall Men" copyright 1941 by The Curtis Publishing Company. Reprinted from *Collected Stories of William Faulkner,* by permission of Random House, Inc.

Charles Scribner's Sons for "A Woman With A Past" (copyright 1930 The Curtis Publishing Company; renewal copyright © 1958 The Curtis Publishing Company and Frances Scott Fitzgerald Lanahan) from *Taps at Reveille* by F. Scott Fitzgerald. For "Haircut" (copyright 1925 Ellis A. Lardner; renewal copyright 1953) from *The Love Nest and Other Stories* by Ring Lardner. For "Ha'Penny" from *Tales From A Troubled Land* by Alan Paton. Copyright © 1961 Alan Paton. For "In Another Country" (copyright 1927 Charles Scribner's Sons; renewal copyright © 1955) from *Men Without Women* by Ernest Hemingway. For "One of the Girls in Our Party" (copyright 1935 Charles Scribner's Sons; renewal copyright © 1963 Paul Gitlin) from *From Death To Morning* by Thomas Wolfe. For "The Rivals" from *King of the Mountain* by George Garrett. Copyright © 1957 George Garrett.

Jessica Jane Stuart for "Bright Moment," by permission of the author.

The Viking Press, Inc. for "Across the Bridge" from *21 Stories* by Graham Greene. Copyright 1949 by Graham Greene. For "The Story-Teller" by Saki, from *The Short Stories of Saki* by Saki. Copyright 1930, 1957, by The Viking Press, Inc.

Our acknowledgments would not be complete were we not to express our thanks to the boys and girls of Pelham Memorial High School and to Miss Carol Bell, one of their teachers, for their help in the appraisal of these stories. Our thanks, too, to Ruth M. Ridout, who assisted in many invaluable ways.

We are particularly indebted to Mr. Paul Millane of Charles Scribner's Sons for more than a year of valuable suggestions, patient understanding, and thoughtful editing of this work.

Contents

Preface

These stories should appeal especially to college preparatory students of the senior high school. The questions which follow each story are essentially a part of a program of learning.

We have attempted to pose questions that will lead the student into thinking: finding evidence, drawing conclusions, and answering intelligently. Perhaps there is some relation between the nature of these questions and those of the works on programed instruction. Many of the questions are designed to suggest answers by drawing upon knowledge the student already possesses but which he may not have used in similar contexts. In several instances, a question that may have caused initial difficulty is answered indirectly in subsequent questions in the same section.

For a few stories there are many questions. Such stories may well be read first as the questions for those stories were designed to introduce technical terms, to help the student to look for significant details, and to point out techniques used by the authors. Other stories, such as Faulkner's "The Tall Men," which might be read toward the end of the unit or course, are followed by questions of a more general, philosophic nature. It is suggested that the teacher begin with such stories as "The Tell-Tale Heart," "The Minister's Black Veil," "The Tale," "The Rivals," and "Haircut."

Students should study the questions and formulate their answers in advance of class discussion. During the class period, the responses of various students and the directed discussion will help to stress the proper responses and to correct the erroneous ones.

After reading these stories, many students may want to attempt writing their own stories. A special section of this book contains a number of short short stories. Ambitious students should have their attention called to that section and to Mr. Stuart's chapter on how he writes his stories.

Some Introductory Notes

Because the short story is an important form of writing, it is helpful to understand what a short story is and how it differs from nonfiction, such as the essay or the article, as well as from other fiction, such as the novel.

The short story has often been associated with the idea of *oneness of impression.* This impression is attained by developing a single incident in one locale, with a small group of characters, and covering a single, relatively short span of time. For prose to qualify as a short story, it must also be fictitious, and not be exact description of an actual happening.

But such a definition of the short story is not always applicable, therefore another must be constructed. To begin with, *the short story is prose writing rather than verse.* Although the short story is neither verse nor poetry, it may have a rhythmic pattern, as in some of the stories of Ernest Hemingway. You can feel the rhythm in the first two sentences of "In Another Country," on page 182 of this book. The short story may even contain images such as the following from "A Woman With A Past," by F. Scott Fitzgerald, on page 98:

> Since then, Adele had probably painted him a neat little landscape of Josephine's past.

Despite the fact that the author may have obtained an idea for his story from a true incident, to qualify as a short story *it must have some element of the fictitious in it.* The author must take the material and reshape it, delete unnecessary details, and add to it in order to make it something more than a mere recital of factual material. The person who first told him the details may no more recognize his original report than the hen can recognize her egg in the omelet. The author has taken the raw material and with the skill of a master chef made it something new with flavor and substance. An important ingredient the author has used is *imagination,* and when imagination is used to interpret or illuminate, a form of fiction has been created.

The author always begins with facts or an idea involving people or characters. Even in animal stories, the animals take on the qualities of people or are used as symbols of people, as in Aesop's *Fables.* In the short story, something has to happen to or within those people, and the reader expects them to be "true to life," to behave as normal human beings would behave under those circumstances. However, in many psychological novels, the author is concerned with the behavior of characters whose mental processes are not those of normal men or women. But even then, the characters are expected to conduct themselves in a pattern consistent with their circumstances. Whether a particular act of a character is true to life or not must be judged not on what we would do under those circumstances, but on what *this particular character would do in that particular place under those particular circumstances.*

For the character to act or react he must be faced with

a problem, and being faced with a problem, he must become involved in a *conflict*. This conflict takes many forms. In longer stories and in drama, it may be the relationship between man and God (as humorously developed in "Rain on Tanyard Hollow"). It may involve his relations with nature; it may involve his relationships with animals, a favorite device in many children's stories. It may involve man and his soul, heart or mind, as in Edgar Allan Poe's "The Tell-Tale Heart."

These relationships involving conflict are the incidents which make up plot, and *fiction must have a plot.*

For man to exist he must have a place where he lives, where he meets a problem, and where he must make his decision to think, believe, or to act. *This place where the character exists and acts, together with the time in which the incidents occur, becomes setting.*

Although it is not usually included in the term of short story, the "short short story" may contain from one thousand to twenty-five hundred words. There are no fixed limits, but the short story generally is fictitious prose not exceeding ten thousand words. A story running to about thirty-five thousand words may be referred to as a novella or novelette; anything in excess of that is referred to as a novel.

Thus, a short story definition that will be acceptable and not allow too many exceptions might be expressed as follows: (1) *a unified work in prose,* (2) *usually no longer than ten thousand words,* (3) *containing elements of the fictitious,* (4) *dealing in a dramatic manner with a character who is faced with a problem about which he must make* a *decision, and* (5) *who then acts in a reasonable manner in accordance with the circumstances.*

The popular short story, emphasizing plot, is the favorite reading of the unsophisticated. It may stress action, as in stories of war, the pioneer days, or the lumber camps. It may be built around the romantic concept of love in which the boy meets girl, boy loses girl, and boy gets girl. These stories are largely concerned with plot, and the action is easily understood on an elementary level.

The literary short story also contains plot, but it is even more concerned with the style in which the story is told. In its telling, the author may leave something implied rather than stated. Someone once said that the poet leaves more untold than he tells, and this may be true, in part, of the good short story writer.

Definitions of the short story stress the *oneness of impression.* Edgar Allan Poe, who, according to many critics, originated the literary short story, said, "Having conceived, with deliberate care, a certain unique or single effect to be wrought out, (the author) then combines such events as may best aid him in establishing this preconceived effect . . . *There should be no word written, of which the tendency, direct or indirect, is not to be the one pre-established design.*" (Italics ours.)

The construction of a short story plot usually has five stages: (*1*) the setting, (*2*) the opening incident, (*3*) the complication, (*4*) the making of a decision or performance of an act, and (*5*) the conclusion. In many stories the conclusion, often as little as one line, may give total meaning to the story and therefore must be considered with great care. Unlike the novel, these parts seem to blend, and they are so interrelated that it is frequently undesirable to separate one from the other in the reading of the story. But this is not the case in a study of the short story. For instance, the situation which usually gives the setting may also give invaluable information about the principal character. This is particularly true of the regional story in which the character is influenced by his environment, as in Alan Paton's stories of South Africa.

Most people read short stories rapidly, reading the story only for the yarn it tells. Many stories, particularly those of the popular magazines, require nothing more. Such stories, of course, have a legitimate function in providing their readers with a vicarious experience enabling them to participate in a life normally closed to them: the landlocked Midwesterner who reads of life at sea; the lonely, small-town girl who reads of love in glamorous Capri; the city boy who reads of the limitless space and adventure of the old West.

The mature and discriminating reader, on the other hand, is less apt to dwell on a level of fantasy but looks for something more in his reading than a mere tale of adventure. He will be alert for symbols, for hidden meanings, for comments on life and its meaning. He will be conscious of the fact that the author may have had a purpose in writing over and above the obvious one of interesting or entertaining the reader. Such a reader will want to determine what the author thought about life and its meaning as expressed in his work. This, then, is what is meant by the word *theme,* and theme is an essential part of all great writing.

A good short story is like good poetry; it can be read quickly for the immediate impression or effect. But to stop there is to miss the greater values to be found in the work.

In reading these short stories the student will do well to read each of them twice. The first time, he should read the story through for its initial effect and let the author tell his story so that the "certain unique or single effect" can become clear. The second time the story is read, it should be read carefully.

One should also make special note of the punctuation. For example, a dash before a particular word may give that word a special significance. In "The Tale," page 31, Conrad frequently uses the dash to indicate the woman's uncertainty in expressing herself. Later he uses the dash again when the young officer reports on the mysterious ship. He has the young man report that the ship was "a stranger—a neutral." By so doing, Conrad emphasizes the young man's belief that the ship is on legitimate business.

The reader should study the details of the setting and try to estimate the personality of the principal character at the beginning of the story. He should also reflect upon the use of symbols and other figurative language.

The student should determine what the turning point is in the principal character's thinking or behavior and note how the story ends. Does it end in a fashion consistent with that character's personality at that time, in that place, under the circumstances? What does the last sentence of the story add to what has gone before? Does it cast meaning on the character and his behavior?

Finally, the reader should try to answer the question, "What is the author trying to say?"

SHERWOOD ANDERSON

1876–1941

The Egg

A MIDWESTERNER, *Sherwood Anderson is best known for his novel,* Winesburg, Ohio, *which is made up of the stories of many characters in a small American city. Born in Clyde, Ohio, Anderson lived there until late in his teens when he went to Chicago. He joined the army and served in the Spanish-American War. He returned to Chicago, and influenced by Carl Sandburg, Theodore Dreiser, and other Chicago writers, he published his first novel.*

In the early twenties Anderson moved to New York, then later to a farm in Virginia and became a newspaper editor. This followed his decision early in the century to abandon a business career and, according to Maxwell Geismar, to choose to be "among the fools of life, rather than the fools of material power." This contempt for financial success may be reflected in the story which follows.

My father was, I am sure, intended by nature to be a cheerful, kindly man. Until he was thirty-four years old he worked as a farm hand for a man named Thomas Butterworth whose place lay near the town of Bidwell, Ohio. He had then a horse of his own and on Saturday evenings drove into town to spend a few hours in social intercourse with other farm hands. In town he drank several glasses of beer and stood about in Ben Head's saloon—crowded on Saturday evenings with visiting farm hands. Songs were sung and glasses thumped on the bar. At ten o'clock father drove home along a lonely country road, made his horse comfortable for the night and himself went to bed, quite happy in his position in life. He had at that time no notion of trying to rise in the world.

It was in the spring of his thirty-fifth year that father married my mother, then a country school teacher, and in the following spring I came wriggling and crying into the world. Something happened to the two people. They became ambitious. The American passion for getting up in the world took possession of them.

It may have been that mother was responsible. Being a school teacher she had no doubt read books and magazines. She had, I presume, read of how Garfield, Lincoln, and other Americans rose from poverty to fame and greatness and as I lay beside her—in the days of her lying-in—she may have dreamed that I would some day rule men and cities. At any rate she induced father to give up his place as a farm hand, sell his horse and embark on an independent enterprise of his own. She was a tall silent woman with a long nose and troubled gray eyes. For herself she wanted nothing. For father and myself she was incurably ambitious.

The first venture into which the two people went turned out badly. They rented ten acres of poor stony land on Griggs's Road, eight miles from Bidwell, and launched into chicken raising. I grew into boyhood on the place and got my first impressions of life there. From the beginning they were impressions of disaster and if, in my turn, I am a gloomy man inclined to see the darker side of life, I attribute it to the fact that what should have been for me the happy joyous days of childhood were spent on a chicken farm.

One unversed in such matters can have no notion of the many and tragic things that can happen to a chicken. It is born out of an egg, lives for a few weeks as a tiny fluffy thing such as you will see pictured on Easter cards, then becomes hideously naked, eats quantities of corn and meal bought by the sweat of your father's brow, gets diseases called pip, cholera, and other names, stands looking with stupid eyes at the sun, becomes sick and dies. A few hens and now and then a rooster, intended to serve God's mysterious ends, struggle through to maturity. The hens lay eggs out of which come other chickens and the dreadful cycle is thus made complete. It is all unbelievably complex. Most philosophers must have been raised on chicken farms. One hopes for so much from a chicken and is so dreadfully disillusioned. Small chickens, just setting out on the journey of life, look so bright and alert and they are in fact so dreadfully stupid. They are so much like people they mix one up in one's judgments of life. If disease does not kill them they wait until your expectations are thoroughly aroused and then walk under the wheels of a wagon—to go squashed and dead back to their maker. Vermin infest their youth, and fortunes must be spent for curative powders. In later life I have seen how a literature has been built up on the subject of fortunes to be made out of the raising of chickens. It is intended to be read by the gods who have just eaten of the tree of the knowledge of good and evil. It is a hopeful literature and declares that much may be done by simple ambitious people who own a few hens. Do not be led astray by it. It was not written for you. Go hunt for gold on the frozen hills of Alaska, put your faith in the honesty of a politician, believe if you will that the world is daily growing better and that good will triumph over evil, but do not read and believe the literature that is written concerning the hen. It was not written for you.

I, however, digress. My tale does not primarily concern itself with the hen. If correctly told it will center on the egg. For ten years my father and mother struggled to make our chicken farm pay and then they gave up that struggle and began another. They moved into the town of Bidwell, Ohio, and embarked in the restaurant business. After ten years of worry with incubators that did not hatch, and with tiny—and in their own way lovely—balls of fluff that passed on into semi-naked pullethood and from that into dead henhood, we threw all aside and packing our belongings on a wagon drove down Griggs's Road toward Bidwell, a tiny caravan of hope looking for a new place from which to start on our upward journey through life.

We must have been a sad looking lot, not, I fancy, unlike refugees fleeing from a battlefield. Mother and I walked in the road. The wagon that contained our goods had been borrowed for the day from Mr. Albert Griggs, a neighbor. Out of its sides stuck the legs of cheap chairs and at the back of the pile of beds, tables, and boxes filled with kitchen utensils was a crate of live chickens, and on top of that the baby carriage in which I had been wheeled about in my infancy.

Why we stuck to the baby carriage I don't know. It was unlikely other children would be born and the wheels were broken. People who have few possessions cling tightly to those they have. That is one of the facts that make life so discouraging.

Father rode on top of the wagon. He was then a bald-headed man of forty-five, a little fat and from long association with mother and the chickens he had become habitually silent and discouraged. All during our ten years on the chicken farm he had worked as a laborer on neighboring farms and most of the money he had earned had been spent for remedies to cure chicken diseases, on Wilmer's White Wonder Cholera Cure or Professor Bidlow's Egg Producer or some other preparations that mother found advertised in the poultry papers. There were two little patches of hair on father's head just above his ears. I remember that as a child I used to sit looking at him when he had gone to sleep in a chair before the stove on Sunday afternoons in the winter. I had at that time already begun to read books and have notions of my own and the bald path that led over the top of his head was, I fancied, something like a broad road, such a road as Caesar might have made on which to lead his legions out of Rome and into the wonders of an unknown world. The tufts of hair that grew above father's ears were, I thought, like forests. I fell into a half-sleeping, half-waking state and dreamed I was a tiny thing going along the road into a far beautiful place where there were no chicken farms and where life was a happy eggless affair.

One might write a book concerning our flight from the

chicken farm into town. Mother and I walked the entire eight miles—she to be sure that nothing fell from the wagon and I to see the wonders of the world. On the seat of the wagon beside father was his greatest treasure. I will tell you of that.

On a chicken farm where hundreds and even thousands of chickens come out of eggs surprising things sometimes happen. Grotesques are born out of eggs as out of people. The accident does not often occur—perhaps once in a thousand births. A chicken is, you see, born that has four legs, two pairs of wings, two heads or what not. The things do not live. They go quickly back to the hand of their maker that has for a moment trembled. The fact that the poor little things could not live was one of the tragedies of life to father. He had some sort of notion that if he could but bring into henhood or roosterhood a five-legged hen or a two-headed rooster his fortune would be made. He dreamed of taking the wonder about to county fairs and growing rich by exhibiting it to other farm hands.

At any rate he saved all the little monstrous things that had been born on our chicken farm. They were preserved in alcohol and put each in its own glass bottle. These he had carefully put into a box and on our journey into town it was carried on the wagon seat beside him. He drove the horses with one hand and with the other clung to the box. When we got to our destination the box was taken down at once and the bottles removed. All during our days as keepers of a restaurant in the town of Bidwell, Ohio, the grotesques in their little glass bottles sat on a shelf back of the counter. Mother sometimes protested but father was a rock on the subject of his treasure. The grotesques were, he declared, valuable. People, he said, liked to look at strange and wonderful things.

Did I say that we embarked in the restaurant business in the town of Bidwell, Ohio? I exaggerated a little. The town itself lay at the foot of a low hill and on the shore of a small river. The railroad did not run through the town and the station was a mile away to the north at a place called Pickleville. There had been a cider mill and pickle factory at the station, but before the time of our coming they had both gone out of business. In the morning and in the evening busses came down to the station along a road called Turner's Pike from the hotel on the main street of Bidwell. Our going to the out-of-the-way place to embark in the restaurant business was mother's idea. She talked of it for a year and then one day went off and rented an empty store building opposite the railroad station. It was her idea that the restaurant would be profitable. Traveling men, she said, would be always waiting around to take trains out of town and town people would come to the station to await incoming trains. They would come to the restaurant to buy pieces of pie and drink coffee. Now that I am older I know that she had another motive in going. She was ambitious for me. She wanted me to rise in the world, to get into a town school and become a man of the towns.

At Pickleville father and mother worked hard as they always had done. At first there was the necessity of putting our place into shape to be a restaurant. That took a month. Father built a shelf on which he put tins of vegetables. He painted a sign on which he put his name in large red letters. Below his name was the sharp command—"EAT HERE"—that was so seldom obeyed. A showcase was bought and filled with cigars and tobacco. Mother scrubbed the floor and the walls of the room. I went to school in the town and was glad to be away from the farm and from the presence of the discouraged, sad-looking chickens. Still I was not very joyous. In the evening I walked home from school along Turner's Pike and remembered the children I had seen playing in the town school yard. A troop of little girls had gone hopping about and singing. I tried that. Down along the frozen road I went hopping solemnly on one leg. "Hippity Hop To The Barber Shop," I sang shrilly. Then I stopped and looked doubtfully about. I was afraid of being seen in my gay mood. It must have seemed to me that I was doing a thing that should not be done by one who, like myself, had been raised on a chicken farm where death was a daily visitor.

Mother decided that our restaurant should remain open at night. At ten in the evening a passenger train went north past our door followed by a local freight. The freight crew had switching to do in Pickleville and when the work was done they came to our restaurant for hot coffee and food. Sometimes one of them ordered a fried egg. In the morning at four they returned north-bound and again visited us. A little trade began to grow up. Mother slept at night and during the day tended the restaurant and fed our boarders while father slept. He slept in the same bed mother had occupied during the night and I went off to the town of Bidwell and to school. During the long nights, while mother and I slept, father cooked meats that were to go into sandwiches for the lunch baskets of our boarders. Then an idea in regard to getting up in the world came into his head. The American spirit took hold of him. He also became ambitious.

In the long nights when there was little to do father had time to think. That was his undoing. He decided that he had in the past been an unsuccessful man because he had not been cheerful enough and that in the future he would adopt a cheerful outlook on life. In the early morning he came upstairs and got into bed with mother. She woke and the two talked. From my bed in the corner I listened.

It was father's idea that both he and mother should try to entertain the people who came to eat at our restaurant. I cannot now remember his words, but he gave the impression of one about to become in some obscure way a kind of public entertainer. When people, particularly young people from the town of Bidwell, came into our place, as on very rare occasions they did, bright entertaining conversation was to be made. From father's words I gathered that something of the jolly innkeeper effect was to be sought. Mother must have been doubtful from the first, but she said nothing discouraging. It was father's notion that a passion for the company of himself and mother would spring up in the breasts of the younger people of the town of Bidwell. In the evening bright happy groups would come singing down Turner's Pike. They would troop shouting with joy and laughter into our place. There would be song and festivity. I do not mean to give the impression that father spoke so elaborately of the matter. He was as I have said an uncommunicative man. "They want some place to go. I tell you they want some place to go," he said over and over. That was as far as he got. My own imagination has filled in the blanks.

For two or three weeks this notion of father's invaded our house. We did not talk much, but in our daily lives tried earnestly to make smiles take the place of glum looks. Mother smiled at the boarders and I, catching the infection, smiled at our cat. Father became a little feverish in his anxiety to please. There was no doubt, lurking somewhere in him, a touch of the spirit of the showman. He did not waste much of his ammunition on the railroad men he served at night but seemed to be waiting for a young man or woman from Bidwell to come in to show what he could do. On the counter in the restaurant there was a wire basket kept always filled with eggs, and it must have been before his eyes when the idea of being entertaining was born in his brain. There was something pre-natal about the way eggs kept themselves connected with the development of his idea. At any rate an egg ruined his new impulse in life. Late one night I was awakened by a roar of anger coming from father's throat. Both mother and I sat upright in our beds. With trembling hands she lighted a lamp that stood on a table by her head. Downstairs the front door of our restaurant went shut with a bang and in a few minutes father tramped up the stairs. He held an egg in his hand and his hand trembled as though he were having a chill. There was a half-insane light in his eyes. As he stood glaring at us I was sure he intended throwing the egg at either mother or me. Then he laid it gently on the table beside the lamp and dropped on his knees beside mother's bed. He began to cry like a boy and I, carried away by his grief, cried with him. The two of us filled the little upstairs room with our wailing voices. It is ridiculous, but of the picture we made I can remember only the fact that mother's hand continually stroked the bald path that ran across the top of his head. I have forgotten what mother said to him and how she induced him to tell her of what had happened downstairs. His explanation also has gone out of my mind. I remember only my own grief and fright and the shiny path over my father's head glowing in the lamp light as he knelt by the bed.

As to what happened downstairs. For some unexplainable reason I know the story as well as though I had been a witness to my father's discomfiture. One in time gets to know many unexplainable things. On that evening young Joe Kane, son of a merchant of Bidwell, came to Pickleville to meet his father, who was expected on the ten o'clock evening train from the South. The train was three hours late and Joe came into our place to loaf about and to wait for its arrival. The local freight train came in and the freight crew were fed. Joe was left alone in the restaurant with father.

From the moment he came into our place the Bidwell young man must have been puzzled by my father's actions. It was his notion that father was angry at him for hanging around. He noticed that the restaurant keeper was apparently disturbed by his presence and he thought of going out. However, it began to rain and he did not fancy the long walk to town and back. He bought a five-cent cigar and ordered a cup of coffee. He had a newspaper in his pocket and took it out and began to read. "I'm waiting for the evening train. It's late," he said apologetically.

For a long time father, whom Joe Kane had never seen before, remained silently gazing at his visitor. He was no doubt suffering from an attack of stage fright. As so often happens in life he had thought so much and so often of the situation that now confronted him that he was somewhat nervous in its presence.

For one thing, he did not know what to do with his hands. He thrust one of them nervously over the counter and shook hands with Joe Kane. "How-de-do," he said. Joe Kane put his newspaper down and stared at him. Father's eye lighted on the basket of eggs that sat on the counter and he began to talk. "Well," he began hesitatingly, "well, you have heard of Christopher Columbus, eh?" He seemed to be angry. "That Christopher Columbus was a cheat," he declared emphatically. "He talked of making an egg stand on its end. He talked, he did, and then he went and broke the end of the egg."

My father seemed to his visitor to be beside himself at the duplicity of Christopher Columbus. He muttered and swore. He declared it was wrong to teach children that Christopher Columbus was a great man when, after all, he cheated at the critical moment. He had declared he would make an egg stand on end and then when his bluff had been called he had done a trick. Still grumbling at Columbus, father took an egg from the basket on the counter and began to walk up and down. He rolled the egg between the palms of his hands. He smiled genially. He began to mumble words regarding the effect to be produced on an egg by the electricity that comes out of the human body. He declared that without breaking its shell and by virtue of rolling it back and forth in his hands he could stand the egg on its end. He explained that the warmth of his hands and the gentle rolling movement he gave the egg created a new center of gravity, and Joe Kane was mildly interested. "I have handled thousands of eggs," father said. "No one knows more about eggs than I do."

He stood the egg on the counter and it fell on its side. He tried the trick again and again, each time rolling the egg between the palms of his hands and saying the words regarding the wonders of electricity and the laws of gravity. When after a half hour's effort he did succeed in making the egg stand for a moment he looked up to find that his visitor was no longer watching. By the time he had succeeded in calling Joe Kane's attention to the success of his effort the egg had again rolled over and lay on its side.

Afire with the showman's passion and at the same time a good deal disconcerted by the failure of his first effort, father now took the bottles containing the poultry monstrosities down from their place on the shelf and began to show them to his visitor. "How would you like to have seven legs and two heads like this fellow?" he asked, exhibiting the most remarkable of his treasures. A cheerful smile played over his face. He reached over the counter and tried to slap Joe Kane on the shoulder as he had seen men do in Ben Head's saloon when he was a young farm hand and drove to town on

Saturday evenings. His visitor was made a little ill by the sight of the body of the terribly deformed bird floating in the alcohol in the bottle and got up to go. Coming from behind the counter father took hold of the young man's arm and led him back to his seat. He grew a little angry and for a moment had to turn his face away and force himself to smile. Then he put the bottles back on the shelf. In an outburst of generosity he fairly compelled Joe Kane to have a fresh cup of coffee and another cigar at his expense. Then he took a pan and filling it with vinegar, taken from a jug that sat beneath the counter, he declared himself about to do a new trick. "I will heat this egg in this pan of vinegar," he said. "Then I will put it through the neck of a bottle without breaking the shell. When the egg is inside the bottle it will resume its normal shape and the shell will become hard again. Then I will give the bottle with the egg in it to you. You can take it about with you wherever you go. People will want to know how you got the egg in the bottle. Don't tell them. Keep them guessing. That is the way to have fun with this trick."

Father grinned and winked at his visitor. Joe Kane decided that the man who confronted him was mildly insane but harmless. He drank the cup of coffee that had been given him and began to read his paper again. When the egg had been heated in vinegar father carried it on a spoon to the counter and going into a back room got an empty bottle. He was angry because his visitor did not watch him as he began to do his trick, but nevertheless went cheerfully to work. For a long time he struggled, trying to get the egg to go through the neck of the bottle. He put the pan of vinegar back on the stove, intending to reheat the egg, then picked it up and burned his fingers. After a second bath in the hot vinegar the shell of the egg had been softened a little but not enough for his purpose. He worked and worked and a spirit of desperate determination took possession of him. When he thought that at last the trick was about to be consummated the delayed train came in at the station and Joe Kane started to go nonchalantly out at the door. Father made a last desperate effort to conquer the egg and make it do the thing that would establish his reputation as one who knew how to entertain guests who came into his restaurant. He worried the egg. He attempted to be somewhat rough with it. He swore and the sweat stood out on his forehead. The egg broke under his hand. When the contents spurted over his clothes, Joe Kane, who had stopped at the door, turned and laughed.

A roar of anger rose from my father's throat. He danced and shouted a string of inarticulate words. Grabbing another egg from the basket on the counter, he threw it, just missing the head of the young man as he dodged through the door and escaped.

Father came upstairs to mother and me with an egg in his hand. I do not know what he intended to do. I imagine he had some idea of destroying it, of destroying all eggs, and that he intended to let mother and me see him begin. When, however, he got into the presence of mother something happened to him. He laid the egg gently on the table and dropped on his knees by the bed as I have already explained. He later decided to close the restaurant for the night and to come upstairs and get into bed. When he did so he blew out the light and after much muttered conversation both he and mother went to sleep. I suppose I went to sleep also, but my sleep was troubled. I awoke at dawn and for a long time looked at the egg that lay on the table. I wondered why eggs had to be and why from the egg came the hen who again laid the egg. The question got into my blood. It has stayed there, I imagine, because I am the son of my father. At any rate, the problem remains unsolved in my mind. And that, I conclude, is but another evidence of the complete and final triumph of the egg—at least as far as my family is concerned.

THE EGG

1. What is the difference in the father before and after his marriage? Notice particularly the last two sentences of paragraph two which express Anderson's view of much of the illness of Americans in the early part of this century.
2. What sardonic humor do you find in the first two pages?
3. Anderson says his story "If correctly told . . . will center on the egg." How does the egg link the two parts of the story?
4. In leaving the country for the town and the ". . . upward journey through life" why does Anderson describe the family as a sad-looking lot? Why is the figure ". . . not, I fancy, un-

like refugees fleeing from a battlefield" used? To carry the figure further, to what do refugees flee? Do they have a well-defined objective ahead of them?

5. How do the mother's and father's senses of values differ?
6. After he opens his restaurant, how does the "American spirit" take hold of the father? What is the immediate result?
7. Could Anderson's picture of an almost hysterical father be true to life? What makes you believe or disbelieve it? How do you account for the apparent change in the father when he comes ". . . into the presence of mother"?
8. Why did the boy wonder ". . . why eggs had to be and why from the egg came the hen who again laid the egg"? What question is Anderson raising in the reader's mind?

HEYWOOD BROUN

1888–1939

The Fifty-First Dragon

HEYWOOD BROUN *was an admirable paradox; a man of tolerant disposition, he became wrathful at any evidence of injustice. His very real concern for the unjustly accused cost him more than one job.*

Mr. Broun's interest in writing began as early as his prep school days when he became editor of his paper at the Horace Mann School in New York City. Later he served his apprenticeship as a sports writer, and in 1912 he began the first of his famous columns. During World War I he served overseas as a newspaper correspondent.

Mr. Broun's published works include biography, essays, and novels.

Of all the pupils at the knight school Gawaine le Cœur-Hardy was among the least promising. He was tall and sturdy, but his instructors soon discovered that he lacked spirit. He would hide in the woods when the jousting class was called, although his companions and members of the faculty sought to appeal to his better nature by shouting to him to come out and break his neck like a man. Even when they told him that the lances were padded, the horses no more than ponies and the field unusually soft for late autumn, Gawaine refused to grow enthusiastic. The Headmaster and the Assistant Professor of Pleasaunce were discussing the case one spring afternoon and the Assistant Professor could see no remedy but expulsion.

"No," said the Headmaster, as he looked out at the purple hills which ringed the school, "I think I'll train him to slay dragons."

"He might be killed," objected the Assistant Professor.

"So he might," replied the Headmaster brightly, but he added, more soberly, "we must consider the greater good. We are responsible for the formation of this lad's character."

"Are the dragons particularly bad this year?" interrupted the Assistant Professor. This was characteristic. He always seemed restive when the head of the school began to talk ethics and the ideals of the institution.

"I've never known them worse," replied the Headmaster. "Up in the hills to the south last week they killed a number of peasants, two cows and a prize pig. And if this dry spell holds there's no telling when they may start a forest fire simply by breathing around indiscriminately."

"Would any refund on the tuition fee be necessary in case of an accident to young Cœur-Hardy?"

"No," the principal answered, judicially, "that's all covered in the contract. But as a matter of fact he won't be killed. Before I send him up in the hills I'm going to give him a magic word."

"That's a good idea," said the Professor. "Sometimes they work wonders."

From that day on Gawaine specialized in dragons. His

course included both theory and practice. In the morning there were long lectures on the history, anatomy, manners and customs of dragons. Gawaine did not distinguish himself in these studies. He had a marvelously versatile gift for forgetting things. In the afternoon he showed to better advantage, for then he would go down to the South Meadow and practice with a battle-ax. In this exercise he was truly impressive, for he had enormous strength as well as speed and grace. He even developed a deceptive display of ferocity. Old alumni say that it was a thrilling sight to see Gawaine charging across the field toward the dummy paper dragon which had been set up for his practice. As he ran he would brandish his ax and shout "A murrain on thee!" or some other vivid bit of campus slang. It never took him more than one stroke to behead the dummy dragon.

Gradually his task was made more difficult. Paper gave way to papier-mâché and finally to wood, but even the toughest of these dummy dragons had no terrors for Gawaine. One sweep of the ax always did the business. There were those who said that when the practice was protracted until dusk and the dragons threw long, fantastic shadows across the meadow Gawaine did not charge so impetuously nor shout so loudly. It is possible there was malice in this charge. At any rate, the Headmaster decided by the end of June that it was time for the test. Only the night before a dragon had come close to the school grounds and had eaten some of the lettuce from the garden. The faculty decided that Gawaine was ready. They gave him a diploma and a new battle-ax and the Headmaster summoned him to a private conference.

"Sit down," said the Headmaster. "Have a cigarette."

Gawaine hesitated.

"Oh, I know it's against the rules," said the Headmaster. "But after all, you have received your preliminary degree. You are no longer a boy. You are a man. Tomorrow you will go out into the world, the great world of achievement."

Gawaine took a cigarette. The Headmaster offered him a match, but he produced one of his own and began to puff away with a dexterity which quite amazed the principal.

"Here you have learned the theories of life," continued the Headmaster, resuming the thread of his discourse, "but after all, life is not a matter of theories. Life is a matter of facts. It calls on the young and the old alike to face these facts, even though they are hard and sometimes unpleasant. Your problem, for example, is to slay dragons."

"They say that those dragons down in the south wood are five hundred feet long," ventured Gawaine, timorously.

"Stuff and nonsense!" said the Headmaster. "The curate saw one last week from the top of Arthur's Hill. The dragon was sunning himself down in the valley. The curate didn't have an opportunity to look at him very long because he felt it was his duty to hurry back to make a report to me. He said the monster, or shall I say, the big lizard?—wasn't an inch over two hundred feet. But the size has nothing at all to do with it. You'll find the big ones even easier than the little ones. They're far slower on their feet and less aggressive, I'm told. Besides, before you go I'm going to equip you in such fashion that you need have no fear of all the dragons in the world."

"I'd like an enchanted cap," said Gawaine.

"What's that?" answered the Headmaster, testily.

"A cap to make me disappear," explained Gawaine.

The Headmaster laughed indulgently. "You mustn't believe all those old wives' stories," he said. "There isn't any such thing. A cap to make you disappear, indeed! What would you do with it? You haven't even appeared yet. Why, my boy, you could walk from here to London, and nobody would so much as look at you. You're nobody. You couldn't be more invisible than that."

Gawaine seemed dangerously close to a relapse into his old habit of whimpering. The Headmaster reassured him: "Don't worry; I'll give you something much better than an enchanted cap. I'm going to give you a magic word. All you have to do is to repeat this magic charm once and no dragon can possibly harm a hair of your head. You can cut off his head at your leisure."

He took a heavy book from the shelf behind his desk and began to run through it. "Sometimes," he said, "the charm is a whole phrase or even a sentence. I might, for instance, give you 'To make the'—No, that might not do. I think a single word would be best for dragons."

"A short word," suggested Gawaine.

"It can't be too short or it wouldn't be potent. There isn't so much hurry as all that. Here's a splendid magic word: 'Rumplesnitz.' Do you think you can learn that?"

Gawaine tried and in an hour or so he seemed to have the word well in hand. Again and again he interrupted the lesson to inquire, "And if I say 'Rumplesnitz' the dragon can't possibly hurt me?" And always the Headmaster replied, "If you only say 'Rumplesnitz,' you are perfectly safe."

Toward morning Gawaine seemed resigned to his career. At daybreak the Headmaster saw him to the edge of the forest and pointed him to the direction in which he should proceed. About a mile away to the southwest a cloud of steam hovered over an open meadow in the woods and the Headmaster assured Gawaine that under the steam he would find a dragon. Gawaine went forward slowly. He wondered whether it would be best to approach the dragon on the run as he did in his practice in the South Meadow or to walk slowly toward him, shouting "Rumplesnitz" all the way.

The problem was decided for him. No sooner had he come to the fringe of the meadow than the dragon spied him and began to charge. It was a large dragon and yet it seemed decidedly aggressive in spite of the Headmaster's statement to the contrary. As the dragon charged it released huge clouds of hissing steam through its nostrils. It was almost as if a gigantic teapot had gone mad. The dragon came forward so fast and Gawaine was so frightened that he had time to say "Rumplesnitz" only once. As he said it, he swung his battle-ax and off popped the head of the dragon. Gawaine had to admit that it was even easier to kill a real dragon than a wooden one if only you said "Rumplesnitz."

Gawaine brought the ears home and a small section of the tail. His schoolmates and the faculty made much of him, but the Headmaster wisely kept him from being spoiled by insisting that he go on with his work. Every clear day Gawaine rose at dawn and went out to kill dragons. The Headmaster kept him at home when it rained, because he said the woods were damp and unhealthy at such times and that he didn't want the boy to run needless risks. Few good days passed in which Gawaine failed to get a dragon. On one particularly fortunate day he killed three, a husband and wife and a visiting relative. Gradually he developed a technique. Pupils who sometimes watched him from the hilltops a long way off said that he often allowed the dragon to come within a few feet before he said "Rumplesnitz." He came to say it with a mocking sneer. Occasionally he did stunts. Once when an excursion party from London was watching him he went into action with his right hand tied behind his back. The dragon's head came off just as easily.

As Gawaine's record of killings mounted higher the Headmaster found it impossible to keep him completely in hand. He fell into the habit of stealing out at night and engaging in long drinking bouts at the village tavern. It was after such a debauch that he rose a little before dawn one fine August morning and started out after his fiftieth dragon. His head was heavy and his mind was sluggish. He was heavy in other respects as well, for he had adopted the somewhat vulgar practice of wearing his medals, ribbons and all, when he went out dragon hunting. The decorations began on his chest and ran all the way down to his abdomen. They must have weighed at least eight pounds.

Gawaine found a dragon in the same meadow where he had killed the first one. It was a fair-sized dragon, but evidently an old one. Its face was wrinkled and Gawaine thought he had never seen so hideous a countenance. Much to the lad's disgust, the monster refused to charge and Gawaine was obliged to walk toward him. He whistled as he went. The dragon regarded him hopelessly, but craftily. (Of course it had heard of Gawaine.) Even when the lad raised his battle-ax the dragon made no move. It knew that there was no salvation in the quickest thrust of the head, for it had been informed that this hunter was protected by an enchantment. It merely waited, hoping something would turn up. Gawaine raised the battle ax and suddenly lowered it again. He had grown very pale and he trembled violently. The dragon suspected a trick. "What's the matter?" it asked, with false solicitude.

"I've forgotten the magic word," stammered Gawaine.

"What a pity," said the dragon. "So that was the secret. It doesn't seem quite sporting to me, all this magic stuff, you know. Not cricket, as we used to say when I was a little dragon; but after all, that's a matter of opinion."

Gawaine was so helpless with terror that the dragon's confidence rose immeasurably and it could not resist the temptation to show off a bit.

"Could I possibly be of any assistance?" it asked. "What's the first letter of the magic word?"

"It begins with an 'r,' " said Gawaine weakly.

"Let's see," mused the dragon, "that doesn't tell us much, does it? What sort of a word is this? Is it an epithet, do you think?"

Gawaine could do no more than nod.

"Why, of course," exclaimed the dragon, "reactionary Republican."

Gawaine shook his head.

"Well, then," said the dragon, "we'd better get down to business. Will you surrender?"

With the suggestion of a compromise Gawaine mustered up enough courage to speak.

"What will you do if I surrender?" he asked.

"Why, I'll eat you," said the dragon.

"And if I don't surrender?"

"I'll eat you just the same."

"Then it doesn't make any difference, does it?" moaned Gawaine.

"It does to me," said the dragon with a smile. "I'd rather you didn't surrender. You'd taste much better if you didn't."

The dragon waited for a long time for Gawaine to ask "Why?" but the boy was too frightened to speak. At last the dragon had to give the explanation without his cue line. "You see," he said, "if you don't surrender you'll taste better because you'll die game."

This was an old and ancient trick of the dragon's. By means of some such quip he was accustomed to paralyze his victims with laughter and then to destroy them. Gawaine was sufficiently paralyzed as it was, but laughter had no part in his helplessness. With the last word of the joke the dragon drew back his head and struck. In that second there flashed into the mind of Gawaine the magic word "Rumplesnitz," but there was no time to say it. There was time only to strike and, without a word, Gawaine met the onrush of the dragon with a full swing. He put all his back and shoulders into it. The impact was terrific and the head of the dragon flew away almost a hundred yards and landed in a thicket.

Gawaine did not remain frightened very long after the death of the dragon. His mood was one of wonder. He was enormously puzzled. He cut off the ears of the monster almost in a trance. Again and again he thought to himself, "I didn't say 'Rumplesnitz'!" He was sure of that and yet there was no question that he had killed the dragon. In fact, he had never killed one so utterly. Never before had he driven a head for anything like the same distance. Twenty-five yards was perhaps his best previous record. All the way back to the knight school he kept rumbling about in his mind seeking an explanation for what had occurred. He went to the Headmaster immediately and after closing the door told him what had happened. "I didn't say 'Rumplesnitz,'" he explained with great earnestness.

The Headmaster laughed. "I'm glad you've found out," he said. "It makes you ever so much more of a hero. Don't you see that? Now you know that it was you who killed all these dragons and not that foolish little word 'Rumplesnitz.'"

Gawaine frowned. "Then it wasn't a magic word after all?" he asked.

"Of course not," said the Headmaster, "you ought to be

too old for such foolishness. There isn't any such thing as a magic word."

"But you told me it was magic," protested Gawaine. "You said it was magic and now you say it isn't."

"It wasn't magic in a literal sense," answered the Headmaster, "but it was much more wonderful than that. The word gave you confidence. It took away your fears. If I hadn't told you that you might have been killed the very first time. It was your battle-ax did the trick."

Gawaine surprised the Headmaster by his attitude. He was obviously distressed by the explanation. He interrupted a long philosophic and ethical discourse by the Headmaster with, "If I hadn't of hit 'em all mighty hard and fast any one of 'em might have crushed me like a, like a—" He fumbled for a word.

"Egg shell," suggested the Headmaster.

"Like a egg shell," assented Gawaine, and he said it many times. All through the evening meal people who sat near him heard him muttering, "Like a egg shell, like a egg shell."

The next day was clear, but Gawaine did not get up at dawn. Indeed, it was almost noon when the Headmaster found him cowering in bed, with the clothes pulled over his head. The principal called the Assistant Professor of Pleasaunce, and together they dragged the boy toward the forest.

"He'll be all right as soon as he gets a couple more dragons under his belt," explained the Headmaster.

The Assistant Professor of Pleasaunce agreed. "It would

be a shame to stop such a fine run," he said. "Why, counting that one yesterday, he's killed fifty dragons."

They pushed the boy into a thicket above which hung a meager cloud of steam. It was obviously quite a small dragon. But Gawaine did not come back that night or the next. In fact, he never came back. Some weeks afterward brave spirits from the school explored the thicket, but they could find nothing to remind them of Gawaine except the metal part of his medals. Even the ribbons had been devoured.

The Headmaster and the Assistant Professor of Pleasaunce agreed that it would be just as well not to tell the school how Gawaine had achieved his record and still less how he came to die. They held that it might have a bad effect on school spirit. Accordingly, Gawaine has lived in the memory of the school as its greatest hero. No visitor succeeds in leaving the building today without seeing a great shield which hangs on the wall of the dining hall. Fifty pairs of dragons' ears are mounted upon the shield and underneath in gilt letters is "Gawaine le Cœur-Hardy," followed by the simple inscription, "He killed fifty dragons." The record has never been equaled.

THE FIFTY-FIRST DRAGON

1. How is the setting established in the first paragraph?
2. How is the humorous tone of the story established in the first paragraph?

3. How may Gawaine be compared with today's athletes in some schools?

4. Is there any significance in the bit about the headmaster, Gawaine, and the cigarette?

5. What is satiric or ironic about the headmaster's statement, "You haven't even appeared yet. Why, my boy, you could walk from here to London, and nobody would so much as look at you"?

6. Why does Mr. Broun say that Gawaine came to say "Rumplesnitz" with a mocking sneer? Relate this to the conclusion of the story.

7. What was the effect on Gawaine when he saw that he had killed the dragon without saying the magic word? Why did he go to the headmaster for an explanation? What does this conduct suggest to you about Gawaine's intelligence?

8. Why was Gawaine killed?

9. List some "Rumplesnitzes" people depend on today.

JOSEPH CONRAD

1857–1924

The Tale

JOSEPH CONRAD, *whose real name was Jósef Teodor Korzeniowski, was born in Poland and spent his early years at sea. Later he became a British citizen. Learning English from newspapers, he was able to pass his examinations in seamanship. His experiences afloat inspired much of his writing. Although his great novels are concerned with seafaring men, they are noted for strong character delineation and their special style.*

Stanley Kunitz in Twentieth Century Authors *says that Conrad "... always carried a 'guilt complex.'" In "The Tale" we find an expression of such a complex on the part of the narrator.*

Outside the large single window the crepuscular light was dying out slowly in a great square gleam without colour, framed rigidly in the gathering shades of the room.

It was a long room. The irresistible tide of the night ran into the most distant part of it, where the whispering of a man's voice, passionately interrupted and passionately renewed, seemed to plead against the answering murmurs of infinite sadness.

At last no answering murmur came. His movement when he rose slowly from his knees by the side of the deep, shadowy couch holding the shadowy suggestion of a reclining woman revealed him tall under the low ceiling, and sombre all over except for the crude discord of the white collar under the shape of his head and the faint, minute spark of a brass button here and there on his uniform.

He stood over her a moment, masculine and mysterious in his immobility, before he sat down on a chair near by. He could see only the faint oval of her upturned face and, extended on her black dress, her pale hands, a moment before abandoned to his kisses and now as if too weary to move.

He dared not make a sound, shrinking as a man would do from the prosaic necessities of existence. As usual, it was the woman who had the courage. Her voice was heard first—almost conventional while her being vibrated yet with conflicting emotions.

"Tell me something," she said.

The darkness hid his surprise and then his smile. Had he not just said to her everything worth saying in the world—and that not for the first time!

"What am I to tell you?" he asked, in a voice creditably steady. He was beginning to feel grateful to her for that something final in her tone which had eased the strain.

"Why not tell me a tale?"

"A tale!" He was really amazed.

"Yes. Why not?"

These words came with a slight petulance, the hint of a loved woman's capricious will, which is capricious only because it feels itself to be a law, embarrassing sometimes and always difficult to elude.

"Why not?" he repeated, with a slightly mocking accent,

as though he had been asked to give her the moon. But now he was feeling a little angry with her for that feminine mobility that slips out of an emotion as easily as out of a splendid gown.

He heard her say, a little unsteadily, with a sort of fluttering intonation which made him think suddenly of a butterfly's flight:

"You used to tell—your—your simple and—and professional tales—tales very well at one time. Or well enough to interest me. You had a—sort of art—in the days—the days before the war."

"Really?" he said, with involuntary gloom. "But now, you see, the war is going on," he continued in such a dead, equable tone that she felt a slight chill far over her shoulders. And yet she persisted. For there's nothing more unswerving in the world than a woman's caprice.

"It could be a tale not of this world," she explained.

"You want a tale of the other, the better world?" he asked, with a matter-of-fact surprise. "You must evoke for that task those who have already gone there."

"No. I don't mean that. I mean another—some other—world. In the universe—not in heaven."

"I am relieved. But you forget that I have only five days' leave."

"Yes. And I've also taken a five days' leave from—from my duties."

"I like that word."

"What word?"

"Duty."

"It is horrible—sometimes."

"Oh, that's because you think it's narrow. But it isn't. It contains infinities, and—and so—"

"What is this jargon?"

He disregarded the interjected scorn. "An infinity of absolution, for instance," he continued. "But as to this 'another world'—who's going to look for it and for the tale that is in it?"

"You," she said, with a strange, almost rough, sweetness of assertion.

He made a shadowy movement of assent in his chair, the irony of which not even the gathered darkness could render mysterious.

"As you will. In that world, then, there was once upon a time a Commanding Officer and a Northman. Put in the capitals, please, because they had no other names. It was a world of seas and continents and islands—"

"Like the earth," she murmured, bitterly.

"Yes. What else could you expect from sending a man made of our common, tormented clay on a voyage of discovery? What else could he find? What else could you understand or care for, or feel the existence of even? There was comedy in it, and slaughter."

"Always like the earth," she murmured.

"Always. And since I could find in the universe only what was deeply rooted in the fibres of my being there was love in it, too. But we won't talk of that."

"No. We won't," she said, in a neutral tone which concealed perfectly her relief—or her disappointment. Then after a pause she added: "It's going to be a comic story."

"Well—" he paused, too. "Yes. In a way. In a very grim way. It will be human, and, as you know, comedy is but a matter of the visual angle. And it won't be a noisy story. All the long guns in it will be dumb—as dumb as so many telescopes."

"Ah, there are guns in it, then! And may I ask—where?"

"Afloat. You remember that the world of which we speak had its seas. A war was going on in it. It was a funny world and terribly in earnest. Its war was being carried on over the land, over the water, under the water, up in the air, and even under the ground. And many young men in it, mostly in wardrooms and mess-rooms, used to say to each other—pardon the unparliamentary word—they used to say, 'It's a damned bad war, but it's better than no war at all.' Sounds flippant, doesn't it?"

He heard a nervous, impatient sigh in the depths of the couch while he went on without a pause.

"And yet there is more in it than meets the eye. I mean more wisdom. Flippancy, like comedy, is but a matter of visual first-impression. That world was not very wise. But there was in it a certain amount of common working sagacity. That, however, was mostly worked by the neutrals in diverse ways, public and private, which had to be watched; watched by acute minds and also by actual sharp eyes. They had to be very sharp indeed, too, I assure you."

"I can imagine," she murmured, appreciatively.

"What is there that you can't imagine?" he pronounced, soberly. "You have the world in you. But let us go back to our commanding officer, who, of course, commanded a ship of a sort. My tales if often professional (as you remarked just now) have never been technical. So I'll just tell you that the ship was of a very ornamental sort once, with lots of grace and elegance and luxury about her. Yes, once! She was like a pretty woman who had suddenly put on a suit of sackcloth and stuck revolvers in her belt. But she floated lightly, she moved nimbly, she was quite good enough."

"That was the opinion of the commanding officer?" said the voice from the couch.

"It was. He used to be sent out with her along certain coasts to see—what he could see. Just that. And sometimes he had some preliminary information to help him, and sometimes he had not. And it was all one, really. It was about as useful as information trying to convey the locality and intentions of a cloud, of a phantom taking shape here and there and impossible to seize, would have been.

"It was in the early days of the war. What at first used to amaze the commanding officer was the unchanged face of the waters, with its familiar expression, neither more friendly nor more hostile. On fine days the sun strikes sparks upon the blue; here and there a peaceful smudge of smoke hangs in the distance, and it is impossible to believe that the familiar clear horizon traces the limit of one great circular ambush.

"Yes, it is impossible to believe, till some day you see a ship not your own ship (that isn't so impressive), but some ship in company, blow up all of a sudden and plop under almost before you know what has happened to her. Then you begin to believe. Henceforth you go out for the work to see—what you can see; and you keep on it with the conviction that some day you will die from something you have not seen. One envies the soldiers at the end of the day, wiping the sweat and blood from their faces, counting the dead fallen to their hands, looking at the devastated fields, the torn earth that seems to suffer and bleed with them. One does, really. The final brutality of it—the taste of primitive passion—the ferocious frankness of the blow struck with one's hand—the direct call and the straight response. Well, the sea gave you nothing of that, and seemed to pretend that there was nothing the matter with the world."

She interrupted, stirring a little.

"Oh, yes. Sincerity—frankness—passion—three words of your gospel. Don't I know them!"

"Think! Isn't it ours—believed in common?" he asked, anxiously, yet without expecting an answer, and went on at once: "Such were the feelings of the commanding officer. When the night came trailing over the sea, hiding what looked like the hypocrisy of an old friend, it was a relief. The night blinds you frankly—and there are circumstances when the sunlight may grow as odious to one as falsehood itself. Night is all right.

"At night the commanding officer could let his thoughts get away—I won't tell you where. Somewhere where there was no choice but between truth and death. But thick weather, though it blinded one, brought no such relief. Mist is deceitful, the dead luminosity of the fog is irritating. It seems that you *ought* to see.

"One gloomy, nasty day the ship was steaming along her beat in sight of a rocky, dangerous coast that stood out intensely black like an India-ink drawing on grey paper. Presently the second in command spoke to his chief. He thought he saw something on the water, to seaward. Small wreckage, perhaps.

" 'But there shouldn't be any wreckage here, sir,' he remarked.

" 'No,' said the commanding officer. 'The last reported submarined ships were sunk a long way to the westward. But one never knows. There may have been others since then not reported nor seen. Gone with all hands.'

"That was how it began. The ship's course was altered to pass the object close; for it was necessary to have a good look at what one could see. Close, but without touching it; for it was not advisable to come in contact with objects of any form whatever floating casually about. Close, but without stopping or even diminishing speed; for in those times it was not prudent to linger on any particular spot, even for a moment. I may tell you at once that the object was not dangerous in itself. No use in describing it. It may have been nothing more remarkable than, say, a barrel of a certain shape and colour. But it was significant.

"The smooth bow-wave hove it up as if for a closer inspection, and then the ship, brought again to her course, turned her back on it with indifference, while twenty pairs of eyes on her deck stared in all directions trying to see—what they could see.

"The commanding officer and his second in command discussed the object with understanding. It appeared to them to be not so much a proof of the sagacity as of the activity of certain neutrals. This activity had in many cases taken the form of replenishing the stores of certain submarines at sea. This was generally believed, if not absolutely known. But the very nature of things in those early days pointed that way. The object, looked at closely and turned away from with apparent indifference, put it beyond doubt that something of the sort had been done somewhere in the neighborhood.

"The object in itself was more than suspect. But the fact of its being left in evidence roused other suspicions. Was it the result of some deep and devilish purpose? As to that all speculation soon appeared to be a vain thing. Finally the two officers came to the conclusion that it was left there most likely by accident, complicated possibly by some unforeseen necessity; such, perhaps, as the sudden need to get away quickly from the spot, or something of that kind.

"Their discussion had been carried on in curt, weighty phrases, separated by long, thoughtful silences. And all the time their eyes roamed about the horizon in an everlasting, almost mechanical effort of vigilance. The younger man summed up grimly:

" 'Well, it's evidence. That's what this is. Evidence of what we were pretty certain of before. And plain, too.'

"'And much good it will do to us,' retorted the commanding officer. 'The parties are miles away; the submarine, devil only knows where, ready to kill; and the noble neutral slipping away to the eastward, ready to lie!'

"The second in command laughed a little at the tone. But he guessed that the neutral wouldn't even have to lie very much. Fellows like that, unless caught in the very act, felt themselves pretty safe. They could afford to chuckle. That fellow was probably chuckling to himself. It's very possible he had been before at the game and didn't care a rap for the bit of evidence left behind. It was a game in which practice made one bold and successful, too.

"And again he laughed faintly. But his commanding officer was in revolt against the murderous stealthiness of methods and the atrocious callousness of complicities that seemed to taint the very source of men's deep emotions and noblest activities; to corrupt their imagination which builds up the final conceptions of life and death. He suffered—"

The voice from the sofa interrupted the narrator.

"How well I can understand that in him!"

He bent forward slightly.

"Yes. I, too. Everything should be open in love and war. Open as the day, since both are the call of an ideal which it is so easy, so terribly easy, to degrade in the name of Victory."

He paused, then went on:

"I don't know that the commanding officer delved so deep as that into his feelings. But he did suffer from them—a sort of disenchanted sadness. It is possible, even, that he suspected himself of folly. Man is various. But he had no time for much introspection, because from the southwest a wall of fog had advanced upon his ship. Great convolutions of vapours flew over, swirling about masts and funnel, which looked as if they were beginning to melt. Then they vanished.

"The ship was stopped, all sounds ceased, and the very fog became motionless, growing denser and as if solid in its amazing dumb immobility. The men at their stations lost sight of each other. Footsteps sounded stealthy; rare voices, impersonal and remote, died out without resonance. A blind white stillness took possession of the world.

"It looked, too, as if it would last for days. I don't mean to say that the fog did not vary a little in its density. Now and then it would thin out mysteriously, revealing to the men a more or less ghostly presentment of their ship. Several times the shadow of the coast itself swam darkly before their eyes through the fluctuating opaque brightness of the great white cloud clinging to the water.

"Taking advantage of these moments, the ship had been moved cautiously nearer the shore. It was useless to remain out in such thick weather. Her officers knew every nook and cranny of the coast along their beat. They thought that she would be much better in a certain cove. It wasn't a large place, just ample room for a ship to swing at her anchor. She would have an easier time of it till the fog lifted up.

"Slowly, with infinite caution and patience, they crept closer and closer, seeing no more of the cliffs than an evanescent dark loom with a narrow border of angry foam at its foot. At the moment of anchoring the fog was so thick that for all they could see they might have been a thousand miles out in the open sea. Yet the shelter of the land could be felt. There was a peculiar quality in the stillness of the air. Very faint, very elusive, the wash of the ripple against the encircling land reached their ears, with mysterious sudden pauses.

"The anchor dropped, the leads were laid in. The commanding officer went below into his cabin. But he had not been there very long when a voice outside his door requested his presence on deck. He thought to himself: 'What is it now?' He felt some impatience at being called out again to face the wearisome fog.

"He found that it had thinned again a little and had taken on a gloomy hue from the dark cliffs which had no form, no outline, but asserted themselves as a curtain of shadows all round the ship, except in one bright spot, which was the entrance from the open sea. Several officers were looking that way from the bridge. The second in command met him with the breathlessly whispered information that there was another ship in the cove.

"She had been made out by several pairs of eyes only a couple of minutes before. She was lying at anchor very near the entrance—a mere vague blot on the fog's brightness. And the commanding officer by staring in the direction pointed out to him by eager hands ended by distinguishing it at last himself. Indubitably a vessel of some sort.

" 'It's a wonder we didn't run slap into her when coming in,' observed the second in command.

" 'Send a boat on board before she vanishes,' said the

commanding officer. He surmised that this was a coaster. It could hardly be anything else. But another thought came into his head suddenly. 'It is a wonder,' he said to his second in command, who had rejoined him after sending the boat away.

"By that time both of them had been struck by the fact that the ship so suddenly discovered had not manifested her presence by ringing her bell.

" 'We came in very quietly, that's true,' concluded the younger officer. 'But they must have heard our leadsman at least. We couldn't have passed her more than fifty yards off. The closest shave! They may even have made us out, since they were aware of something coming in. And the strange thing is that we never heard a sound from her. The fellows on board must have been holding their breath.'

" 'Aye,' said the commanding officer, thoughtfully.

"In due course the boarding-boat returned, appearing suddenly alongside, as though she had burrowed her way under the fog. The officer in charge came up to make his report, but the commanding officer didn't give him time to begin. He cried from a distance:

" 'Coaster, isn't she?'

" 'No, sir. A stranger—a neutral,' was the answer.

" 'No. Really! Well, tell us all about it. What is she doing here?'

"The young man stated then that he had been told a long and complicated story of engine troubles. But it was plausible enough from a strictly professional point of view and it had the usual features; disablement, dangerous drifting along the shore, weather more or less thick for days, fear of a gale, ultimately a resolve to go in and anchor anywhere on the coast, and so on. Fairly plausible.

" 'Engines still disabled?' inquired the commanding officer.

" 'No, sir. She has steam on them.'

"The commanding officer took his second aside. 'By Jove!' he said, 'you were right! They were holding their breaths as we passed them. They were.'

"But the second in command had his doubts now.

" 'A fog like this does muffle small sounds, sir,' he remarked. 'And what could his object be, after all?'

" 'To sneak out unnoticed,' answered the commanding officer.

" 'Then why didn't he? He might have done it, you know. Not exactly unnoticed, perhaps. I don't suppose he could have slipped his cable without making some noise. Still, in a minute or so he would have been lost to view—clean gone before we had made him out fairly. Yet he didn't.'

"They looked at each other. The commanding officer shook his head. Such suspicions as the one which had entered his head are not defended easily. He did not even state it openly. The boarding officer finished his report. The cargo of the ship was of a harmless and useful character. She was bound to an English port. Papers and everything in perfect order. Nothing suspicious to be detected anywhere.

"Then passing to the men, he reported the crew on deck as the usual lot. Engineers of the well-known type, and very full of their achievement in repairing the engines. The mate surly. The master a rather fine specimen of Northman, civil enough, but appeared to have been drinking. Seemed to be recovering from a regular bout of it.

" 'I told him I couldn't give him permission to proceed. He said he wouldn't dare to move his ship her own length out in such weather as this, permission or no permission. I left a man on board, though.'

" 'Quite right.'

"The commanding officer, after communing with his suspicions for a time, called his second aside.

" 'What if she were the very ship which had been feeding some infernal submarine or other?' he said in an undertone.

"The other started. Then, with conviction:

" 'She would get off scot-free. You couldn't prove it, sir.'

" 'I want to look into it myself.'

" 'From the report we've heard I'm afraid you couldn't even make a case for reasonable suspicion, sir.'

" 'I'll go on board all the same.'

"He had made up his mind. Curiosity is the great motive power of hatred and love. What did he expect to find? He could not have told anybody—not even himself.

"What he really expected to find there was the atmosphere, the atmosphere of gratuitous treachery, which in his view nothing could excuse; for he thought that even a passion of unrighteousness for its own sake could not excuse that. But could he detect it? Sniff it? Taste it? Receive some mysterious communication which would turn his invincible suspicions into a certitude strong enough to provoke action with all its risks?

"The master met him on the after-deck, looming up in the fog amongst the blurred shapes of the usual ship's fittings. He was a robust Northman, bearded, and in the force of his age. A round leather cap fitted his head closely. His hands were rammed deep into the pockets of his short leather jacket. He kept them there while he explained that at sea he lived in the chart-room, and led the way there, striding carelessly. Just before reaching the door under the bridge he staggered a little, recovered himself, flung it open, and stood aside, leaning his shoulder as if involuntarily against the side of the house, and staring vaguely into the fog-filled space. But he followed the commanding officer at once, flung the door to, snapped on the electric light, and hastened to thrust his hands back into his pockets, as though afraid of being seized by them either in friendship or in hostility.

"The place was stuffy and hot. The usual chart-rack overhead was full, and the chart on the table was kept unrolled by an empty cup standing on a saucer half-full of some spilt dark liquid. A slightly nibbled biscuit reposed on the chronometer-case. There were two settees, and one of them had been made up into a bed with a pillow and some blankets, which were now very much tumbled. The Northman let himself fall on it, his hands still in his pockets.

" 'Well, here I am,' he said, with a curious air of being surprised at the sound of his own voice.

"The commanding officer from the other settee observed the handsome, flushed face. Drops of fog hung on the yellow beard and moustaches of the Northman. The much darker eyebrows ran together in a puzzled frown, and suddenly he jumped up.

" 'What I mean is that I don't know where I am. I really don't,' he burst out, with extreme earnestness. 'Hang it all! I got turned around somehow. The fog has been after me for a week. More than a week. And then my engines broke down. I will tell you how it was.'

"He burst out into loquacity. It was not hurried, but it was insistent. It was not continuous for all that. It was broken by the most queer, thoughtful pauses. Each of these pauses lasted no more than a couple of seconds, and each had the profundity of an endless meditation. When he began again nothing betrayed in him the slightest consciousness of these intervals. There was the same fixed glance, the same unchanged earnestness of tone. He didn't know. Indeed, more than one of these pauses occurred in the middle of a sentence.

"The commanding officer listened to the tale. It struck him as more plausible than simple truth is in the habit of being. But that, perhaps, was prejudice. All the time the Northman was speaking the commanding officer had been aware of an inward voice, a grave murmur in the depths of his very own self, telling another tale, as if on purpose to keep alive in him his indignation and his anger with that baseness of greed or of mere outlook which lies often at the root of simple ideas.

"It was the story that had been already told to the boarding officer an hour or so before. The commanding officer nodded slightly at the Northman from time to time. The latter came to an end and turned his eyes away. He added, as an afterthought:

" 'Wasn't it enough to drive a man out of his mind with worry? And it's my first voyage to this part, too. And the ship's my own. Your officer has seen the papers. She isn't much, as you can see for yourself. Just an old cargo-boat. Bare living for my family.'

"He raised a big arm to point at a row of photographs plastering the bulkhead. That movement was ponderous, as if the arm had been made of lead. The commanding officer said, carelessly:

" 'You will be making a fortune yet for your family with this old ship.'

" 'Yes, if I don't lose her,' said the Northman, gloomily.

" 'I mean—out of this war,' added the commanding officer.

"The Northman stared at him in a curiously unseeing and at the same time interested manner, as only eyes of a particular blue shade can stare.

" 'And you wouldn't be angry at it,' he said, 'would you? You are too much of a gentleman. We didn't bring this on you. And suppose we sat down and cried. What good would that be? Let those cry who made the trouble,' he concluded, with energy. 'Time's money, you say. Well—*this* time *is* money. Oh! isn't it!'

"The commanding officer tried to keep under the feeling of immense disgust. He said to himself that it was unreasonable. Men were like that—moral cannibals feeding on each other's misfortunes. He said aloud:

"'You have made it perfectly plain how it is that you are here. Your log-book confirms you very minutely. Of course, a log-book may be cooked. Nothing easier.'

"The Northman never moved a muscle. He was gazing at the floor; he seemed not to have heard. He raised his head after a while.

"'But you can't suspect me of anything,' he muttered, negligently.

"The commanding officer thought: 'Why should he say this?'

"Immediately afterwards the man before him added: 'My cargo is for an English port.'

"His voice had turned husky for the moment. The commanding officer reflected: 'That's true. There can be nothing. I can't suspect him. Yet why was he lying with steam up in this fog—and then, hearing us come in, why didn't he give some sign of life? Why? Could it be anything else but a guilty conscience? He could tell by the leadsmen that this was a man-of-war.'

"Yes—why? The commanding officer went on thinking: 'Suppose I ask him and then watch his face. He will betray himself in some way. It's perfectly plain that the fellow *has* been drinking. Yes, he has been drinking; but he will have a lie ready all the same.' The commanding officer was one of those men who are made morally and almost physically uncomfortable by the mere thought of having to beat down a lie. He shrank from the act in scorn and disgust, which were invincible because more temperamental than moral.

"So he went out on deck instead and had the crew mustered formally for his inspection. He found them very much what the report of the boarding officer had led him to expect. And from their answers to his questions he could discover no flaw in the log-book story.

"He dismissed them. His impression of them was—a picked lot; have been promised a fistful of money each if this came off; all slightly anxious, but not frightened. Not a single one of them likely to give the show away. They don't feel in danger of their life. They know England and English ways too well!

"He felt alarmed at catching himself thinking as if his vaguest suspicions were turning into a certitude. For, indeed, there was no shadow of reason for his inferences. There was nothing to give away.

"He returned to the chart-room. The Northman had lingered behind there; and something subtly different in his bearing, more bold in his blue, glassy stare, induced the commanding officer to conclude that the fellow had snatched at the opportunity to take another swig at the bottle he must have had concealed somewhere.

"He noticed, too, that the Northman on meeting his eyes put on an elaborately surprised expression. At least, it seemed elaborated. Nothing could be trusted. And the Englishman felt himself with astonishing conviction faced by an enormous lie, solid like a wall, with no way round to get at the truth, whose ugly murderous face he seemed to see peeping over at him with a cynical grin.

" 'I dare say,' he began suddenly, 'you are wondering at

my proceedings, though I am not detaining you, am I? You wouldn't dare to move in this fog?'

"'I don't know where I am,' the Northman ejaculated earnestly. 'I really don't.'

"He looked around as if the very chart-room fittings were strange to him. The commanding officer asked him whether he had not seen any unusual objects floating about while he was at sea.

"'Objects! What objects? We were groping blind in the fog for days.'

"'We had a few clear intervals,' said the commanding officer. 'And I'll tell you what we have seen and the conclusion I've come to about it.'

"He told him in a few words. He heard the sound of a sharp breath indrawn through closed teeth. The Northman with his hand on the table stood absolutely motionless and dumb. He stood as if thunderstruck. Then he produced a fatuous smile.

"Or at least so it appeared to the commanding officer. Was this significant, or of no meaning whatever? He didn't know, he couldn't tell. All the truth had departed out of the world as if drawn in, absorbed in this monstrous villainy this man was—or was not—guilty of.

"'Shooting's too good for people that conceive neutrality in this pretty way,' remarked the commanding officer, after a silence.

"'Yes, yes, yes,' the Northman assented, hurriedly—then added an unexpected and dreamy-voiced 'Perhaps.'

"Was he pretending to be drunk, or only trying to appear

sober? His glance was straight, but it was somewhat glazed. His lips outlined themselves firmly under his yellow moustache. But they twitched. Did they twitch? And why was he drooping like this in his attitude?

" 'There's no perhaps about it,' pronounced the commanding officer sternly.

"The Northman had straightened himself. And unexpectedly he looked stern, too.

" 'No. But what about the tempters? Better kill that lot off. There's about four, five, six million of them,' he said, grimly; but in a moment changed into a whining key. 'But I had better hold my tongue. You have some suspicions.'

" 'No, I've no suspicions,' declared the commanding officer.

"He never faltered. At that moment he had the certitude. The air of the chart-room was thick with guilt and falsehood braving the discovery, defying simple right, common decency, all humanity of feeling, every scruple of conduct.

"The Northman drew a long breath. 'Well, we know that you English are gentlemen. But let us speak the truth. Why should we love you so very much? You haven't done anything to be loved. We don't love the other people, of course. They haven't done anything for that either. A fellow comes along with a bag of gold . . . I haven't been in Rotterdam my last voyage for nothing.'

" 'You may be able to tell something interesting, then, to our people when you come into port,' interjected the officer.

" 'I might. But you keep some people in your pay at Rotterdam. Let them report. I am a neutral—am I not? . . . Have you ever seen a poor man on one side and a bag of gold on the other? Of course, I couldn't be tempted. I haven't the nerve for it. Really I haven't. It's nothing to me. I am just talking openly for once.'

"'Yes. And I am listening to you,' said the commanding officer, quietly.

"The Northman leaned forward over the table. 'Now that I know you have no suspicions, I talk. You don't know what a poor man is. I do. I am poor myself. This old ship, she isn't much, and she is mortgaged, too. Bare living, no more. Of course, I wouldn't have the nerve. But a man who has nerve! See. The stuff he takes aboard looks like any other cargo—packages, barrels, tins, copper tubes—what not. He doesn't see it work. It isn't real to him. But he sees the gold. That's real. Of course, nothing could induce me. I suffer from an internal disease. I would either go crazy from anxiety—or—or—take to drink or something. The risk is too great. Why—ruin!'

"'It should be death.' The commanding officer got up, after this curt declaration, which the other received with a hard stare oddly combined with an uncertain smile. The officer's gorge rose at the atmosphere of murderous complicity which surrounded him, denser, more impenetrable, more acrid than the fog outside.

"'It's nothing to me,' murmured the Northman, swaying visibly.

"'Of course not,' assented the commanding officer, with a great effort to keep his voice calm and low. The certitude was strong with him. 'But I am going to clear all you fellows off this coast at once. And I will begin with you. You must leave in half an hour.'

"By that time the officer was walking along the deck with the Northman at his elbow.

" 'What! In this fog?' the latter cried out, huskily.

" 'Yes, you will have to go in this fog.'

" 'But I don't know where I am. I really don't.'

"The commanding officer turned round. A sort of fury possessed him. The eyes of the two men met. Those of the Northman expressed a profound amazement.

" 'Oh, you don't know how to get out.' The commanding officer spoke with composure, but his heart was beating with anger and dread. 'I will give you your course. Steer south-by-east-half-east for about four miles and then you will be clear to haul to the eastward for your port. The weather will clear up before very long.'

" 'Must I? What could induce me? I haven't the nerve.'

" 'And yet you must go. Unless you want to—'

" 'I don't want to,' panted the Northman. 'I've enough of it.'

"The commanding officer got over the side. The Northman remained still as if rooted to the deck. Before his boat reached his ship the commanding officer heard the steamer beginning to pick up her anchor. Then, shadowy in the fog, she steamed out on the given course.

" 'Yes,' he said to his officers, 'I let him go.' "

The narrator bent forward towards the couch, where no movement betrayed the presence of a living person.

"Listen," he said, forcibly. "That course would lead the Northman straight on a deadly ledge of rock. And the commanding officer gave it to him. He steamed out—ran on it—and went down. So he had spoken the truth. He did not know where he was. But it proves nothing. Nothing either way. It may have been the only truth in all his story. And yet . . . He seems to have been driven out by a menacing stare—nothing more."

He abandoned all pretence.

"Yes, I gave that course to him. It seemed to me a supreme test. I believe—no, I don't believe. I don't know. At the time I was certain. They all went down; and I don't know whether I have done stern retribution—or murder; whether I have added to the corpses that litter the bed of the unreadable sea the bodies of men completely innocent or basely guilty. I don't know. I shall never know."

He rose. The woman on the couch got up and threw her arms round his neck. Her eyes put two gleams in the deep shadow of the room. She knew his passion for truth, his horror of deceit, his humanity.

"Oh, my poor, poor—"

"I shall never know," he repeated sternly, disengaged himself, pressed her hands to his lips, and went out.

THE TALE

1. A definition of a tale is something "which is told; an oral recitation or recital." (*Webster's New Collegiate Dictionary,* 1958) How does this definition explain the title of this story?

2. What has he told her that was "everything worth saying in the world"?

3. Where does the tale proper begin? What is the purpose of the introductory material?

4. Twice Conrad refers to the commanding officer's looking for "—what he could see." Why does he repeat the phrase and twice precede it with a dash?

5. Why may "sunlight grow as odious as falsehood itself"? Don't we usually associate light with truth?

6. Note particularly the paragraph beginning, "And again he laughed faintly." As you read the rest of the story could you determine whether or not this paragraph correctly described the nature of the commanding officer?

7. Why does the voice from the sofa interrupt after, "He suffered—" with the line, "How well I can understand that in him!" Does her comment identify the commanding officer?

8. Note the fog which caused the men at their stations to lose sight of each other. What is the symbolic purpose of the lack of vision in so much of this tale?

9. After the discovery of the ship, the commanding officer and the second in command have different views regarding her. How does this foreshadow the last line of the story?

10. Do the pauses in the Northman's explanation tell you anything about him?

11. In what way is this story like "The Lady or the Tiger"? Is there more to this story than there is to that one?

12. Both Conrad and Hemingway have appeal to men readers. What traits do they have in common? In what ways do they differ?

STEPHEN CRANE

1871–1900

The Bride Comes to Yellow Sky

STEPHEN CRANE, *a native of New Jersey, attended Lafayette College and Syracuse University. He served as a war correspondent during the Greco-Turkish and the Spanish-American Wars. Although he wrote novels and some poetry, some of his best writing is in his short stories. His best-known novel,* The Red Badge of Courage, *tells of the conflicts within a young man facing battle for the first time.*

One of the first American realists, Mr. Crane lived for a time in England and died in Germany.

The great Pullman was whirling onward with such dignity of motion that a glance from the window seemed simply to prove that the plains of Texas were pouring eastward. Vast flats of green grass, dull-hued spaces of mesquit and cactus, little groups of frame houses, woods of light and tender trees, all were sweeping into the east, sweeping over the horizon, a precipice.

A newly married pair had boarded this coach at San Antonio. The man's face was reddened from many days in the wind and sun, and a direct result of his new black clothes was that his brick-coloured hands were constantly performing in a most conscious fashion. From time to time he looked down respectfully at his attire. He sat with a hand on each knee, like a man waiting in a barber's shop. The glances he devoted to other passengers were furtive and shy.

The bride was not pretty, nor was she very young. She wore a dress of blue cashmere, with small reservations of velvet here and there, and with steel buttons abounding. She continually twisted her head to regard her puff sleeves, very stiff, straight, and high. They embarrassed her. It was quite apparent that she had cooked, and that she expected to cook, dutifully. The blushes caused by the careless scrutiny of some passengers as she had entered the car were strange to see upon this plain, under-class countenance, which was drawn in placid, almost emotionless lines.

They were evidently very happy. "Ever been in a parlour-car before?" he asked, smiling with delight.

"No," she answered; "I never was. It's fine, ain't it?"

"Great! And then after a while we'll go forward to the diner, and get a big lay-out. Finest meal in the world. Charge a dollar."

"Oh, do they?" cried the bride. "Charge a dollar? Why, that's too much—for us—ain't it, Jack?"

"Not this trip, anyhow," he answered bravely. "We're going to go the whole thing."

Later he explained to her about the trains. "You see, it's a thousand miles from one end of Texas to the other; and this train runs right across it, and never stops but four times." He had the pride of an owner. He pointed out to her the dazzling fittings of the coach; and in truth her eyes opened wider as she contemplated the sea-green figured velvet, the shining brass, silver, and glass, the wood that gleamed as darkly brilliant as the surface of a pool of oil. At one end a bronze figure sturdily held a support for a separated chamber, and at convenient places on the ceiling were frescos in olive and silver.

To the minds of the pair, their surroundings reflected the glory of their marriage that morning in San Antonio; this was the environment of their new estate; and the man's face in particular beamed with an elation that made him appear ridiculous to the Negro porter. This individual at times surveyed them from afar with an amused and superior grin. On other occasions he bullied them with skill in ways that did not make it exactly plain to them that they were being bullied. He subtly used all the manners of the most unconquerable kind of snobbery. He oppressed them; but of this oppression they had small knowledge, and they speedily forgot that infrequently a number of travellers covered them with stares of derisive enjoyment. Historically there was supposed to be something infinitely humorous in their situation.

"We are due in Yellow Sky at 3:42," he said, looking tenderly into her eyes.

"Oh, are we?" she said, as if she had not been aware of it. To evince surprise at her husband's statement was part of her wifely amiability. She took from a pocket a little silver watch; and as she held it before her, and stared at it with a frown of attention, the new husband's face shone.

"I bought it in San Anton' from a friend of mine," he told her gleefully.

"It's seventeen minutes past twelve," she said, looking up at him with a kind of shy and clumsy coquetry. A passenger, noting this play, grew excessively sardonic, and winked at himself in one of the numerous mirrors.

At last they went to the dining-car. Two rows of Negro waiters, in glowing white suits, surveyed their entrance with the interest, and also the equanimity, of men who had been forewarned. The pair fell to the lot of a waiter who happened to feel pleasure in steering them through their meal. He viewed them with the manner of a fatherly pilot, his countenance radiant with benevolence. The patronage, entwined with the ordinary deference, was not plain to them. And yet, as they returned to their coach, they showed in their faces a sense of escape.

To the left, miles down a long purple slope, was a little ribbon of mist where moved the keening Rio Grande. The train was approaching it at an angle, and the apex was Yellow Sky. Presently it was apparent that, as the distance from Yellow Sky grew shorter, the husband became commensurately restless. His brick-red hands were more insistent in their prominence. Occasionally he was even rather absent-minded and far-away when the bride leaned forward and addressed him.

As a matter of truth, Jack Potter was beginning to find the shadow of a deed weigh upon him like a leaden slab. He, the town marshal of Yellow Sky, a man known, liked, and feared in his corner, a prominent person, had gone to San Antonio to meet a girl he believed he loved, and there, after the usual prayers, had actually induced her to marry him, without consulting Yellow Sky for any part of the transaction. He was now bringing his bride before an innocent and unsuspecting community.

Of course people in Yellow Sky married as it pleased them, in accordance with a general custom; but such was Potter's thought of his duty to his friends, or of their idea of his duty, or of an unspoken form which does not control men in these matters, that he felt he was heinous. He had committed an extraordinary crime. Face to face with this girl in San Antonio, and spurred by his sharp impulse, he had gone headlong over all the social hedges. At San Antonio he was like a man hidden in the dark. A knife to sever any friendly duty, any form, was easy to his hand in that remote city. But the hour of Yellow Sky—the hour of daylight—was approaching.

He knew full well that his marriage was an important thing to his town. It could only be exceeded by the burning of the new hotel. His friends could not forgive him. Frequently he had reflected on the advisability of telling them by telegraph, but a new cowardice had been upon him. He feared to do it. And now the train was hurrying him toward a scene of amazement, glee, and reproach. He glanced out of the window at the line of haze swinging slowly in toward the train.

Yellow Sky had a kind of brass band, which played painfully, to the delight of the populace. He laughed without heart as he thought of it. If the citizens could dream of his prospective arrival with his bride, they would parade the band at the station and escort them, amid cheers and laughing congratulations, to his adobe home.

He resolved that he would use all the devices of speed and plainscraft in making the journey from the station to his house. Once within that safe citadel, he could issue some sort of vocal bulletin, and then not go among the citizens until they had time to wear off a little of their enthusiasm.

The bride looked anxiously at him. "What's worrying you, Jack?"

He laughed again. "I'm not worrying, girl; I'm only thinking of Yellow Sky."

She flushed in comprehension.

A sense of mutual guilt invaded their minds and developed a finer tenderness. They looked at each other with eyes softly aglow. But Potter often laughed the same nervous laugh; the flush upon the bride's face seemed quite permanent.

The traitor to the feelings of Yellow Sky narrowly watched the speeding landscape. "We're nearly there," he said.

Presently the porter came and announced the proximity of Potter's home. He held a brush in his hand, and, with all his airy superiority gone, he brushed Potter's new clothes as the latter slowly turned this way and that way. Potter fumbled out a coin and gave it to the porter, as he had seen others do. It was a heavy and muscle-bound business, as that of a man shoeing his first horse.

The porter took their bag, and as the train began to slow

they moved forward to the hooded platform of the car. Presently the two engines and their long string of coaches rushed into the station of Yellow Sky.

"They have to take water here," said Potter, from a constricted throat and in mournful cadence, as one announcing death. Before the train stopped his eye had swept the length of the platform, and he was glad and astonished to see there was none upon it but the station-agent, who, with a slightly hurried and anxious air, was walking toward the water-tanks. When the train had halted, the porter alighted first, and placed in position a little temporary step.

"Come on, girl," said Potter, hoarsely. As he helped her down they each laughed on a false note. He took the bag from the negro, and bade his wife cling to his arm. As they slunk rapidly away, his hang-dog glance perceived that they were unloading the two trunks, and also that the station-agent, far ahead near the baggage-car, had turned and was running toward him, making gestures. He laughed, and groaned as he laughed, when he noted the first effect of his marital bliss upon Yellow Sky. He gripped his wife's arm firmly to his side, and they fled. Behind them the porter stood, chuckling fatuously.

II

The California express on the Southern Railway was due at Yellow Sky in twenty-one minutes. There were six men at the bar of the Weary Gentleman saloon. One was a drummer who talked a great deal and rapidly; three were Texans who did not care to talk at that time; and two were Mexican sheep-herders, who did not talk as a general practice in the Weary Gentleman saloon. The barkeeper's dog lay on the board walk that crossed in front of the door. His head was on his paws, and he glanced drowsily here and there with the constant vigilance of a dog that is kicked on occasion. Across the sandy street were some vivid green grass-plots, so wonderful in appearance, amid the sands that burned near them in a blazing sun, that they caused a doubt in the mind. They exactly resembled the grass mats used to represent lawns on the stage. At the cooler end of the railway station, a man without a coat sat in a tilted chair and smoked his pipe. The fresh-cut bank of the Rio Grande circled near the town, and there could be seen beyond it a great plum-coloured plain of mesquit.

Save for the busy drummer and his companions in the saloon, Yellow Sky was dozing. The new-comer leaned gracefully upon the bar, and recited many tales with the confidence of a bard who has come upon a new field.

"—and at the moment that the old man fell downstairs with the bureau in his arms, the old woman was coming up with two scuttles of coal, and of course—"

The drummer's tale was interrupted by a young man who suddenly appeared in the open door. He cried: "Scratchy Wilson's drunk, and has turned loose with both hands." The two Mexicans at once set down their glasses and faded out of the rear entrance of the saloon.

The drummer, innocent and jocular, answered: "All

right, old man. S'pose he has? Come in and have a drink, anyhow."

But the information had made such an obvious cleft in every skull in the room that the drummer was obliged to see its importance. All had become instantly solemn. "Say," said he, mystified, "what is this?" His three companions made the introductory gesture of eloquent speech; but the young man at the door forestalled them.

"It means, my friend," he answered, as he came into the saloon, "that for the next two hours this town won't be a health resort."

The barkeeper went to the door, and locked and barred it; reaching out of the window, he pulled in heavy wooden shutters, and barred them. Immediately a solemn, chapel-like gloom was upon the place. The drummer was looking from one to another.

"But say," he cried, "what is this, anyhow? You don't mean there is going to be a gun-fight?"

"Don't know whether there'll be a fight or not," answered one man, grimly; "but there'll be some shootin'—some good shootin'."

The young man who had warned them waved his hand. "Oh, there'll be a fight fast enough, if any one wants it. Anybody can get a fight out there in the street. There's a fight just waiting."

The drummer seemed to be swayed between the interest of a foreigner and a perception of personal danger.

"What did you say his name was?" he asked.

"Scratchy Wilson," they answered in chorus.

"And will he kill anybody? What are you going to do? Does this happen often? Does he rampage around like this once a week or so? Can he break in that door?"

"No; he can't break down that door," replied the barkeeper. "He's tried it three times. But when he comes you'd better lay down on the floor, stranger. He's dead sure to shoot at it, and a bullet may come through."

Thereafter the drummer kept a strict eye upon the door. The time had not yet been called for him to hug the floor, but, as a minor precaution, he sidled near to the wall. "Will he kill anybody?" he said again.

The men laughed low and scornfully at the question.

"He's out to shoot, and he's out for trouble. Don't see any good in experimentin' with him."

"But what do you do in a case like this? What do you do?"

A man responded: "Why, he and Jack Potter—"

"But," in chorus the other men interrupted, "Jack Potter's in San Anton'."

"Well, who is he? What's he got to do with it?"

"Oh, he's the town marshal. He goes out and fights Scratchy when he gets on one of these tears."

"Wow!" said the drummer, mopping his brow. "Nice job he's got."

The voices had toned away to mere whisperings. The drummer wished to ask further questions, which were born of an increasing anxiety and bewilderment; but when he attempted them, the men merely looked at him in irritation and motioned him to remain silent. A tense waiting hush was upon them. In the deep shadows of the room their eyes shone as they listened for sounds from the street. One man made three gestures at the barkeeper; and the latter, moving like a ghost, handed him a glass and a bottle. The man poured a full glass of whisky, and set down the bottle noiselessly. He gulped the whisky in a swallow, and turned again toward the door in immovable silence. The drummer saw that the barkeeper, without a sound, had taken a Winchester from beneath the bar. Later he saw this individual beckoning to him, so he tiptoed across the room.

"You better come with me back of the bar."

"No, thanks," said the drummer, perspiring; "I'd rather be where I can make a break for the back door."

Whereupon the man of bottles made a kindly but peremptory gesture. The drummer obeyed it, and, finding himself seated on a box with his head below the level of the bar, balm was laid upon his soul at sight of various zinc and copper fittings that bore a resemblance to armour-plate. The barkeeper took a seat comfortably upon an adjacent box.

"You see," he whispered, "this here Scratchy Wilson is a wonder with a gun—a perfect wonder; and when he goes on the war-trail, we hunt our holes—naturally. He's about the last one of the old gang that used to hang out along the river here. He's a terror when he's drunk. When he's sober he's all right—kind of simple—wouldn't hurt a fly—nicest fellow in town. But when he's drunk—whoo!"

There were periods of stillness. "I wish Jack Potter was back from San Anton'," said the barkeeper. "He shot Wilson up once—in the leg—and he would sail in and pull out the kinks of this thing."

Presently they heard from a distance the sound of a shot, followed by three wild yowls. It instantly removed a bond from the men in the darkened saloon. There was a shuffling of feet. They looked at each other. "Here he comes," they said.

III

A man in a maroon-coloured flannel shirt, which had been purchased for purposes of decoration, and made principally by some Jewish women on the East Side of New York, rounded a corner and walked into the middle of the main street of Yellow Sky. In either hand the man held a long, heavy, blue-black revolver. Often he yelled, and these cries rang through a semblance of a deserted village, shrilly flying over the roofs in a volume that seemed to have no relation to the ordinary vocal strength of a man. It was as if the surrounding stillness formed the arch of a tomb over him. These cries of ferocious challenge rang against walls of silence. And his boots had red tops with gilded imprints, of the kind beloved in winter by little sledding boys on the hillsides of New England.

The man's face flamed in a rage begot of whisky. His eyes, rolling, and yet keen for ambush, hunted the still doorways and windows. He walked with the creeping movement of the midnight cat. As it occurred to him, he roared menacing information. The long revolvers in his hands were as easy as straws; they were moved with an electric swiftness. The little fingers of each hand played sometimes in a musician's way. Plain from the low collar of the shirt, the cords of his neck straightened and sank, straightened and sank, as passion moved him. The only sounds were his terrible invitations. The calm adobes preserved their demeanour at the passing of this small thing in the middle of the street.

There was no offer of fight—no offer of fight. The man called to the sky. There were no attractions. He bellowed and fumed and swayed his revolvers here and everywhere.

The dog of the barkeeper of the Weary Gentleman saloon had not appreciated the advance of events. He yet lay dozing in front of his master's door. At sight of the dog, the man paused and raised his revolver humorously. At sight of the man, the dog sprang up and walked diagonally away, with a sullen head, and growling. The man yelled, and the dog broke into a gallop. As it was about to enter an alley, there was a loud noise, a whistling, and something spat the ground directly before it. The dog screamed, and, wheeling in terror, galloped headlong in a new direction. Again there was a noise, a whistling, and sand was kicked viciously before it. Fear-stricken, the dog turned and flurried like an animal in a pen. The man stood laughing, his weapons at his hips.

Ultimately the man was attracted by the closed door of the Weary Gentleman saloon. He went to it and, hammering with a revolver, demanded drink.

The door remaining imperturbable, he picked up a bit of paper from the walk, and nailed it to the framework with a knife. He then turned his back contemptuously upon this popular resort and, walking to the opposite side of the street and spinning there on his heel quickly and lithely, fired at the bit of paper. He missed it by a half-inch. He swore at himself, and went away. Later he comfortably fusilladed the windows of his most intimate friend. The man was playing with this town; it was a toy for him.

But still there was no offer of fight. The name of Jack Potter, his ancient antagonist, entered his mind, and he concluded that it would be a glad thing if he should go to Potter's house, and by bombardment induce him to come out and fight. He moved in the direction of his desire, chanting Apache scalp-music.

When he arrived at it, Potter's house presented the same still front as had the other adobes. Taking up a strategic position, the man howled a challenge. But this house regarded him as might a great stone god. It gave no sign. After a decent wait, the man howled further challenges, mingling with them wonderful epithets.

Presently there came the spectacle of a man churning himself into deepest rage over the immobility of a house. He fumed at it as the winter wind attacks a prairie cabin in the North. To the distance there should have gone the sound of a tumult like the fighting of two hundred Mexicans. As necessity bade him, he paused for breath or to reload his revolvers.

IV

Potter and his bride walked sheepishly and with speed. Sometimes they laughed together shamefacedly and low.

"Next corner, dear," he said finally.

They put forth the efforts of a pair walking bowed against a strong wind. Potter was about to raise a finger to point the first appearance of the new home when, as they circled the corner, they came face to face with a man in a maroon-coloured shirt, who was feverishly pushing cartridges into a large revolver. Upon the instant the man dropped his revolver to the ground and, like lightning, whipped another from its holster. The second weapon was aimed at the bridegroom's chest.

There was a silence. Potter's mouth seemed to be merely a grave for his tongue. He exhibited an instinct to at once loosen his arm from the woman's grip, and he dropped the bag to the sand. As for the bride, her face had gone as yellow as old cloth. She was a slave to hideous rites, gazing at the apparitional snake.

The two men faced each other at a distance of three paces. He of the revolver smiled with a new and quiet ferocity.

"Tried to sneak up on me," he said. "Tried to sneak up on me!" His eyes grew more baleful. As Potter made a slight movement, the man thrust his revolver venomously forward. "No; don't you do it, Jack Potter. Don't you move a finger toward a gun just yet. Don't you move an eyelash. The time has come for me to settle with you, and I'm goin' to do it my own way, and loaf along with no interferin'. So if you don't want a gun bent on you, just mind what I tell you."

Potter looked at his enemy. "I ain't got a gun on me, Scratchy," he said. "Honest, I ain't." He was stiffening and steadying, but yet somewhere at the back of his mind a vision of the Pullman floated: the sea-green figured velvet, the shining brass, silver, and glass, the wood that gleamed as darkly brilliant as the surface of a pool of oil—all the glory of the marriage, the environment of the new estate. "You know I fight when it comes to fighting, Scratchy Wilson; but I ain't got a gun on me. You'll have to do all the shootin' yourself."

His enemy's face went livid. He stepped forward, and lashed his weapon to and fro before Potter's chest. "Don't you tell me you ain't got no gun on you, you whelp. Don't tell me no lie like that. There ain't a man in Texas ever seen you without a gun. Don't take me for no kid." His eyes blazed with light, and his throat worked like a pump.

"I ain't takin' you for no kid," answered Potter. His heels had not moved an inch backward. "I'm takin' you for a damn fool. I tell you I ain't got a gun, and I ain't. If you're goin' to shoot me up, you better begin now; you'll never get a chance like this again."

So much enforced reasoning had told on Wilson's rage; he was calmer. "If you ain't got a gun, why ain't you got a gun?" he sneered. "Been to Sunday-school?"

"I ain't got a gun because I've just come from San Anton' with my wife. I'm married," said Potter. "And if I'd thought there was going to be any galoots like you prowling around when I brought my wife home, I'd had a gun, and don't you forget it."

"Married!" said Scratchy, not at all comprehending.

"Yes, married. I'm married," said Potter, distinctly.

"Married?" said Scratchy. Seemingly for the first time, he saw the drooping, drowning woman at the other man's side. "No!" he said. He was like a creature allowed a glimpse of another world. He moved a pace backward, and his arm, with the revolver, dropped to his side. "Is this the lady?" he asked.

"Yes; this is the lady," answered Potter.

There was another period of silence.

"Well," said Wilson at last, slowly, "I s'pose it's all off now."

"It's all off if you say so, Scratchy. You know I didn't make the trouble." Potter lifted his valise.

"Well, I 'low it's off, Jack," said Wilson. He was looking at the ground. "Married!" He was not a student of chivalry; it was merely that in the presence of this foreign condition he was a simple child of the earlier plains. He picked up his starboard revolver, and placing both weapons in their holsters, he went away. His feet made funnel-shaped tracks in the heavy sand.

THE BRIDE COMES TO YELLOW SKY

1. How does Crane build suspense about the reception of Potter and his bride?

2. Where is the physical conflict first suggested?
3. Why does the traveling salesman ask twice, "Will he kill anybody"?
4. Which details in the description of Scratchy Wilson make him seem a dangerous man?
5. Why is the incident of the dog important?
6. What one sentence best indicates the courage of Potter?
7. Why is the bride described as "drowning" during the altercation between Potter and Wilson?
8. Are you satisfied with the quiet ending? Why?
9. Notice that this story has four distinct scenes. How does Crane manage to sustain unity, or oneness of impression?
10. Would you classify this story as a Western? A humorous story? An adventure story? Or what other type?

WILLIAM FAULKNER

1897–1962

The Tall Men

WILLIAM FAULKNER, *Pulitzer and Nobel Prize winner, was a descendant of two once-wealthy and influential Southern families. Born in Mississippi, Faulkner made that state his home all his life. During World War I he declined to serve in the American forces because of his dislike for "the Yankees" and enlisted in the Canadian Air Force. His first novel,* Soldier's Pay, *was based on his war experiences.*

Mr. Faulkner's interests, in addition to writing, were hunting, fishing, and farming.

They passed the dark bulk of the cotton gin. Then they saw the lamplit house and the other car, the doctor's coupé, just stopping at the gate, and they could hear the hound baying.

"Here we are," the old deputy marshal said.

"What's that other car?" the younger man said, the stranger, the state draft investigator.

"Doctor Schofield's," the marshal said. "Lee McCallum asked me to send him out when I telephoned we were coming."

"You mean you warned them?" the investigator said. "You telephoned ahead that I was coming out with a warrant for these two evaders? Is this how you carry out the orders of the United States Government?"

The marshal was a lean, clean old man who chewed tobacco, who had been born and lived in the county all his life.

"I understood all you wanted was to arrest these two McCallum boys and bring them back to town," he said.

"It was!" the investigator said. "And now you have warned them, given them a chance to run. Possibly put the Government to the expense of hunting them down with troops. Have you forgotten that you are under a bond yourself?"

"I ain't forgot it," the marshal said. "And ever since we left Jefferson I been trying to tell you something for you not to forget. But I reckon it will take these McCallums to impress that on you. . . . Pull in behind the other car. We'll try to find out first just how sick whoever it is that is sick is."

The investigator drew up behind the other car and switched off and blacked out his lights. "These people," he said. Then he thought, *But this doddering, tobacco-chewing old man is one of them, too, despite the honor and pride of his office, which should have made him different.* So he didn't speak it aloud, removing the keys and getting out of the car, and then locking the car itself, rolling the windows up first, thinking, *These people who lie about and conceal the ownership of land and property in order to hold relief jobs which they have no intention of performing, standing on their constitutional rights against having to work, who jeopardize the very job itself through petty and transparent subterfuge to acquire a free mattress which they intend to attempt to sell; who would relinquish even the job, if by so doing they could receive free food and a place, any rathole, in town to sleep in; who, as farmers, make false statements to get seed loans which they will later misuse, and then react in loud vituperative outrage and astonishment when caught at it. And then, when at long last a suffering and threatened Government asks one thing of them in return, one thing simply, which is to put their names down on a selective-service list, they refuse to do it.*

The old marshal had gone on. The investigator followed, through a stout paintless gate in a picket fence, up a broad brick walk between rows of old shabby cedars, toward the rambling and likewise paintless sprawl of the two-story house in the open hall of which the soft lamplight glowed and the lower story of which, as the investigator now perceived, was of logs.

He saw a hall full of soft lamplight beyond a stout paintless gallery running across the log front, from beneath which the same dog which they had heard, a big hound, came booming again, to stand foursquare facing them in the walk, bellowing, until a man's voice spoke to it from the house. He followed the marshal up the steps onto the gallery. Then he saw the man standing in the door, waiting for them to approach—a man of about forty-five, not tall, but blocky, with a brown, still face and horseman's hands, who looked at him once, brief and hard, and then no more, speaking to the marshal, "Howdy, Mr. Gombault. Come in."

"Howdy, Rafe," the marshal said. "Who's sick?"

"Buddy," the other said. "Slipped and caught his leg in the hammer mill this afternoon."

"Is it bad?" the marshal said.

"It looks bad to me," the other said. "That's why we sent for the doctor instead of bringing him in to town. We couldn't get the bleeding stopped."

"I'm sorry to hear that," the marshal said. "This is Mr. Pearson." Once more the investigator found the other looking at him, the brown eyes still, courteous enough in the brown face, the hand he offered hard enough, but the clasp quite limp, quite cold. The marshal was still speaking. "From Jackson. From the draft board." Then he said, and the investigator could discern no change whatever in his tone: "He's got a warrant for the boys."

The investigator could discern no change whatever anywhere. The limp hard hand merely withdrew from his, the still face now looking at the marshal. "You mean we have declared war?"

"No," the marshal said.

"That's not the question, Mr. McCallum," the investigator said. "All required of them was to register. Their numbers might not even be drawn this time; under the law of averages, they probably would not be. But they refused—failed, anyway—to register."

"I see," the other said. He was not looking at the investigator. The investigator couldn't tell certainly if he was even looking at the marshal, although he spoke to him, "You want to see Buddy? The doctor's with him now."

"Wait," the investigator said. "I'm sorry about your brother's accident, but I—" The marshal glanced back at him for a moment, his shaggy gray brows beetling, with something at once courteous yet a little impatient about the glance, so that during the instant the investigator sensed from the old marshal the same quality which had been in the other's brief look. The investigator was a man of better than average intelligence; he was already becoming aware of something a little different here from what he had expected. But he had been in relief work in the state several years, dealing almost exclusively with country people, so he still believed he knew them. So he looked at the old marshal, thinking, *Yes. The same sort of people, despite the office, the authority and responsibility which should have changed him.* Thinking again, *These people. These people.* "I intend to take the night train back to Jackson," he said. "My reservation is already made. Serve the warrant and we will—"

"Come along," the old marshal said. "We are going to have plenty of time."

So he followed—there was nothing else to do—fuming and seething, attempting in the short length of the hall to regain control of himself in order to control the situation, because he realized now that if the situation were controlled, it would devolve upon him to control it; that if their departure with their prisoners were expedited, it must be himself and not the old marshal who would expedite it. He had been right. The doddering old officer was not only at bottom one of these people, he had apparently been corrupted anew to his old, inherent, shiftless sloth and unreliability merely by entering the house. So he followed in turn, down the hall and into a bedroom; whereupon he looked about him not only with amazement but with something very like terror. The room was a big room, with a bare unpainted floor, and besides the bed, it contained only a chair or two and one other piece of old-fashioned furniture. Yet to the investigator it seemed so filled with tremendous men cast in the same mold as the man who had met them that the very walls themselves must bulge. Yet they were not big, not tall, and it was not vitality, exuberance, because they made no sound, merely looking quietly at him where he stood in the door, with faces bearing an almost identical stamp of kinship—a thin, almost frail old man of about seventy, slightly taller than the others; a second one, white-haired, too, but otherwise identical with the man who had met them at the door; a third one about the same age as the man who had met them, but with something delicate in his face and something tragic and dark and wild in the same dark eyes; the two absolutely identical blue-eyed youths; and lastly the blue-eyed man on the bed over which the doctor, who might have been a city doctor, in his neat city suit, leaned—all of them turning to look quietly at him and the marshal as they entered. And he saw, past the doctor, the slit trousers of the man on the bed and the exposed, bloody, mangled leg, and he turned sick, stopping just inside the door under that quiet, steady regard while the marshal went up to the man who lay on the bed, smoking a cob pipe, a big, old-fashioned, wicker-covered demijohn, such as the investigator's grandfather had kept his whisky in, on the table beside him.

"Well, Buddy," the marshal said, "this is bad."

"Ah, it was my own damn fault," the man on the bed said. "Stuart kept warning me about that frame I was using."

"That's correct," the second old one said.

Still the others said nothing. They just looked steadily and quietly at the investigator until the marshal turned slightly and said, "This is Mr. Pearson. From Jackson. He's got a warrant for the boys."

Then the man on the bed said, "What for?"

"That draft business, Buddy," the marshal said.

"We're not at war now," the man on the bed said.

"No," the marshal said. "It's that new law. They didn't register."

"What are you going to do with them?"

"It's a warrant, Buddy. Swore out."

"That means jail."

"It's a warrant," the old marshal said. Then the investigator saw that the man on the bed was watching him, puffing steadily at the pipe.

"Pour me some whisky, Jackson," he said.

"No," the doctor said. "He's had too much already."

"Pour me some whisky, Jackson," the man on the bed said. He puffed steadily at the pipe, looking at the investigator. "You come from the Government?" he said.

"Yes," the investigator said. "They should have registered. That's all required of them yet. They did not—" His voice ceased, while the seven pairs of eyes contemplated him, and the man on the bed puffed steadily.

"We would have still been here," the man on the bed said. "We wasn't going to run." He turned his head. The two youths were standing side by side at the foot of the bed. "Anse, Lucius," he said.

To the investigator it sounded as if they answered as one, "Yes, father."

"This gentleman has come all the way from Jackson to say the Government is ready for you. I reckon the quickest place to enlist will be Memphis. Go upstairs and pack."

The investigator started, moved forward. "Wait!" he cried.

But Jackson, the eldest, had forestalled him. He said, "Wait," also, and now they were not looking at the investigator. They were looking at the doctor.

"What about his leg?" Jackson said.

"Look at it," the doctor said. "He almost amputated it himself. It won't wait. And he can't be moved now. I'll need my nurse to help me, and some ether, provided he hasn't had too much whisky to stand the anesthetic too. One of you can drive to town in my car. I'll telephone—"

"Ether?" the man on the bed said. "What for? You just said yourself it's pretty near off now. I could whet up one of Jackson's butcher knives and finish it myself, with another drink or two. Go on. Finish it."

"You couldn't stand any more shock," the doctor said. "This is whisky talking now."

"Shucks," the other said. "One day in France we was running through a wheat field and I saw the machine gun, coming across the wheat, and I tried to jump it like you would jump a fence rail somebody was swinging at your middle, only I never made it. And I was on the ground then, and along toward dark that began to hurt, only about that time something went whang on the back of my helmet, like when you hit a anvil, so I never knowed nothing else until I woke up. There was a heap of us racked up along a bank outside a field dressing station, only it took a long time for the doctor to get around to all of us, and by that time it was hurting bad. This here ain't hurt none to speak of since I got a-holt of this johnny-jug. You go on and finish it. If it's help you need, Stuart and Rafe will help you. . . . Pour me a drink, Jackson."

This time the doctor raised the demijohn and examined the level of the liquor. "There's a good quart gone," he said, "If you've drunk a quart of whisky since four o'clock, I doubt if you could stand the anesthetic. Do you think you could stand it if I finished it now?"

"Yes, finish it. I've ruined it; I want to get shut of it."

The doctor looked about at the others, at the still, identical faces watching him. "If I had him in town, in the hospital, with a nurse to watch him, I'd probably wait until he got over this first shock and got the whisky out of his system. But he can't be moved now, and I can't stop the bleeding like this, and even if I had ether or a local anesthetic—"

"Shucks," the man on the bed said. "God never made no better local nor general comfort or anesthetic neither than what's in this johnny-jug. And this ain't Jackson's leg nor Stuart's nor Rafe's nor Lee's. It's mine. I done started it; I reckon I can finish cutting it off any way I want to."

But the doctor was still looking at Jackson. "Well, Mr. McCallum?" he said. "You're the oldest."

But it was Stuart who answered. "Yes," he said. "Finish it. What do you want? Hot water, I reckon."

"Yes," the doctor said. "Some clean sheets. Have you got a big table you can move in here?"

"The kitchen table," the man who had met them at the door said. "Me and the boys—"

"Wait," the man on the bed said. "The boys won't have time to help you." He looked at them again. "Anse, Lucius," he said.

Again it seemed to the investigator that they answered as one, "Yes, father."

"This gentleman yonder is beginning to look impatient. You better start. Come to think of it, you won't need to pack. You will have uniforms in a day or two. Take the truck. There won't be nobody to drive you to Memphis and bring the truck back, so you can leave it at the Gayoso Feed Company until we can send for it. I'd like for you to enlist into the old Sixth Infantry, where I used to be. But I reckon that's too much to hope, and you'll just have to chance where they send you. But it likely won't matter, once you are in. The Government done right by me in my day, and it will do right by you. You just enlist wherever they want to send you, need you, and obey your sergeants and officers until you find out how to be soldiers. Obey them, but remember your name and don't take nothing from no man. You can go now."

"Wait!" the investigator cried again; again he started, moved forward into the center of the room. "I protest this!

I'm sorry about Mr. McCallum's accident. I'm sorry about the whole business. But it's out of my hands and out of his hands now. This charge, failure to register according to law, has been made and the warrant issued. It cannot be evaded this way. The course of the action must be completed before any other step can be taken. They should have thought of this when these boys failed to register. If Mr. Gombault refuses to serve this warrant, I will serve it myself and take these men back to Jefferson with me to answer this charge as made. And I must warn Mr. Gombault that he will be cited for contempt!"

The old marshal turned, his shaggy eyebrows beetling again, speaking down to the investigator as if he were a child, "Ain't you found out yet that me or you neither ain't going nowhere for a while?"

"What?" the investigator cried. He looked about at the grave faces once more contemplating him with that remote and speculative regard. "Am I being threatened?" he cried.

"Ain't nobody paying any attention to you at all," the marshal said. "Now you just be quiet for a while, and you will be all right, and after a while we can go back to town."

So he stopped again and stood while the grave, contemplative faces freed him once more of that impersonal and unbearable regard, and saw the two youths approach the bed and bend down in turn and kiss their father on the mouth, and then turn as one and leave the room, passing him without even looking at him. And sitting in the lamplit hall beside the old marshal, the bedroom door closed now, he heard the truck start up and back and turn and go down the road, the sound of it dying away, ceasing, leaving the still, hot night—the Mississippi Indian summer, which had already outlasted half of November—filled with the loud last shrilling of the summer's cicadas, as though they, too, were aware of the imminent season of cold weather and of death.

"I remember old Anse," the marshal said pleasantly, chattily, in that tone in which an adult addresses a strange child. "He's been dead fifteen–sixteen years now. He was about sixteen when the old war broke out, and he walked all the way to Virginia to get into it. He could have enlisted and fought right here at home, but his ma was a Carter, so wouldn't nothing do him but to go all the way back to Virginia to do his fighting, even though he hadn't never seen Virginia before himself; walked all the way back to a land he hadn't never even seen before and enlisted in Stonewall Jackson's army and stayed in it all through the Valley, and right up to Chancellorsville, where them Carolina boys shot Jackson by mistake, and right on up to that morning in 'Sixty-five when Sheridan's cavalry blocked the road from Appomattox to the Valley, where they might have got away again. And he walked back to Mississippi with just about what he had carried away with him when he left, and he got married and built the first story of this house—this here log story we're in right now—and started getting them boys—Jackson and Stuart and Raphael and Lee and Buddy.

"Buddy come along late, late enough to be in the other war, in France in it. You heard him in there. He brought back two medals, an American medal and a French one, and no man knows till yet how he got them, just what he done. I don't believe he even told Jackson and Stuart and them. He hadn't hardly got back home, with them numbers on his uniform and the wound stripes and them two medals, before he had found him a girl, found her right off, and a year later them twin boys was born, the livin', spittin' image of old Anse McCallum. If old Anse had just been about seventy-five years younger, the three of them might have been thriblets. I remember them—two little critters exactly alike, and wild as spikehorn bucks, running around here day and night both with a pack of coon dogs until they got big enough to help Buddy and Stuart and Lee with the farm and the gin, and Rafe with the horses and mules, when he would breed and raise and train them and take them to Memphis to sell, right on up to three, four years back, when they went to the agricultural college for a year to learn more about white-face cattle.

"That was after Buddy and them had quit raising cotton. I remember that too. It was when the Government first begun to interfere with how a man farmed his own land, raised his cotton. Stabilizing the price, using up the surplus, they called it, giving a man advice and help, whether he wanted it or not. You may have noticed them boys in yonder tonight; curious folks almost, you might call them. That first year, when county agents was trying to explain the new system to farmers, the agent come out here and tried to explain it to Buddy and Lee and Stuart, explaining how they could cut down the crop, but that the Government would pay farmers the difference, and so they would actually be better off than trying to farm by themselves.

" 'Why, we're much obliged,' Buddy says, 'But we don't

need no help. We'll just make the cotton like we always done; if we can't make a crop of it, that will just be our lookout and our loss, and we'll try again.'

"So they wouldn't sign no papers nor no cards nor nothing. They just went on and made the cotton like old Anse had taught them to; it was like they just couldn't believe that the Government aimed to help a man whether he wanted help or not, aimed to interfere with how much of anything he could make by hard work on his own land, making the crop and ginning it right here in their own gin, like they had always done, and hauling it to town to sell, hauling it all the way into Jefferson before they found out they couldn't sell it because, in the first place, they had made too much of it and, in the second place, they never had no card to sell what they would have been allowed. So they hauled it back. The gin wouldn't hold all of it, so they put some of it under Rafe's mule shed and they put the rest of it right here in the hall where we are setting now, where they would have to walk around it all winter and keep themselves reminded to be sho and fill out that card next time.

"Only next year they didn't fill out no papers neither. It was like they still couldn't believe it, still believed in the freedom and liberty to make or break according to a man's fitness and will to work, guaranteed by the Government that old Anse had tried to tear in two once and failed, and admitted in good faith he had failed and taken the consequences, and that had give Buddy a medal and taken care of him when he was far away from home in a strange land and hurt.

"So they made that second crop. And they couldn't sell it

to nobody neither because they never had no cards. This time they built a special shed to put it under, and I remember how in that second winter Buddy come to town one day to see Lawyer Gavin Stevens. Not for legal advice how to sue the Government or somebody into buying the cotton, even if they never had no card for it, but just to find out why. 'I was for going ahead and signing up for it,' Buddy says, 'if that's going to be the new rule. But we talked it over, and Jackson ain't no farmer, but he knowed father longer than the rest of us, and he said father would have said no, and I reckon now he would have been right.'

"So they didn't raise any more cotton; they had a plenty of it to last a while—twenty-two bales, I think it was. That was when they went into whiteface cattle, putting old Anse's cotton land into pasture, because that's what he would have wanted them to do if the only way they could raise cotton was by the Government telling them how much they could raise and how much they could sell it for, and where, and when, and then pay them for not doing the work they didn't do. Only even when they didn't raise cotton, every year the county agent's young fellow would come out to measure the pasture crops they planted so he could pay them for that, even if they never had no not-cotton to be paid for. Except that he never measured no crop on this place. 'You're welcome to look at what we are doing,' Buddy says. 'But don't draw it down on your map.'

" 'But you can get money for this,' the young fellow says. 'The Government wants to pay you for planting all this.'

" 'We are aiming to get money for it,' Buddy says. 'When

we can't, we will try something else. But not from the Government. Give that to them that want to take it. We can make out.'

"And that's about all. Them twenty-two bales of orphan cotton are down yonder in the gin right now, because there's room for it in the gin now because they ain't using the gin no more. And them boys grew up and went off a year to the agricultural college to learn right about whiteface cattle, and then come back to the rest of them—these here curious folks living off here to themselves, with the rest of the world all full of pretty neon lights burning night and day both, and easy, quick money scattering itself around everywhere for any man to grab a little, and every man with a shiny new automobile already wore out and throwed away and the new one delivered before the first one was even paid for, and everywhere a fine loud grabble and snatch of AAA and WPA and a dozen other three-letter reasons for a man not to work. Then this here draft comes along, and these curious folks ain't got around to signing that neither, and you come all the way up from Jackson with your paper all signed and regular, and we come out here, and after a while we can go back to town. A man gets around, don't he?"

"Yes," the investigator said. "Do you suppose we can go back to town now?"

"No," the marshal told him in that same kindly tone, "not just yet. But we can leave after a while. Of course you will miss your train. But there will be another one tomorrow."

He rose, though the investigator had heard nothing. The investigator watched him go down the hall and open the bedroom door and enter and close it behind him. The investigator sat quietly, listening to the night sounds and looking at the closed door until it opened presently and the marshal came back, carrying something in a bloody sheet, carrying it gingerly.

"Here," he said. "Hold it a minute."

"It's bloody," the investigator said.

"That's all right," the marshal said. "We can wash when we get through." So the investigator took the bundle and stood holding it while he watched the old marshal go back down the hall and on through it and vanish and return presently with a lighted lantern and a shovel. "Come along," he said. "We're pretty near through now."

The investigator followed him out of the house and across the yard, carrying gingerly the bloody, shattered, heavy bundle in which it still seemed to him he could feel some warmth of life, the marshal striding on ahead, the lantern swinging against his leg, the shadow of his striding scissoring and enormous along the earth, his voice still coming back over his shoulder, chatty and cheerful, "Yes, sir. A man gets around and he sees a heap; a heap of folks in a heap of situations. The trouble is, we done got into the habit of confusing the situations with the folks. Take yourself, now," he said in that same kindly tone, chatty and easy; "you mean all right. You just went and got yourself all fogged up with rules and regulations. That's our trouble. We done invented ourselves so many alphabets and rules and recipes that we can't see anything else; if what we see can't be fitted to an alphabet or a rule, we are lost. We have come to be like critters doctor folks might have created in laboratories, that have learned how to slip off their bones and guts and still live, still be kept alive indefinite and forever maybe even without even knowing the bones and the guts are gone. We have slipped our backbone; we have about decided a man don't need a backbone any more; to have one is old-fashioned. But the groove where the backbone used to be is still there, and the backbone has been kept alive, too, and someday we're going to slip back onto it. I don't know just when nor just how much of a wrench it will take to teach us, but someday."

They had left the yard now. They were mounting a slope; ahead of them the investigator could see another clump of cedars, a small clump, somehow shaggily formal against the starred sky. The marshal entered it and stopped and set the lantern down and, following with the bundle, the investigator saw a small rectangle of earth enclosed by a low brick coping. Then he saw the two graves, or the head-stones—two plain granite slabs set upright in the earth.

"Old Anse and Mrs. Anse," the marshal said. "Buddy's wife wanted to be buried with her folks. I reckon she would have been right lonesome up here with just McCallums. Now, let's see." He stood for a moment, his chin in his hand; to the investigator he looked exactly like an old lady trying to decide where to set out a shrub. "They was to run from left to right, beginning with Jackson. But after the boys was born, Jackson and Stuart was to come up here by their pa and ma, so Buddy could move up some and make room. So he will be about here." He moved the lantern nearer and took up the shovel. Then he saw the investigator still holding the bundle. "Set it down," he said. "I got to dig first."

"I'll hold it," the investigator said.

"Nonsense, put it down," the marshal said. "Buddy won't mind."

So the investigator put the bundle down on the brick coping and the marshal began to dig, skillfully and rapidly, still talking in that cheerful, interminable voice, "Yes, sir. We done forgot about folks. Life has done got cheap, and life ain't cheap. Life's a pretty durn valuable thing. I don't mean just getting along from one WPA relief check to the next one, but honor and pride and discipline that make a man worth preserving, make him of any value. That's what we got to learn again. Maybe it takes trouble, bad trouble, to teach it back to us; maybe it was the walking to Virginia because that's where his ma come from, and losing a war and then walking back, that taught it to old Anse. Anyway, he seems to learned it, and to learned it good enough to bequeath it to his boys. Did you notice how all Buddy had to do was to tell them boys of his it was time to go, because the Government had sent them word? And how they told him good-by? Growned men kissing one another without hiding and without shame. Maybe that's what I am trying to say. . . . There," he said. "That's big enough."

He moved quickly, easily; before the investigator could stir, he had lifted the bundle into the narrow trench and was covering it, covering it as rapidly as he had dug, smoothing the earth over it with the shovel. Then he stood up and raised the lantern—a tall, lean old man, breathing easily and lightly.

"I reckon we can go back to town now," he said.

THE TALL MEN

1. There are three voices in this story. Whose are they? What does each voice reveal about the person or persons it represents?

2. What change takes place in the investigator? How is this revealed? How do you account for the change?

3. What is meant by "I reckon she [Buddy's wife] would have been lonesome up here with just McCallums"?

4. What do you think was Mr. Faulkner's purpose in writing the story?

5. Do you agree with Buddy's and the boys' philosophy? Prepare (a) to defend it, or (b) to show its inapplicability to today's living.

   In answering the questions listed above perhaps you may want to consider the following:

   a. Why is the investigator introduced as "the stranger"?
   b. What one adjective would you use to describe him as he appears to be in his second and third speeches?

c. In what significant way does Mr. Faulkner contrast the marshal with the investigator?

d. What was the something the marshal had ". . . been trying to tell him [the investigator] for him not to forget"?

e. What do we learn (from the investigator's thoughts) about judging people before we know them?

f. How do you explain the investigator's feeling that the room was "filled with tremendous men" when they were "not big, not tall, and it was not vitality, exuberance . . ."?

g. Does Buddy's direction to the boys to go to Memphis to enlist come as a surprise to you? How does this correspond with the guiding principle under which the men had lived?

h. Buddy tells the boys to obey their officers, ". . . but remember your name and don't take nothing from no man." How does this speech reveal the character of the men?

i. What is meant by the marshal's saying, "Ain't nobody paying any attention to you at all"?

j. What are the steps by which Mr. Faulkner provides for continuity of family traits for nearly one hundred years?

k. Notice the paragraph about not filling out papers the second year. What was the attitude of the men toward government? What did they believe the government guaranteed to its citizens?

l. Why did the boys go to agricultural college "to learn about whiteface cattle . . ."?

m. What is meant by "confusing the situation with the folks"?

n. What speech of the marshal's shows that he believes essentially the same things as the McCallum men? What are the things the marshal values?

o. Why does the marshal bury the leg?

p. These boys, according to the investigator, were draft dodgers. In what way could they and the other men of their family be considered true patriots in the broadest sense?

F. SCOTT FITZGERALD

1896–1940

A Woman with a Past

BORN IN *the Middle West, Fitzgerald attended private school and then Princeton University. More concerned with college publications and university club shows than with studies, Fitzgerald left Princeton without his degree. During World War I he served as a lieutenant in the army.*

When Fitzgerald was twenty-three, This Side of Paradise, *his first novel, was published. The following year he was successful in placing many short stories in popular American magazines. In 1924 he went to Paris to live, and it was while he was there that his greatest novel,* The Great Gatsby, *was published.*

Fitzgerald is best remembered as a chronicler of American life among the well-to-do of the Twenties, and he was particularly skillful in his depiction of young people of that time.

I

Driving slowly through New Haven, two of the young girls became alert. Josephine and Lillian darted soft frank glances into strolling groups of three or four undergraduates, into larger groups on corners, which swung about as one man to stare at their receding heads. Believing that they recognized an acquaintance in a solitary loiterer, they waved wildly, whereupon the youth's mouth fell open, and as they turned the next corner he made a dazed dilatory gesture with his hand. They laughed, "We'll send him a post card when we get back to school tonight, to see if it really was him."

Adele Craw, sitting on one of the little seats, kept on talking to Miss Chambers, the chaperone. Glancing sideways at her, Lillian winked at Josephine without batting an eye, but Josephine had gone into a reverie.

This was New Haven—city of her adolescent dreams, of glittering proms where she would move on air among men as intangible as the tunes they danced to. City sacred as Mecca, shining as Paris, hidden as Timbuctoo. Twice a year the lifeblood of Chicago, her home, flowed into it, and twice a year flowed back, bringing Christmas or bringing summer. Bingo, bingo, bingo, that's the lingo; love of mine, I pine for one of your glances; the darling boy on the left there; underneath the stars I wait.

Seeing it for the first time, she found herself surprisingly unmoved—the men they passed seemed young and rather bored with the possibilities of the day, glad of anything to stare at; seemed undynamic and purposeless against the background of bare elms, lakes of dirty snow and buildings crowded together under the February sky. A wisp of hope, a well-turned-out derby-crowned man, hurrying with stick and suitcase toward the station, caught her attention, but his reciprocal glance was too startled, too ingenuous. Josephine wondered at the extent of her own disillusionment.

She was exactly seventeen and she was blasé. Already she had been a sensation and a scandal; she had driven mature men to a state of disequilibrium; she had, it was said, killed her grandfather, but as he was over eighty at the time perhaps he just died. Here and there in the Middle West were discouraged little spots which upon inspection turned out to be the youths who had once looked full into her green and wistful eyes. But her love affair of last summer had ruined her faith in the all-sufficiency of men. She had grown bored with the waning September days—and it seemed as though it had happened once too often. Christmas with its provocative shortness, its travelling glee clubs, had brought no one new. There remained to her only a persistent, a physical hope; hope in her stomach that there was someone whom she would love more than he loved her.

They stopped at a sporting-goods store and Adele Craw, a pretty girl with clear honorable eyes and piano legs, purchased the sporting equipment which was the reason for their trip—they were the spring hockey committee for the school. Adele was in addition the president of the senior class and the school's ideal girl. She had lately seen a change for the better in Josephine Perry—rather as an honest citizen might guilelessly approve a peculator retired on his profits. On the other hand, Adele was simply incomprehensible to Josephine—admirable, without doubt, but a member of another species. Yet with the charming adaptability that she had hitherto reserved for men, Josephine was trying hard not to disillusion her, trying to be honestly interested in the small, neat, organized politics of the school.

Two men who had stood with their backs to them at another counter turned to leave the store, when they caught sight of Miss Chambers and Adele. Immediately they came forward. The one who spoke to Miss Chambers was thin and rigid of face. Josephine recognized him as Miss Brereton's nephew, a student at New Haven, who had spent several week-ends with his aunt at the school. The other man Josephine had never seen before. He was tall and broad, with blond curly hair and an open expression in which strength of purpose and a nice consideration were pleasantly mingled. It was not the sort of face that generally appealed to Josephine. The eyes were obviously without a secret, without a sidewise gambol, without a desperate flicker to show that they had a life of their own apart from the mouth's speech. The mouth itself was large and masculine; its smile was an act of kindness and control. It was rather with curiosity as to the sort of man who would be attentive to Adele Craw that Josephine continued to look at him, for his voice that obviously couldn't lie greeted Adele as if this meeting was the pleasant surprise of his day.

In a moment Josephine and Lillian were called over and introduced.

"This is Mr. Waterbury"—that was Miss Brereton's nephew—"and Mr. Dudley Knowleton."

Glancing at Adele, Josephine saw on her face an expression of tranquil pride, even of possession. Mr. Knowleton spoke politely, but it was obvious that though he looked at the younger girls he did not quite see them. But since they were friends of Adele's he made suitable remarks, eliciting the fact that they were both coming down to New Haven to their first prom the following week. Who were their hosts?

Sophomores; he knew them slightly. Josephine thought that was unnecessarily superior. Why, they were the charter members of the Loving Brothers' Association—Ridgeway Saunders and George Davey—and on the glee-club trip the girls they picked out to rush in each city considered themselves a sort of élite, second only to the girls they asked to New Haven.

"And oh, I've got some bad news for you," Knowleton said to Adele. "You may be leading the prom. Jack Coe went to the infirmary with appendicitis, and against my better judgment I'm the provisional chairman." He looked apologetic. "Being one of these stone-age dancers, the two-step king, I don't see how I ever got on the committee at all."

When the car was on its way back to Miss Brereton's school, Josephine and Lillian bombarded Adele with questions.

"He's an old friend from Cincinnati," she explained demurely. "He's captain of the baseball team and he was last man for Skull and Bones."

"You're going to the prom with him?"

"Yes. You see, I've known him all my life."

Was there a faint implication in this remark that only those who had known Adele all her life knew her at her true worth?

"Are you engaged?" Lillian demanded.

Adele laughed. "Mercy, I don't think of such matters. It doesn't seem to be time for that sort of thing yet, does it?" ["Yes," interpolated Josephine silently.] "We're just good friends. I think there can be a perfectly healthy friendship between a man and a girl without a lot of—"

"Mush," supplied Lillian helpfully.

"Well, yes, but I don't like that word. I was going to say without a lot of sentimental romantic things that ought to come later."

"Bravo, Adele!" said Miss Chambers somewhat perfunctorily.

But Josephine's curiosity was unappeased.

"Doesn't he say he's in love with you, and all that sort of thing?"

"Mercy, no! Dud doesn't believe in such stuff any more than I do. He's got enough to do at New Haven serving on the committees and the team."

"Oh!" said Josephine.

She was oddly interested. That two people who were attracted to each other should never even say anything about it but be content to "not believe in such stuff," was something new in her experience. She had known girls who had no beaus, others who seemed to have no emotions, and still others who lied about what they thought and did; but here was a girl who spoke of the attentions of the last man tapped for Skull and Bones as if they were two of the limestone gargoyles that Miss Chambers had pointed out on the just completed Harkness Hall. Yet Adele seemed happy—happier than Josephine, who had always believed that boys and girls were made for nothing but each other, and as soon as possible.

In the light of his popularity and achievements, Knowleton seemed more attractive. Josephine wondered if he would remember her and dance with her at the prom, or if that depended on how well he knew her escort, Ridgeway Saunders. She tried to remember whether she had smiled at him when he was looking at her. If she had really smiled he would remember her and dance with her. She was still trying to be sure of that over her two French irregular verbs and her ten stanzas of the Ancient Mariner that night; but she was still uncertain when she fell asleep.

II

Three gay young sophomores, the founders of the Loving Brothers' Association, took a house together for Josephine, Lillian and a girl from Farmington and their three mothers. For the girls it was a first prom, and they arrived at New Haven with all the nervousness of the condemned; but a Sheffield fraternity tea in the afternoon yielded up such a plethora of boys from home, and boys who had visited there, and friends of those boys, and new boys with unknown possibilities but obvious eagerness, that they were glowing with self-confidence as they poured into the glittering crowd that thronged the armory at ten.

It was impressive; for the first time Josephine was at a function run by men upon men's standards—an outward projection of the New Haven world from which women were excluded and which went on mysteriously behind the scenes.

She perceived that their three escorts, who had once seemed the very embodiments of worldliness, were modest fry in this relentless microcosm of accomplishment and success. A man's world! Looking around her at the glee-club concert, Josephine had felt a grudging admiration for the good fellowship, the good feeling. She envied Adele Craw, barely glimpsed in the dressing-room, for the position she automatically occupied by being Dudley Knowleton's girl tonight. She envied her more stepping off under the draped bunting through a gateway of hydrangeas at the head of the grand march, very demure and faintly unpowdered in a plain white dress. She was temporarily the centre of all attention, and at the sight something that had long lain dormant in Josephine awakened—her sense of a problem, a scarcely defined possibility.

"Josephine," Ridgeway Saunders began, "you can't realize how happy I am now that it's come true. I've looked forward to this so long, and dreamed about it—"

She smiled up at him automatically, but her mind was elsewhere, and as the dance progressed the idea continued to obsess her. She was rushed from the beginning; to the men from the tea were added a dozen new faces, a dozen confident or timid voices, until, like all the more popular girls, she had her own queue trailing her about the room. Yet all this had happened to her before, and there was something missing. One might have ten men to Adele's two, but Josephine was abruptly aware that here a girl took on the importance of the man who had brought her.

She was discomforted by the unfairness of it. A girl

earned her popularity by being beautiful and charming. The more beautiful and charming she was, the more she could afford to disregard public opinion. It seemed absurd that simply because Adele had managed to attach a baseball captain, who mightn't know anything about girls at all, or be able to judge their attractions, she should be thus elevated in spite of her thick ankles, her rather too pinkish face.

Josephine was dancing with Ed Bement from Chicago. He was her earliest beau, a flame of pigtail days in dancing school when one wore white cotton stockings, lace drawers with a waist attached and ruffled dresses with the inevitable sash.

"What's the matter with me?" she asked Ed, thinking aloud. "For months I've felt as if I were a hundred years old, and I'm just seventeen and that party was only seven years ago."

"You've been in love a lot since then," Ed said.

"I haven't," she protested indignantly. "I've had a lot of silly stories started about me, without any foundation, usually by girls who were jealous."

"Jealous of what?"

"Don't get fresh," she said tartly. "Dance me near Lillian."

Dudley Knowleton had just cut in on Lillian. Josephine spoke to her friend; then waiting until their turns would bring them face to face over a space of seconds, she smiled at Knowleton. This time she made sure that smile intersected as well as met glance, that he passed beside the circumference of her fragrant charm. If this had been named like French perfume of a later day it might have been called

"Please." He bowed and smiled back; a minute later he cut in on her.

It was in an eddy in a corner of the room and she danced slower so that he adapted himself, and for a moment they went around in a slow circle.

"You looked so sweet leading the march with Adele," she told him. "You seemed so serious and kind, as if the others were all a lot of children. Adele looked sweet too." And she added on an inspiration, "At school I've taken her for a model."

"You have!" She saw him conceal his sharp surprise as he said, "I'll have to tell her that."

He was handsomer than she had thought, and behind his cordial good manners there was a sort of authority. Correctly attentive to her, she saw his eyes search the room quickly to see if all went well; he spoke quietly, in passing, to the orchestra leader, who came down deferentially to the edge of his dais. Last man for Bones. Josephine knew what that meant—her father had been Bones. Ridgeway Saunders and the rest of the Loving Brothers' Association would certainly not be Bones. She wondered, if there had been a Bones for girls, whether she would be tapped—or Adele Craw with her ankles, symbol of solidity.

Come on o-ver here,
Want to have you near;
Come on join the part-y,
Get a wel-come heart-y.

"I wonder how many boys here have taken you for a model," she said. "If I were a boy you'd be exactly what I'd like to be. Except I'd be terribly bothered having girls falling in love with me all the time."

"They don't," he said simply. "They never have."

"Oh, yes—but they hide it because they're so impressed with you, and they're afraid of Adele."

"Adele wouldn't object." And he added hastily, "—if it ever happened. Adele doesn't believe in being serious about such things."

"Are you engaged to her?"

He stiffened a little. "I don't believe in being engaged till the right time comes."

"Neither do I," agreed Josephine readily. "I'd rather have one good friend than a hundred people hanging around being mushy all the time."

"Is that what that crowd does that keep following you around tonight?"

"What crowd?" she asked innocently.

"The 50 per cent of the sophomore class that's rushing you."

"A lot of parlor snakes," she said ungratefully.

Josephine was radiantly happy now as she turned beautifully through the newly enchanted hall in the arms of the chairman of the prom committee. Even this extra time with him she owed to the awe which he inspired in her entourage; but a man cut in eventually and there was a sharp fall in her elation. The man was impressed that Dudley Knowleton had danced with her; he was more respectful, and his modulated admiration bored her. In a little while, she hoped, Dudley Knowleton would cut back, but as midnight passed, dragging on another hour with it, she wondered if after all it had only been a courtesy to a girl from Adele's school. Since then Adele had probably painted him a neat little landscape of Josephine's past. When finally he approached her she grew tense and watchful, a state which made her exteriorly pliant and tender and quiet. But instead of dancing he drew her into the edge of a row of boxes.

"Adele had an accident on the cloakroom steps. She turned her ankle a little and tore her stocking on a nail. She'd like to borrow a pair from you because you're staying near here and we're way out at the Lawn Club."

"Of course."

"I'll run over with you—I have a car outside."

"But you're busy, you mustn't bother."

"Of course I'll go with you."

There was thaw in the air; a hint of thin and lucid spring hovered delicately around the elms and cornices of buildings whose bareness and coldness had so depressed her the week before. The night had a quality of asceticism, as if the essence of masculine struggle were seeping everywhere through the little city where men of three centuries had brought their energies and aspirations for winnowing. And Dudley Knowleton sitting beside her, dynamic and capable, was symbolic of it all. It seemed that she had never met a man before.

"Come in, please," she said as he went up the steps of the house with her. "They've made it very comfortable."

There was an open fire burning in the dark parlor. When she came downstairs with the stockings she went in and stood beside him, very still for a moment, watching it with him. Then she looked up, still silent, looked down, looked at him again.

"Did you get the stockings?" he asked, moving a little.

"Yes," she said breathlessly. "Kiss me for being so quick."

He laughed as if she had said something witty and moved toward the door. She was smiling and her disappointment was deeply hidden as they got into the car.

"It's been wonderful meeting you," she told him. "I can't tell you how many ideas I've gotten from what you said."

"But I haven't any ideas."

"You have. All that about not getting engaged till the proper time comes. I haven't had much opportunity to talk to a man like you. Otherwise my ideas would be different, I guess. I've just realized that I've been wrong about a lot of things. I used to want to be exciting. Now I want to help people."

"Yes," he agreed, "that's very nice."

He seemed about to say more when they arrived at the armory. In their absence supper had begun; and crossing the great floor by his side, conscious of many eyes regarding them, Josephine wondered if people thought that they had been up to something.

"We're late," said Knowleton when Adele went off to put on the stockings. "The man you're with has probably given you up long ago. You'd better let me get you something here."

"That would be too divine."

Afterward, back on the floor again, she moved in a sweet aura of abstraction. The followers of several departed belles merged with hers until now no girl on the floor was cut in on with such frequency. Even Miss Brereton's nephew, Ernest Waterbury, danced with her in stiff approval. Danced? With a tentative change of pace she simply swung from man to man in a sort of hands-right-and-left around the floor. She felt a sudden need to relax, and as if in answer to her mood a new man was presented, a tall, sleek Southerner with a persuasive note:

"You lovely creacha. I been strainin my eyes watchin your cameo face floatin round. You stand out above all these othuz like an Ameliken Beauty Rose over a lot of field daisies."

Dancing with him the second time, Josephine hearkened to his pleadings.

"All right. Let's go outside."

"It wasn't outdaws I was considerin," he explained as they left the floor. "I happen to have a mortgage on a nook right hee in the building."

"All right."

Book Chaffee, of Alabama, led the way through the cloakroom, through a passage to an inconspicuous door.

"This is the private apartment of my friend Sergeant Boone, instructa of the battery. He wanted to be particularly sure it'd be used as a nook tonight and not a readin room or anything like that."

Opening the door he turned on a dim light; she came in and he shut it behind her, and they faced each other.

"Mighty sweet," he murmured. His tall face came down, his long arms wrapped around her tenderly, and very slowly, so that their eyes met for quite a long time, he drew her up to him. Josephine kept thinking that she had never kissed a Southern boy before.

They started apart at the sudden sound of a key turning in the lock outside. Then there was a muffled snicker followed by retreating footsteps, and Book sprang for the door and wrenched at the handle, just as Josephine noticed that this was not only Sergeant Boone's parlor, it was his bedroom as well.

"Who was it?" she demanded. "Why did they lock us in?"

"Some funny boy. I'd like to get my hands on him."

"Will he come back?"

Book sat down on the bed to think. "I couldn't say. Don't even know who it was. But if somebody on the committee came along it wouldn't look too good, would it?"

Seeing her expression change, he came over and put his arm around her. "Don't you worry, honey. We'll fix it."

She returned his kiss, briefly but without distraction. Then she broke away and went into the next apartment, which was hung with boots, uniform coats and various military equipment.

"There's a window up here," she said. It was high in the wall and had not been opened for a long time. Book mounted on a chair and forced it ajar.

"About ten feet down," he reported, after a moment, "but there's a big pile of snow just underneath. You might get a nasty fall and you'll sure soak your shoes and stockin's."

"We've got to get out," Josephine said sharply.

"We'd better wait and give this funny man a chance—"

"I won't wait. I want to get out. Look—throw out all the blankets from the bed and I'll jump on that; or you jump first and spread them over the pile of snow."

After that it was merely exciting. Carefully Book Chaffee wiped the dust from the window to protect her dress; then they were struck silent by a footstep that approached—and passed the outer door. Book jumped, and she heard him kicking profanely as he waded out of the soft drift below. He spread the blankets. At the moment when Josephine swung her legs out the window, there was the sound of voices outside the door and the key turned again in the lock. She landed softly, reaching for his hand, and convulsed with laughter they ran and skidded down the half block toward the corner, and reaching the entrance to the armory, they stood panting for a moment, breathing in the fresh night. Book was reluctant to go inside.

"Why don't you let me conduct you where you're stayin? We can sit around and sort of recuperate."

She hesitated, drawn toward him by the community of their late predicament; but something was calling her inside, as if the fulfillment of her elation awaited her there.

"No," she decided.

As they went in she collided with a man in a great hurry, and looked up to recognize Dudley Knowleton.

"So sorry," he said. "Oh, hello—"

"Won't you dance me over to my box?" she begged him impulsively. "I've torn my dress."

As they started off he said abstractedly: "The fact is, a

little mischief has come up and the buck has been passed to me. I was going along to see about it."

Her heart raced wildly and she felt the need of being another sort of person immediately.

"I can't tell you how much it's meant meeting you. It would be wonderful to have one friend I could be serious with without being all mushy and sentimental. Would you mind if I wrote you a letter—I mean, would Adele mind?"

"Lord, no." His smile had become utterly unfathomable to her. As they reached the box she thought of one more thing:

"Is it true that the baseball team is training at Hot Springs during Easter?"

"Yes. You going there?"

"Yes. Good night, Mr. Knowleton."

But she was destined to see him once more. It was outside the men's coat room, where she waited among a crowd of other pale survivors and their paler mothers, whose wrinkles had doubled and tripled with the passing night. He was explaining something to Adele, and Josephine heard the phrase. "The door was locked, and the window open—"

Suddenly it occurred to Josephine that, meeting her coming in damp and breathless, he must have guessed at the truth—and Adele would doubtless confirm his suspicion. Once again the spectre of her old enemy, the plain and jealous girl, arose before her. Shutting her mouth tight together she turned away.

But they had seen her, and Adele called to her in her cheerful ringing voice:

"Come say good night. You were *so* sweet about the stockings. Here's a girl you won't find doing shoddy, silly things, Dudley." Impulsively she leaned and kissed Josephine on the cheek. "You'll see I'm right, Dudley—next year she'll be the most respected girl in school."

III

As things go in the interminable days of early March, what happened next happened quickly. The annual senior dance at Miss Brereton's school came on a night soaked through with spring, and all the junior girls lay awake listening to the sighing tunes from the gymnasium. Between the numbers, when boys up from New Haven and Princeton wandered about the grounds, cloistered glances looked down from dark open windows upon the vague figures.

Not Josephine, though she lay awake like the others. Such vicarious diversions had no place in the sober pattern she was spinning now from day to day; yet she might as well have been in the forefront of those who called down to the men and threw notes and entered into conversations, for destiny had suddenly turned against her and was spinning a dark web of its own.

> Lit-tle lady, don't be depressed and blue,
> After all we're both in the same can-noo—

Dudley Knowleton was over in the gymnasium fifty yards away, but proximity to a man did not thrill her as it would have done a year ago—not, at least, in the same way. Life, she saw now, was a serious matter, and in the modest darkness a line of a novel ceaselessly recurred to her: "He is a man fit to be the father of my children." What were the seductive graces, the fast lines of a hundred parlor snakes compared to such realities. One couldn't go on forever kissing comparative strangers behind half-closed doors.

Under her pillow now were two letters, answers to her letters. They spoke in a bold round hand of the beginning of baseball practice; they were glad Josephine felt as she did about things; and the writer certainly looked forward to seeing her at Easter. Of all the letters she had ever received they were the most difficult from which to squeeze a single drop of heart's blood—one couldn't even read the "Yours" of the subscription as "Your"—but Josephine knew them by heart. They were precious because he had taken the time to write them; they were eloquent in the very postage stamp because he used so few.

She was restless in her bed—the music had begun again in the gymnasium:

> Oh, my love, I've waited so long for you,
> Oh, my love, I'm singing this song for you—
> Oh-h-h-h—

From the next room there was light laughter, and then from below a male voice, and a long interchange of comic whispers. Josephine recognized Lillian's laugh and the voices of two other girls. She could imagine them as they lay across the window in their nightgowns, their heads just showing from the open window. "Come right down," one boy kept saying. "Don't be formal—come just as you are."

There was a sudden silence, then a quick crunching of footsteps on gravel, a suppressed snicker and a scurry, and the sharp, protesting groan of several beds in the next room and the banging of a door down the hall. Trouble for somebody, maybe. A few minutes later Josephine's door half opened, she caught a glimpse of Miss Kwain against the dim corridor light, and then the door closed.

The next afternoon Josephine and four other girls, all of whom denied having breathed so much as a word into the night, were placed on probation. There was absolutely nothing to do about it. Miss Kwain had recognized their faces in the window and they were all from two rooms. It was an injustice, but it was nothing compared to what happened next. One week before Easter vacation the school motored off on a one-day trip to inspect a milk farm—all save the ones on probation. Miss Chambers, who sympathized with Josephine's misfortune, enlisted her services in entertaining Mr. Ernest Waterbury, who was spending a week-end with his aunt. This was only vaguely better than nothing, for Mr. Waterbury was a very dull, very priggish young man. He was so dull and so priggish that the following morning Josephine was expelled from school.

It had happened like this: They had strolled in the grounds, they had sat down at a garden table and had tea. Ernest Waterbury had expressed a desire to see something in the chapel, just a few minutes before his aunt's car rolled up the drive. The chapel was reached by descending winding mock-medieval stairs; and, her shoes still wet from the garden, Josephine had slipped on the top step and fallen five feet directly into Mr. Waterbury's unwilling arms, where she lay helpless, convulsed with irresistible laughter. It was in this position that Miss Brereton and the visiting trustee had found them.

"But I had nothing to do with it!" declared the ungallant Mr. Waterbury. Flustered and outraged, he was packed back to New Haven, and Miss Brereton, connecting this with last week's sin, proceeded to lose her head. Josephine, humiliated and furious, lost hers, and Mr. Perry, who happened to be in New York, arrived at the school the same night. At his passionate indignation, Miss Brereton collapsed and retracted, but the damage was done, and Josephine packed her trunk. Unexpectedly, monstrously, just as it had begun to mean something, her school life was over.

For the moment all her feelings were directed against Miss Brereton, and the only tears she shed at leaving were of anger and resentment. Riding with her father up to New York, she saw that while at first he had instinctively and whole-heartedly taken her part, he felt also a certain annoyance with her misfortune.

"We'll all survive," he said. "Unfortunately, even that old idiot Miss Brereton will survive. She ought to be running a reform school." He brooded for a moment. "Anyhow, your mother arrives tomorrow and you and she can go down to Hot Springs as you planned."

"Hot Springs!" Josephine cried, in a choked voice. "Oh, no!"

"Why not?" he demanded in surprise. "It seems the best thing to do. Give it a chance to blow over before you go back to Chicago."

"I'd rather go to Chicago," said Josephine breathlessly. "Daddy, I'd much rather go to Chicago."

"That's absurd. Your mother's started East and the arrangements are all made. At Hot Springs you can get out and ride and play golf and forget that old she-devil—"

"Isn't there another place in the East we could go? There's people I know going to Hot Springs who'll know all about this, people that I don't want to meet—girls from school."

"Now, Jo, you keep your chin up—this is one of those times. Sorry I said that about letting it blow over in Chicago; if we hadn't made other plans we'd go back and face every old shrew and gossip in town right away. When anybody slinks off in a corner they think you've been up to something bad. If anybody says anything to you, you tell them the truth—what I said to Miss Brereton. You tell them she said you could come back and I damn well wouldn't let you go back."

"They won't believe it."

There would be, at all events, four days of respite at Hot Springs before the vacations of the schools. Josephine passed this time taking golf lessons from a professional so newly arrived from Scotland that he surely knew nothing of her misadventure; she even went riding with a young man one afternoon, feeling almost at home with him after his admission that he had flunked out of Princeton in February—a confidence, however, which she did not reciprocate in kind. But in the evenings, despite the young man's importunity, she stayed with her mother, feeling nearer to her than she ever had before.

But one afternoon in the lobby Josephine saw by the desk two dozen good-looking young men waiting by a stack of bat cases and bags, and knew that what she dreaded was at hand. She ran upstairs and with an invented headache dined there that night, but after dinner she walked restlessly around their apartment. She was ashamed not only of her situation but of her reaction to it. She had never felt any pity for the unpopular girls who skulked in dressing rooms because they could attract no partners on the floor, or for girls who were outsiders at Lake Forest, and now she was like them—hiding miserably out of life. Alarmed lest already the change was written in her face, she paused in front of the mirror, fascinated as ever by what she found there.

"The darn fools," she said aloud. And as she said it her chin went up and the faint cloud about her eyes lifted. The phrases of the myriad love letters she had received passed before her eyes; behind her, after all, was the reassurance of a hundred lost and pleading faces, of innumerable tender and pleading voices. Her pride flooded back into her till she could see the warm blood rushing up into her cheeks.

There was a knock at the door—it was the Princeton boy.

"How about slipping downstairs?" he proposed. "There's a dance. It's full of Ee-lies, the whole Yale baseball team. I'll pick up one of them and introduce you and you'll have a big time. How about it?"

"All right, but I don't want to meet anybody. You'll just have to dance with me all evening."

"You know that suits *me*."

She hurried into a new spring evening dress of the frailest fairy blue. In the excitement of seeing herself in it, it seemed as if she had shed the old skin of winter and emerged a shining chrysalis with no stain; and going downstairs her feet fell softly just off the beat of the music from below. It was a tune from a play she had seen a week ago in New York, a tune with a future—ready for gayeties as yet unthought of, lovers not yet met. Dancing off, she was certain that life had innumerable beginnings. She had hardly gone ten steps when she was cut in upon by Dudley Knowleton.

"Why, Josephine!" He had never used her first name before—he stood holding her hand. "Why, I'm glad to see you. I've been hoping you'd be here."

She soared skyward on a rocket of surprise and delight. He was actually glad to see her—the expression on his face was obviously sincere. Could it be possible that he hadn't heard?

"Adele wrote me you might be here. She wasn't sure."

—Then he knew and didn't care; he liked her anyhow.

"I'm in sackcloth and ashes," she said.

"Well, they're very becoming to you."

"You know what happened—" she ventured.

"I do. I wasn't going to say anything, but it's generally agreed that Waterbury behaved like a fool—and it's not going to be much help to him in the elections next month. Look—I want you to dance with some men who are just starving for a touch of beauty."

Presently she was dancing with, it seemed to her, the entire team at once. Intermittently Dudley Knowleton cut back in, as well as the Princeton man, who was somewhat indignant at this unexpected competition. There were many girls from many schools in the room, but with an admirable team spirit the Yale men displayed a sharp prejudice in Josephine's favor; already she was pointed out from the chairs along the wall.

But interiorly she was waiting for what was coming, for the moment when she would walk with Dudley Knowleton into the warm, Southern night. It came naturally, just at the end of a number, and they strolled along an avenue of early-blooming lilacs and turned a corner and another corner . . .

"You were glad to see me, weren't you!" Josephine said.

"Of course."

"I was afraid at first. I was sorriest about what happened at school because of you. I'd been trying so hard to be different—because of you."

"You mustn't think of that school business any more. Everybody that matters knows you got a bad deal. Forget it and start over."

"Yes," she agreed tranquilly. She was happy. The breeze and the scent of lilacs—that was she, lovely and intangible;

the rustic bench where they sat and the trees—that was he, rugged and strong beside her, protecting her.

"I'd thought so much of meeting you here," she said after a minute. "You'd been so good for me, that I thought maybe in a different way I could be good for you—I mean I know ways of having a good time that you don't know. For instance, we've certainly got to go horseback riding by moonlight some night. That'll be fun."

He didn't answer.

"I can really be very nice when I like somebody—that's really not often," she interpolated hastily, "not seriously. But I mean when I do feel seriously that a boy and I are really friends I don't believe in having a whole mob of other boys hanging around taking up time. I like to be with him all the time, all day and all evening, don't you?"

He stirred a little on the bench; he leaned forward with his elbows on his knees, looking at his strong hands. Her gently modulated voice sank a note lower.

"When I like anyone I don't even like dancing. It's sweeter to be alone."

Silence for a moment.

"Well, you know"—he hesitated, frowning—"as a matter of fact, I'm mixed up in a lot of engagements made some time ago with some people." He floundered about unhappily. "In fact, I won't even be at the hotel after tomorrow. I'll be at the house of some people down the valley—a sort of house party. As a matter of fact, Adele's getting here tomorrow."

Absorbed in her own thoughts, she hardly heard him at first, but at the name she caught her breath sharply.

"We're both to be at this house party while we're here, and I imagine it's more or less arranged what we're going to do. Of course, in the daytime I'll be here for baseball practice."

"I see." Her lips were quivering. "You won't be—you'll be with Adele."

"I think that—more or less—I will. She'll—want to see you, of course."

Another silence while he twisted his big fingers and she helplessly imitated the gesture.

"You were just sorry for me," she said. "You like Adele—much better."

"Adele and I understand each other. She's been more or less my ideal since we were children together."

"And I'm not your kind of girl." Josephine's voice trembled with a sort of fright. "I suppose because I've kissed a lot of boys and got a reputation for a speed and raised the deuce."

"It isn't that."

"Yes, it is," she declared passionately. "I'm just paying for things." She stood up. "You better take me back inside so I can dance with the kind of boys that like me."

She walked quickly down the path, tears of misery streaming from her eyes. He overtook her by the steps, but she only shook her head and said, "Excuse me for being so fresh. I'll grow up—I got what was coming to me—it's all right."

A little later when she looked around the floor for him he had gone—and Josephine realized with a shock that for the first time in her life she had tried for a man and failed. But, save in the very young, only love begets love, and from the moment Josephine had perceived that his interest in her was merely kindness she realized the wound was not in her heart but in her pride. She would forget him quickly, but she would never forget what she had learned from him. There were two kinds of men, those you played with and those you might marry. And as this passed through her mind, her restless eyes wandered casually over the group of stags, resting very lightly on Mr. Gordon Tinsley, the current catch of Chicago, reputedly the richest young man in the Middle West. He had never paid any attention to young Josephine until tonight. Ten minutes ago he had asked her to go driving with him tomorrow.

But he did not attract her—and she decided to refuse. One mustn't run through people, and, for the sake of a romantic half-hour, trade a possibility that might develop—quite seriously—later, at the proper time. She did not know that this was the first mature thought that she had ever had in her life, but it was.

The orchestra were packing their instruments and the Princeton man was still at her ear, still imploring her to walk out with him into the night. Josephine knew without cogitation which sort of man he was—and the moon was bright even on the windows. So with a certain sense of relaxation she took his arm and they strolled out to the pleasant bower she had so lately quitted, and their faces turned toward each other, like little moons under the great white one which hovered high over the Blue Ridge; his arm dropped softly about her yielding shoulder.

"Well?" he whispered.

"Well?"

A WOMAN WITH A PAST

1. Would you classify this as a love story or as a story of character?
2. Did Josephine like the life she led? What was she looking for in life?
3. How is unity achieved in this story despite the fact that Fitzgerald divides it into three parts and that each part centers around a separate incident?
4. Although Fitzgerald tells us much about Josephine that we cannot admire, how does he succeed in enlisting our sympathy for her in much of the story?
5. There is evidence that Josephine could have almost any man she wanted. Why, then, does she envy Knowleton's attentions to Adele?
6. What incidents occur throughout the story to imply that Josephine may not have had as shady a past as she was believed to have had, but that only bad luck was responsible for her misfortune?

7. Had Josephine learned anything by the end of the story?

8. Fitzgerald has a marked style as a short story writer and novelist. Find examples of his colorful use of words, imagery, paradox, and effective use of comparison and contrast.

GEORGE GARRETT

1929–

The Rivals

THIS AUTHOR *served with the armed forces in the occupation of Trieste, Austria, and Germany. He is now a college English professor at Wesleyan University.*

George Garrett has received many prizes for poetry and drama, and he has also published volumes of verse and short stories. A young man, he shows in "The Rivals" *a familiarity with the thinking of young people, and in this short story he deals with a significant period in a youth's life.*

They paddled across the bay, the boy in the cockpit behind studying the man, watching the twitch across his shoulders as he leaned forward and the quick smooth action of his arms, and the deft, almost rippleless stroke of the paddle. He tried to time his own motions exactly with his father's. The paddles rose and fell together in bright synchronization as the little canvas boat, delicate as a kite on its slight frame, moved swiftly on the still water. The boy saw beads of sweat thick on his father's neck and, as he paddled, he could feel the cool crawling on his own skin of sweat drying in the breeze. Up ahead, across a mile of water, he could see the white line of the outer beach, a frail sandspit humped with irregular dunes, protecting the bay from the Atlantic.

Though he couldn't see the waves breaking on the other side yet, he heard the noise of them like vague thunder.

"Hold it," his father shouted over his shoulder. "I'm pooped."

The boy checked the swing of the paddle in midair, leaned forward in the cockpit and relaxed. The boat bobbed idly with them like a fishing cork.

"They sound big," his father said. "They sound like real rollers to me."

His father had twisted around in the forward cockpit to look at him and grinned. He wants to get out of it, the boy thought. I guess he doesn't want to go through with it.

"They sound the same as they always do to me."

"Well," his father said, "let's see when we get there."

That's exactly like him the boy thought. He would go that far, all the way to the edge of the ocean and then turn back. He wants to go back now, but he knows, he can feel it, that I think he won't keep his promise. So now he'll go that far and then seem to make up his mind that it's too rough today. He'll look at the surf and shake his head and say it's too bad we'll have to wait 'til next summer. Next summer will be too late.

"You know something?" his father said. "I had the oddest notion just when we could first hear the waves. I remembered something out of a clear blue sky that I had forgotten for years. I remembered riding up to the line as a replacement in Normandy, during the war. I was sitting in the cab of the truck because I was the only officer in the group. We turned a curve in the road and for the first time I could hear the sound of artillery firing away up ahead of us. It was the strangest feeling because right up until I heard that sound, I hadn't made up my mind that I was really there or that there was a real war on."

"I bet you were scared, weren't you?"

"Well, yes, you might say so," he said. "But it was more than just being scared. I don't know how to explain it. You can be scared and it's only a physical thing, like being tired or sick at your stomach. This was different. It was that all of a sudden I knew it was me in the cab of the truck, nobody else but me, me alone and nobody there to see me, just me. It was queer."

"It sounds like you were pretty scared to me."

"I can't explain it," his father said. "If you don't understand, I can't explain it to you. You'll have to find out for yourself some day."

He's been drinking, the boy thought. I can smell it. He gets to talking like that when he's been drinking. When he's drunk he starts to tell all about the war. And it's been like that most of the summer. He's going to treat this day just like any other day. He don't care. He don't care that it's the last day before we go home and maybe we'll never have another chance to try the boat in the waves. On top of that he's scared.

"Ready to go?" the boy asked.

"Okay," his father said. "Any time."

They sat up straight in the cockpits and the boy poised, waiting, caught the least sign of movement from his father's back and bent forward. The two paddles flashed and knifed in the water and he could feel in his hands the keen surge of the boat. He could hear the sound of the waves louder now, and looking ahead, squinting against the midmorning sun, he saw first the far horizon where white clouds jutted like a rock coast. He followed the blue below them until he saw and felt the enormous bulk of the ocean, huge and slow, and then, abruptly at the far line of the outer beach a splatter and a flash of pure whiteness.

"I see them!" he shouted. "I see them breaking."

"Yes sir," his father answered. "They're still there all right."

When they were at last in shallow water the boy eased himself out of the cockpit, careful to keep from rocking the boat, and, once his legs were free, leapt aside into the waist-deep water. He hurried, thrashing around in front of his father, and grabbed the short line they used to tie it to the dock, and he pulled the boat up to the edge of the sand. He stood on the beach, feeling the coarse sand that stuck to his wet feet, and watched his father climb awkwardly out of the forward cockpit. His father stretched luxuriantly and smiled.

"That little old boat is hard on you when you've got long legs," he said. "Sometimes it's tough to be tall. They don't seem to make anything the right size."

The boy, slightly built, small for his age, merely nodded.

"Well," his father said, "maybe you won't have to worry about it. You take after your mother more."

"I haven't stopped growing yet."

"You never can tell," his father said. "I knew a fellow that grew almost a foot after he was your age. It's the exception, though."

"All set?"

"I guess so."

They picked up the boat and balanced it on their shoulders, his father in front to lead the way across the dunes. It was heavier than you thought. It seemed so light and frail in the water, but the weight of the boat, slanting from his father's shoulders to his own, dug harshly into the boy's flesh. I won't quit, the boy thought. I'll go all the way to the far beach without stopping if that's what he wants to do.

"Okay?"

"Sure," the boy said. "Let's go."

They struggled forward, slipping in the soft sand, the long unwieldy boat troubling their arms. The boy, his face pressed against the canvas, couldn't see where they were going. He watched his father's feet in the sand ahead and kept in step. They began to climb a dune and he felt the weight settling on his shoulders as they climbed. His arms ached from the strain and the sharp keel cut into his shoulders until he wanted to cry out, but he wouldn't. Then he felt that they were on level sand again and suddenly he could feel the wild chill of the full sea breeze, the top of a dune.

"Want to set her down and take a breather?"

"Not unless you do," the boy said.

"Well, I'm tired," his father said. "I'm not as young as I used to be. Let's set it down. Watch your feet."

They lowered the boat and the boy smiled to himself. The taste of sweat on his tongue was like the light salty taste of blood after a fist fight, the clean taste of a minor victory.

"That's a real nice ground swell," his father said, scanning the surf. "Those waves are rugged."

"How come we came up this dune?" the boy asked. "It would have been easier if we'd gone around."

"It's the same distance any way you go. It doesn't make any difference."

The boy looked out at the surf. It was perfect. Farther out the ocean was calm, but bulging with a ground swell which, as it neared the shore, was broken into huge combers. They started as ragged lines, swelled and surged, rising, rising, until it seemed that the whole sea was rising behind them and would sweep over the entire sandspit. Just at that moment with a brilliance that made him gasp the waves broke into an explosion of white, followed by the deep resounding sound of the tide.

"It's still coming in," the boy said. "It's still high tide."

"That's a blessing."

From the tone of voice the boy detected irony, the last inscrutable mask of the adult world. It seemed to him that whenever his father was forced into some naked corner of truth, just at the moment when you might face the real flesh and blood of him, he simply turned aside, donning a kind of false face behind which he felt wholly secure. It was an odd perception. He seemed to glimpse his father in a Halloween false face, pathetically cocksure of himself, like the emperor in the fairy tale, strutting in his expensive, fine spun, invisible new clothes.

Without a word they picked up the boat and went down the dune, through a forlornly blonde patch of seawheat and onto the coarse, rock-strewn outer beach. They set the boat down facing the sea and sat down beside it. His father, looking into the extravagant surf, lit a cigarette.

"You want one?"

"No thanks," the boy said.

"You can have one if you want it," his father said. "I know you smoke now. It doesn't take Sherlock Holmes to figure it out. If you want a smoke just ask me. I don't care."

"I just don't feel like smoking now."

"I've forgotten about being your age," his father said. "I guess half the pleasure was in the secrecy."

"I just don't feel like smoking now."

It had popped into his head to say *They say it stunts your growth,* but the words wouldn't come. It seemed like when you thought of something smart to answer back, your tongue just wouldn't form the words for you. And he had an idea that if he once, only once, let loose and spoke the truth from his anger and envy, the words would come like a great flood, like vomiting. How could he ever make his father understand then, drowning, overwhelmed in all that rage? The boy felt ashamed, wishing and wishing and not knowing what to do. He sat woodenly and looked into the surf.

"I could use a little pick-me-up," his father said. He stood up, fumbled in the cockpit for the rucksack they used to carry dry towels and sometimes sandwiches. His father opened the rucksack on the sand and took out a pint bottle. He grinned and took a long pull.

"Better be careful," the boy said. "You might get a cramp."

"You can't imagine how this beach was during the first years of the war," his father said. "Between the storms and the submarines it was a regular graveyard. I remember coming out here one day and finding the whole beach just covered with bunches of green bananas. It was such an odd sight I wanted to laugh."

One drink, the boy thought, and he starts to talk about the war. It's funny that he thinks anybody cares. Mother doesn't care, that's for sure. How many times does she have to tell him that's all over now, that's ancient history, why don't you talk about something somebody cares about?

"What do you think?" his father said. "Think we can make it all right?"

"If we're careful," the boy said. "Once we get out beyond the surf the only thing we have to worry about is keeping up with a wave when we're riding it in."

"I don't know," his father said. "This boat is pretty flimsy. A good wave might break it to pieces."

"We could fix it easy enough."

"It's pretty rough out there. I don't think you know how hard it is to handle a boat in the surf."

"We can try it. How can you tell something before you've tried?"

"I don't know," his father said. "It's tricky. I wouldn't want anything to happen to you. Your mother would never forgive me if I let something happen to you."

"What could happen? I can swim."

"I don't know. Most anything could happen if we capsized."

"What's the matter? Are you scared?"

Now at last he had said it. It had come out in the open, not, as he had feared in a tirade or childish tantrum, but in the form of a simple question, as definite and keen as the cutting blade of a jackknife. His father put out his cigarette in the sand and looked away. After a moment he looked back at the boy, grinning.

"That seems like a funny thing to say," his father said. "I was worrying about you."

"You don't have to worry about me."

"It seems kind of silly to me to make such a big issue out of nothing. Try and be reasonable."

"Okay," the boy said. "I *dare* you to do it. That's all there is to it. Just a dare."

"In that case, I guess we have to do it. I'll take your dare."

They seized the boat, raised it, and half-running, staggering, hurried to the water's edge.

"Leave one paddle behind," his father said loudly above the noise of the waves. They would have to shout now to be heard. Until the trial of the boat and themselves was finished they would have the noise of the waves all around them. The boy looked at his paddle. The two paddles were heavy, hand-carved Indian ones his father had bought out West, richly whittled.

"Don't want to lose both," his father cried.

The boy threw his paddle up the beach. His father was already in his cockpit, so the boy shoved the boat out until it floated well in the shallow water, then settled, empty-handed, in the cockpit behind. He watched his father lean forward and briskly begin stroking with the paddle. The boat was headed at a slight angle into the surf and the first wave broke over them, only a little one, almost spent, but the boy could feel the true wildness as the boat bounced and shivered from the impact and water splashed into the cockpit. He gripped tightly and leaned over as his father paddled into the surf, jockeying the boat amid the uproar and the chill spray. He could feel now the power of the waves as they were slammed, spun around, whirled and dashed in a white fury, and he could see his father working, paddling, the muscles in his arms taut and pulsing. It was dreamy, a rare urgency like a dream of falling downstairs. The shapes of the waves, like huge blue animals stampeding, were all around them, and the boy closed his eyes, partly from the fierce sting of the salt. When he opened them it was calm again. They were outside the breakers and his father, laughing gaily above the noise, paddled in a wide circle. The cockpit was full of water and the boat was heavy. The boy fumbled at his feet and found the tin can and began to bail as fast as he could while his father continued to paddle aimlessly around.

"We made it!" his father shouted. "I never thought we would without capsizing, but we made it."

"Here we are!" the boy shouted.

"How about that!"

While the boy bailed, he looked at his father with a kind of awe. The big man, stripped to his trunks, his chest heaving from his effort, his head spray-drenched and glistening in the sun, seemed strangely savage and noble. It hadn't been as the boy imagined it would be. Thinking about taking the boat in the surf, talking about it all summer long, until finally wheedling his father's promise, he had only pictured how it would be coming in with the waves, the glory and the hectic joy. He hadn't wondered how it would be getting through the surf and beyond. He looked back into the turbulence they had come through and he felt something close to fear, for he knew now. And he felt a curious admiration for his father. They had done this together. He passed the bailing can to his father and hunched down, breathing deeply.

"Ready?" his father said when he had finished bailing.

"All set."

His father headed the boat straight for the shore and began to paddle. They caught the crest of a wave and the boy felt it seize the boat, carrying them in a high rush forward. He could feel the wave mounting slowly under them as they sped along, and then they poised almost motionless for a breathless instant on the brink, shot forward in a dazzling flash of foam; it seemed they were falling, falling until they shuddered to a stop as the keel dug into the sand in shallow water. They leapt from the boat and dragged it ashore, fell exhausted on the soft sand. The boy lay on his back looking into the dizzy brightness of the sky and thought he could feel the earth turning under him.

"That wasn't so bad," his father said. "That wasn't so bad at all."

"That was good." The boy said. "Did you ever have a ride like that?"

"Better than a roller coaster."

There weren't words for what the boy felt. He lay there beside his father with the sun and the breeze drying his body and he felt marvelously light as if he were floating on his back in calm water and nothing, not even the percussion of the surf, could interrupt his spent tranquillity. The air seemed full of tunes his blood could dance to.

"All right," his father said. "I had mine. Now it's your turn."

The boy felt his guts knot and tighten like a fist.

"I don't know if I can do it," he said. "I might wreck the boat."

"I'll take that chance," his father said. "You ought to try it once. After all, it was your idea."

The boy tested the weight of the paddle in his hand. It felt oddly heavy. The trouble was you could never finish anything and just leave it that way. His father was giving him the chance to prove himself and he knew he must take it, that was vital, whether he failed or not. He settled himself into the cockpit when they were afloat and paddled. As he fought the boat forward into the surf he knew now what it had been like for his father because now he only had time to act, neither to think nor plan ahead, only to feel what the waves were doing and move instantly in response. The waves rolled over them and he fought in a happy fury until one caught them, smashed over them and sent the boat reeling back to the shore.

"Bail it out and try again."

"I don't know if I can do it."

"There's no harm in trying."

The boy seized the tin can and bailed. It was an awful thing, he thought, to be about to do something that he knew he couldn't. It was different when you didn't know, but he wasn't innocent any more. He knew what to expect. He was thinking, as he bailed, that maybe being a man would be like that, going ahead with something and doing it because you had to even when you knew what the outcome would be. After you once knew, there was no outside mystery any more. There was only the secret of yourself to worry with. He felt suddenly as frail and fragile as a China doll.

He tried again, pointing into the surf, paddling as fast as he could. He fought, his body tensed against the cold and the power, his eyes squinted against the spray. He could see his father, sitting, leaning forward, completely relaxed, and he felt urgently alone. They made a little progress; he could see the calm area behind the waves he was striving for, and he struggled for it. It was then like a shape from a dream; in a timeless moment a wave bulked high above them directly ahead and he could feel the boat slipping back under him in the trough and see his father turning in the cockpit shouting words he couldn't hear as the wave broke over them, turning and turning, and he jumped free of the cockpit, crashed against the sand and rolled in a shower of bright lights, came up gasping for air, hurt, tasting blood in his mouth. He saw the boat dashed empty on the sand and then he saw his father come up out of the foam still shouting, his face twisting in pain. He moved awkwardly in the water to where his father was, grasped him under the arms, strained to pull him up. A wave broke over them and he heard his father scream. Somehow, dragging and pulling, he managed to get his father to the beach. His father lay still with only his head on dry land, breathing hard, white-faced.

"It's my leg," he said finally. "I think I broke my leg."

The boy looked quickly, furtively at his father's legs stretched limp in the water. They had never seemed so long and thin, so easy to be broken. It was a strange thing to think of his father's flesh. He had never really imagined his father as possessing flesh that could be injured, bones that could break.

"Which one?" he heard himself asking. "Which leg is broken?"

"The right one," his father said. "Run up and get the bottle. I need a drink."

The boy raced up the beach to the rucksack, fished the bottle out and returned with it. He stood tensely watching while his father drank.

"Just what the old doctor ordered," his father said. "Go and see about the boat."

He ran down the beach to where the boat had been dashed ashore. The frame was broken in several places, but the canvas wasn't ripped. It would float all right. He got under it and, gradually, slipping in the wet sand, using all the strength he had, he tipped it over and the water poured out of the cockpits. With most of the water out the boat was lighter and he was able to pull it farther ashore, high and dry. When he came back, his father was propped up on his elbows looking at his leg.

"It's a nice clean break," his father said. "Not bad, but we got some trouble."

The boy began to shake and he could feel tears in his eyes and the taste of tears in his mouth. He didn't want to cry but the tears came. He tried to speak but he couldn't.

"Take it easy," his father said.

"It's my fault," the boy said. "I dared you to do it and it's my fault."

"The hell it's your fault. I took the dare didn't I?"

"I didn't mean for anything like this to happen," the boy said, still crying. "I didn't mean for anything to happen. I just wanted to show you. I didn't want you to get hurt."

"What did you want?"

"I can't explain it."

"Try it," his father said roughly. "This one time tell me exactly what you wanted."

"I can't put it in words."

"Try, damn it. It's important to me, believe it or not. Damn it, try and put it in words. How else can I understand you?"

The boy stopped crying and squatted down on his haunches. He looked at the sand, thinking.

"I just wanted to show you I was a man," he whispered. "I wanted to prove it."

His father laughed. He leaned his head back and laughed above the roar of the surf.

"In that case," his father said, "it was worth it. Because now you've got the chance."

The boy looked at him, wondering, and waited.

"Now listen to me," his father said. "You've got to go back without me. Tell your mother to call a doctor and get Joe Soens to come out with his motorboat and pick me up. Tell him to bring somebody. It will take two."

"All right."

"You're going to have to drag the boat over the dunes by yourself. That'll take maybe an hour if you work steady at it. The tide will be running out and it will be hard work paddling across the bay. Can you do it?"

"I think so."

His father's hand seized his arm and the boy could feel the strong fingers digging deep in his muscles, but it didn't hurt. He felt numb.

"Can you do it?" his father asked fiercely.

"Yes," the boy said.

"All right," his father said. "That's all I have to know."

The boy ran down the beach and started to drag the boat toward the dunes, inching it along the sand. He looked up for a moment and saw his father wriggling on his back, getting clear of the water. He saw the tall man in his lonely effort and he felt a new and troubled joy, a joy too deep for guilt or tears or any of the knowledge of childhood. It was a strange and precious feeling, as small as the first moment of a catching flame, but hard too, and brimming with an inner glow like a jewel. He kept dragging the boat, pacing himself, measuring his strength because he had a long way to go.

THE RIVALS

1. Is there a conflict in this story? Between whom does it occur? Is this a common problem in human relationships?
2. What is the attitude of the son at the beginning of the story? Who does the boy think is the better man?

3. What changes the boy's opinion of his father?
4. How has the boy's self-confidence changed when the father says, "Now it's your turn"?
5. In what way is the boy's reaction true to life in the paragraph which begins "The boy seized the tin can and bailed"?
6. How do the relative strengths of the boy and man change after the boat is dashed upon the sand?
7. Why does the father insist that the boy try to "put it in words"? Why was it important to the father?
8. In what way is the boy's reply characteristic of young people under such circumstances?
9. How is our confidence in the boy restored?
10. Explain the sentence "'Can you do it?' his father asked fiercely."
11. What emotion did the boy experience when "he felt a new and troubled joy, a joy too deep for guilt or tears or any of the knowledge of childhood"? What has he finally learned, along with us, about himself?
12. Explain the significance of the last sentence.
13. Explain the title. In what sense were the two "rivals"?
14. What does Mr. Garrett gain as a storyteller by the use of dialogue? Does it help to describe the characters? Which dialogue is particularly effective? What aspect of character does it help to establish?

15. There is much action in this story, and much of it is dramatic. Would you describe this as an action story? Which is the more important here, the action or the characters? What type of story would you say this is?

16. In the preceding question we said that some of the action is dramatic. Can dialogue be dramatic? If so, how does an author use it for dramatic effects in this story? Which dialogue in this story would you say is dramatic?

17. You probably have had experiences something like this in your relationships with adults. Try your hand at a story or vignette telling of one of your experiences.

GRAHAM GREENE

1904–

Across the Bridge

THIS AUTHOR *is one of England's greatest contemporary novelists. He attended Oxford University and later served on the staff of the London* Times. *Much of his work is concerned with serious matters pertaining to sin and redemption, but some of it is of a thriller type (he calls them "entertainments"), including several that have been made into motion pictures such as* This Gun for Hire, The Third Man, *and* Orient Express.

Mr. Greene has served Great Britain in the British Foreign Office in West Africa. He has written one play, novels, a book of memoirs, and short stories.

"They say he's worth a million," Lucia said. He sat there in the little hot damp Mexican square, a dog at his feet, with an air of immense and forlorn patience. The dog attracted your attention at once; for it was very nearly an English setter, only something had gone wrong with the tail and the feathering. Palms wilted over his head, it was all shade and stuffiness round the bandstand, radios talked loudly in Spanish from the little wooden sheds where they changed your pesos into dollars at a loss. I could tell he didn't understand a word from the way he read his newspaper—as I did myself, picking out the words which were like English ones.

"He's been here a month," Lucia said. "They turned him out of Guatemala and Honduras."

You couldn't keep any secrets for five hours in this border town. Lucia had only been twenty-four hours in the place, but she knew all about Mr. Joseph Calloway. The only reason I didn't know about him (and I'd been in the place two weeks) was because I couldn't talk the language any more than Mr. Calloway could. There wasn't another soul in the place who didn't know the story—the whole story of the Halling Investment Trust and the proceedings for extradition. Any man doing dusty business in any of the wooden booths in the town is better fitted by long observation to tell Mr. Calloway's tale than I am, except that I was in—literally—at the finish. They all watched the drama proceed with immense interest, sympathy and respect. For, after all, he had a million.

Every once in a while through the long steamy day, a boy came and cleaned Mr. Calloway's shoes: he hadn't the right words to resist them—they pretended not to know his English. He must have had his shoes cleaned the day Lucia and I watched him at least half a dozen times. At midday he took a stroll across the square to the Antonio Bar and had a bottle of beer, the setter sticking to heel as if they were out for a country walk in England (he had, you may remember, one of the biggest estates in Norfolk). After his bottle of beer, he would walk down between the money-changers' huts to the Rio Grande and look across the bridge into the United States: people came and went constantly in cars. Then back to the square till lunch-time. He was staying in the best hotel, but you don't get good hotels in this border town: nobody stays in them more than a night. The good hotels were on the other side of the bridge: you could see their electric signs twenty stories high from the little square at night, like lighthouses marking the United States.

You may ask what I'd been doing in so drab a spot for a fortnight. There was no interest in the place for anyone; it was just damp and dust and poverty, a kind of shabby replica of the town across the river: both had squares in the same spots; both had the same number of cinemas. One was cleaner than the other, that was all, and more expensive, much more expensive. I'd stayed across there a couple of nights waiting for a man a tourist bureau said was driving down from Detroit to Yucatan and would sell a place in his car for some fantastically small figure—twenty dollars, I think it was. I don't know if he existed or was invented by the optimistic half-caste in the agency; anyway, he never turned up and so I waited, not much caring, on the cheap side of the river. It didn't much matter; I was living. One day I meant to give up the man from Detroit and go home or go south, but it was easier not to decide anything in a hurry. Lucia was just waiting for a car going the other way, but she didn't have to wait so long. We waited together and watched Mr. Calloway waiting—for God knows what.

I don't know how to treat this story—it was a tragedy for Mr. Calloway, it was poetic retribution, I suppose, in the eyes of the shareholders he'd ruined with his bogus transactions, and to Lucia and me, at this stage, it was pure comedy—except when he kicked the dog. I'm not a sentimentalist about dogs, I prefer people to be cruel to animals rather than to human beings, but I couldn't help being revolted at the way he'd kick that animal—with a hint of cold-blooded venom, not in anger but as if he were getting even for some trick it had played him a long while ago. That generally happened when he returned from the bridge: it was the only sign of anything resembling emotion he showed. Otherwise he looked a small, set, gentle creature with silver hair and a silver moustache, and gold-rimmed glasses, and one gold tooth like a flaw in character.

Lucia hadn't been accurate when she said he'd been turned out of Guatemala and Honduras; he'd left voluntarily when the extradition proceedings seemed likely to go through and moved north. Mexico is still not a very centralized state, and it is possible to get round governors as you can't get round cabinet ministers or judges. And so he waited there on the border for the next move. That earlier part of the story is, I suppose, dramatic, but I didn't watch it and I can't invent what I haven't seen—the long waiting in anterooms, the bribes taken and refused, the growing fear of arrest, and then the flight—in gold-rimmed glasses—covering his tracks as well as he could, but this wasn't finance and he was an amateur at escape. And so he'd washed up here, under my eyes and Lucia's eyes, sitting all day under the bandstand, nothing to read but a Mexican paper, nothing to do but look across the river at the United States, quite unaware, I suppose, that everyone knew everything about him, once a day kicking his dog. Perhaps in its semi-setter way it reminded him too much of the Norfolk estate—though that too, I suppose, was the reason he kept it.

And the next act again was pure comedy. I hesitate to think what this man worth a million was costing his country as they edged him out from this land and that. Perhaps somebody was getting tired of the business, and careless; anyway, they sent across two detectives, with an old photograph. He'd grown his silvery moustache since that had been taken, and he'd aged a lot, and they couldn't catch sight of him. They hadn't been across the bridge two hours when everybody knew that there were two foreign detectives in town looking for Mr. Calloway—everybody knew, that is to say, except Mr. Calloway, who couldn't talk Spanish. There were plenty of people who could have told him in English, but they didn't. It wasn't cruelty, it was a sort of awe and respect: like a bull, he was on show, sitting there mournfully in the plaza with his dog, a magnificent spectacle for which we all had ringside seats.

I ran into one of the policemen in the Bar Antonio. He was disgusted; he had had some idea that when he crossed the bridge life was going to be different, so much more colour and sun, and—I suspect—love, and all he found were wide mud streets where the nocturnal rain lay in pools, and mangy dogs, smells and cockroaches in his bedroom, and the nearest to love, the open door of the Academia Comercial, where pretty mestizo girls sat all the morning learning to typewrite. Tip-tap-tip-tap-tip—perhaps they had a dream, too—jobs on the other side of the bridge, where life was going to be so much more luxurious, refined and amusing.

We got into conversation; he seemed surprised that I knew who they both were and what they wanted. He said, "We've got information this man Calloway's in town."

"He's knocking around somewhere," I said.

"Could you point him out?"

"Oh, I don't know him by sight," I said.

He drank his beer and thought a while. "I'll go out and sit in the plaza. He's sure to pass sometime."

I finished my beer and went quickly off and found Lucia. I said, "Hurry, we're going to see an arrest." We didn't care a thing about Mr. Calloway, he was just an elderly man who kicked his dog and swindled the poor, and who deserved anything he got. So we made for the plaza; we knew Calloway would be there, but it had never occurred to either of us that the detectives wouldn't recognize him. There was quite a surge of people round the place; all the fruit-sellers and boot-blacks in town seemed to have arrived together; we had to force our way through, and there in the little green stuffy centre of the place, sitting on adjoining seats, were the two plainclothes men and Mr. Calloway. I've never known the place so silent; everybody was on tiptoe, and the plainclothes men were staring at the crowd looking for Mr. Calloway, and Mr. Calloway sat on his usual seat staring out over the money-changing booths at the United States.

"It can't go on. It just can't," Lucia said. But it did. It got more fantastic still. Somebody ought to write a play about it. We sat as close as we dared. We were afraid all the time we were going to laugh. The semi-setter scratched for fleas and

Mr. Calloway watched the U.S.A. The two detectives watched the crowd, and the crowd watched the show with solemn satisfaction. Then one of the detectives got up and went over to Mr. Calloway. That's the end, I thought. But it wasn't, it was the beginning. For some reason they had eliminated him from their list of suspects. I shall never know why.

The man said, "You speak English?"

"I *am* English," Mr. Calloway said.

Even that didn't tear it, and the strangest thing of all was the way Mr. Calloway came alive. I don't think anybody had spoken to him like that for weeks. The Mexicans were too respectful—he was a man with a million—and it had never occurred to Lucia and me to treat him casually like a human being; even in our eyes he had been magnified by the colossal theft and the world-wide pursuit.

He said, "This is rather a dreadful place, don't you think?"

"It is," the policeman said.

"I can't think what brings anybody across the bridge."

"Duty," the policeman said gloomily. "I suppose you are passing through."

"Yes," Mr. Calloway said.

"I'd have expected over here there'd have been—you know what I mean—life. You read things about Mexico."

"Oh, life," Mr. Calloway said. He spoke firmly and precisely, as if to a committee of shareholders. "That begins on the other side."

"You don't appreciate your own country until you leave it."

"That's very true," Mr. Calloway said. "Very true."

At first it was difficult not to laugh, and then after a while there didn't seem to be much to laugh at; an old man imagining all the fine things going on beyond the international bridge. I think he thought of the town opposite as a combination of London and Norfolk—theatres and cocktail bars, a little shooting and a walk round the field at evening with the dog—that miserable imitation of a setter—poking the ditches. He'd never been across, he couldn't know that it was just the same thing over again—even the same layout; only the streets were paved and the hotels had ten more stories, and life was more expensive, and everything was a little bit cleaner. There wasn't anything Mr. Calloway would have called living—no galleries, no book-shops, just *Film Fun* and the local paper, and *Click* and *Focus* and the tabloids.

"Well," said Mr. Calloway, "I think I'll take a stroll before lunch. You need an appetite to swallow the food here. I generally go down and look at the bridge about now. Care to come too?"

The detective shook his head. "No," he said, "I'm on duty. I'm looking for a fellow." And that, of course, gave *him* away. As far as Mr. Calloway could understand, there was only one "fellow" in the world anyone was looking for—his brain had eliminated friends who were seeking their friends, husbands who might be waiting for their wives, all objectives of any search but just the one. The power of elimination was what had made him a financier—he could forget the people behind the shares.

That was the last we saw of him for a while. We didn't see him going into the Botica Paris to get his aspirin, or walking back from the bridge with his dog. He simply disappeared, and when he disappeared, people began to talk, and the detectives heard the talk. They looked silly enough, and they got busy after the very man they'd been sitting next to in the garden. Then they too disappeared. They, as well as Mr. Calloway, had gone to the state capital to see the Governor and the Chief of Police, and it must have been an amusing sight there too, as they bumped into Mr. Calloway and sat with him in the waiting-rooms. I suspect Mr. Calloway was generally shown in first, for everyone knew he was worth a million. Only in Europe is it possible for a man to be a criminal as well as a rich man.

Anyway, after about a week the whole pack of them returned by the same train. Mr. Calloway travelled Pullman, and the two policemen travelled in the day coach. It was evident that they hadn't got their extradition order.

Lucia had left by that time. The car came and went across the bridge. I stood in Mexico and watched her get out at the United States Customs. She wasn't anything in particular but she looked beautiful at a distance as she gave me a wave out of the United States and got back into the car. And I suddenly felt sympathy for Mr. Calloway, as if there were something over there which you couldn't find here, and turning round I saw him back on his old beat, with the dog at his heels.

I said "Good afternoon," as if it had been all along our habit to greet each other. He looked tired and ill and dusty, and I felt sorry for him—to think of the kind of victory he'd been winning, with so much expenditure of cash and care—the prize this dirty and dreary town, the booths of the money-changers, the awful little beauty parlours with their wicker chairs and sofas looking like the reception rooms of brothels, that hot and stuffy garden by the bandstand.

He replied gloomily, "Good morning," and the dog started to sniff at some ordure and he turned and kicked it with fury, with depression, with despair.

And at that moment a taxi with the two policemen in it passed us on its way to the bridge. They must have seen that kick; perhaps they were cleverer than I had given them credit for, perhaps they were just sentimental about animals, and thought they'd do a good deed, and the rest happened by accident. But the fact remains—those two pillars of the law set about the stealing of Mr. Calloway's dog.

He watched them go by. Then he said, "Why don't you go across?"

"It's cheaper here," I said.

"I mean just for an evening. Have a meal at that place we can see at night in the sky. Go to the theatre."

"There isn't a chance."

He said angrily, sucking his gold tooth, "Well, anyway, get away from here." He stared down the hill and up the other side. He couldn't see that that street climbing up from the bridge contained only the same money-changers' booths as this one.

I said, "Why don't *you* go?"

He said evasively, "Oh—business."

I said, "It's only a question of money. You don't *have* to pass by the bridge."

He said with faint interest, "I don't talk Spanish."

"There isn't a soul here," I said, "who doesn't talk English."

He looked at me with surprise. "Is that so?" he said. "Is that so?"

It's as I have said; he'd never tried to talk to anyone, and they respected him too much to talk to him—he was worth a million. I don't know whether I'm glad or sorry that I told him that. If I hadn't, he might be there now, sitting by the bandstand having his shoes cleaned—alive and suffering.

Three days later his dog disappeared. I found him looking for it, calling it softly and shamefacedly between the palms of the garden. He looked embarrassed. He said in a low angry voice, "I *hate* that dog. The beastly mongrel," and called "Rover, Rover" in a voice which didn't carry five yards. He said, "I bred setters once. I'd have shot a dog like that." It reminded him, I *was* right, of Norfolk, and he lived in the memory, and he hated it for its imperfection. He was a man without a family and without friends, and his only enemy was that dog. You couldn't call the law an enemy; you have to be intimate with an enemy.

Late that afternoon someone told him they'd seen the dog walking across the bridge. It wasn't true, of course, but we didn't know that then—they'd paid a Mexican five pesos to smuggle it across. So all that afternoon and the next Mr. Calloway sat in the garden having his shoes cleaned over and over again, and thinking how a dog could just walk across like that, and a human being, an immortal soul, was bound here in the awful routine of the little walk and the unspeakable meal and the aspirin at the *botica.* That dog was seeing things he couldn't see—that hateful dog. It made him mad—I think literally mad. You must remember the man had been going on for months. He had a million and he was living on two pounds a week, with nothing to spend his money on. He sat there and brooded on the hideous injustice of it. I think he'd have crossed over one day in any case, but the dog was the last straw.

Next day when he wasn't to be seen I guessed he'd gone across, and I went too. The American town is as small as the Mexican. I knew I couldn't miss him if he was there, and I was still curious. A little sorry for him, but not much.

I caught sight of him first in the only drug-store, having a Coca-Cola, and then once outside a cinema looking at the posters; he had dressed with extreme neatness, as if for a party, but there was no party. On my third time round, I came on the detectives—they were having Coca-Colas in the drug-store, and they must have missed Mr. Calloway by inches. I went in and sat down at the bar.

"Hello," I said, "you still about?" I suddenly felt anxious for Mr. Calloway, I didn't want them to meet.

One of them said, "Where's Calloway?"

"Oh," I said, "he's hanging on."

"But not his dog," he said, and laughed. The other looked a little shocked, he didn't like anyone to *talk* cynically about a dog. Then they got up—they had a car outside.

"Have another?" I said.

"No, thanks. We've got to keep moving."

The man bent close and confided to me, "Calloway's on this side."

"No!" I said.

"And his dog."

"He's looking for it," the other said.

"I'm damned if he is," I said, and again one of them looked a little shocked, as if I'd insulted the dog.

I don't think Mr. Calloway was looking for his dog, but his dog certainly found him. There was a sudden hilarious yapping from the car and out plunged the semi-setter and gambolled furiously down the street. One of the detectives—the sentimental one—was into the car before we got to the door and was off after the dog. Near the bottom of the long road to the bridge was Mr. Calloway—I do believe he'd come down to look at the Mexican side when he found there was nothing but the drug-store and the cinemas and the paper shops on the American. He saw the dog coming and yelled at it to go home—"home, home, home," as if they were in Norfolk—it took no notice at all, pelting towards him. Then he saw the police car coming and ran. After that, everything happened too quickly, but I think the order of events was this—the dog started across the road right in front of the car, and Mr. Calloway yelled, at the dog or the car, I don't know which. Anyway, the detective swerved—he said later, weakly, at the inquiry, that he couldn't run over a dog, and down went Mr. Calloway, in a mess of broken glass and gold rims and silver hair, and blood. The dog was on to him before any of us could reach him, licking and whimpering and licking. I saw Mr. Calloway put up his hand, and down it went across the dog's neck and the whimper rose to a stupid bark of triumph, but Mr. Calloway was dead—shock and a weak heart.

"Poor old geezer," the detective said, "I bet he really loved that dog," and it's true that the attitude in which he lay looked more like a caress than a blow. I thought it was meant to be a blow, but the detective may have been right. It all seemed to me a little too touching to be true as the old crook lay there with his arm over the dog's neck, dead with his million between the money-changers' huts, but it's as well to be humble in the face of human nature. He had come across the river for something, and it may, after all, have been the dog he was looking for. It sat there, baying its stupid and mongrel triumph across his body, like a piece of sentimental statuary. The nearest he could get to the fields, the ditches, the horizon of his home. It was comic and it was pitiable; but it wasn't less comic because the man was dead. Death doesn't change comedy to tragedy, and if that last gesture was one of affection, I suppose it was only one more indication of a human being's capacity for self-deception, our baseless optimism that is so much more appalling than our despair.

ACROSS THE BRIDGE

1. What important information do we learn about Mr. Calloway in the introduction?

2. Why is the dog introduced even before Mr. Calloway?
3. At what point does irony first appear? (See Glossary) What other instances of irony are found in this story?
4. Why doesn't the storyteller point out the swindler to the detectives?
5. How is the detectives' failure to recognize Calloway made plausible?
6. What do *Film Fun, Click,* and *Focus* symbolize in their context?
7. Why does Mr. Greene repeatedly use the refrain that Calloway "was worth a million"?
8. Why do "you have to be intimate with an enemy"?
9. Mr. Greene raises the question at the start of this story as to whether it is comedy or tragedy. Why do you think it is one rather than the other? Can you make such a decision?
10. What does Mr. Greene mean by the last sentence?

NATHANIEL HAWTHORNE

1804–1864

The Minister's Black Veil

A CONTEMPORARY *of Poe, Nathaniel Hawthorne also became one of the great early-American storytellers. Born of New England ancestry, Hawthorne seemed to inherit a deep concern for man and his immortal soul. Throughout much of his work he portrays man's confrontation with evil and shows how man seeks to work out his problem. This is particularly evident in his two great novels,* The House of the Seven Gables *and* The Scarlet Letter.

In "The Minister's Black Veil," *Hawthorne pictures a man who is obsessed with this problem.*[1]

The sexton stood in the porch of Milford meeting-house, pulling busily at the bell-rope. The old people of the village came stooping along the street. Children, with bright faces, tripped merrily beside their parents, or mimicked a graver gait, in the conscious dignity of their Sunday clothes. Spruce bachelors looked sidelong at the pretty maidens, and fancied that the Sabbath sunshine made them prettier than on week

[1] Another clergyman in New England, who died about eighty years since, made himself remarkable by the same eccentricity that is here related of the Reverend Mr. Hooper. In his case, however, the symbol had a different import. In early life he had accidentally killed a beloved friend; and from that day till the hour of his own death, he hid his face from men. (Hawthorne's note)

days. When the throng had mostly streamed into the porch, the sexton began to toll the bell, keeping his eye on the Reverend Mr. Hooper's door. The first glimpse of the clergyman's figure was the signal for the bell to cease its summons.

"But what has good Parson Hooper got upon his face?" cried the sexton in astonishment.

All within hearing immediately turned about, and beheld the semblance of Mr. Hooper, pacing slowly his meditative way towards the meeting-house. With one accord they started, expressing more wonder than if some strange minister were coming to dust the cushions of Mr. Hooper's pulpit.

"Are you sure it is our parson?" inquired Goodman Gray of the sexton.

"Of a certainty it is good Mr. Hooper," replied the sexton. "He was to have exchanged pulpits with Parson Shute, of Westbury; but Parson Shute sent to excuse himself yesterday, being to preach a funeral sermon."

The cause of so much amazement may appear sufficiently slight. Mr. Hooper, a gentlemanly person, of about thirty, though still a bachelor, was dressed with due clerical neatness, as if a careful wife had starched his band, and brushed the weekly dust from his Sunday's garb. There was but one thing remarkable in his appearance. Swathed about his forehead, and hanging down over his face, so low as to be shaken by his breath, Mr. Hooper had on a black veil. On a nearer view it seemed to consist of two folds of crape, which entirely concealed his features, except the mouth and chin, but probably did not intercept his sight, further than to give a darkened aspect to all living and inanimate things. With this gloomy shade before him, good Mr. Hooper walked onward, at a slow and quiet pace, stooping somewhat, and looking on the ground, as is customary with abstracted men, yet nodding kindly to those of his parishioners who still waited on the meeting-house steps. But so wonder-struck were they that his greeting hardly met with a return.

"I can't really feel as if good Mr. Hooper's face was behind that piece of crape," said the sexton.

"I don't like it," muttered an old woman, as she hobbled into the meeting-house. "He has changed himself into something awful, only by hiding his face."

"Our parson has gone mad!" cried Goodman Gray, following him across the threshold.

A rumor of some unaccountable phenomenon had preceded Mr. Hooper into the meeting-house, and set all the congregation astir. Few could refrain from twisting their heads towards the door; many stood upright, and turned directly about; while several little boys clambered upon the seats, and came down again with a terrible racket. There was a general bustle, a rustling of the women's gowns and shuffling of the men's feet, greatly at variance with that hushed repose which should attend the entrance of the minister. But Mr. Hooper appeared not to notice the perturbation of his people. He entered with an almost noiseless step, bent his head mildly to the pews on each side, and bowed as he passed his oldest parishioner, a white-haired great-grandsire, who occupied an arm-chair in the centre of the aisle. It was strange to observe how slowly this venerable man became conscious of something singular in the appearance of his pastor. He seemed not fully to partake of the prevailing wonder, till Mr. Hooper had ascended the stairs, and showed himself in the pulpit, face to face with his congregation, except for the black veil. That mysterious emblem was never once withdrawn. It shook with his measured breath as he gave out the psalm; it threw its obscurity between him and the holy page, as he read the Scriptures; and while he prayed, the veil lay heavily on his uplifted countenance. Did he seek to hide it from the dread Being whom he was addressing?

Such was the effect of this simple piece of crape, that more than one woman of delicate nerves was forced to leave the meeting-house. Yet perhaps the pale-faced congregation was almost as fearful a sight to the minister, as his black veil to them.

Mr. Hooper had the reputation of a good preacher, but not an energetic one: he strove to win his people heavenward by mild, persuasive influences, rather than to drive them thither by the thunders of the Word. The sermon which he now delivered was marked by the same characteristics of style and manner as the general series of his pulpit oratory. But there was something, either in the sentiment of the discourse itself, or in the imagination of the auditors, which made it greatly the most powerful effort that they had ever heard from their pastor's lips. It was tinged, rather more darkly than usual, with the gentle gloom of Mr. Hooper's temperament. The subject had reference to secret sin, and those sad mysteries which we hide from our nearest and dearest, and would fain conceal from our own consciousness, even forgetting that the Omniscient can detect them. A subtle power was breathed into his words. Each member of the congregation, the most innocent girl, and the man of hardened breast, felt as if the preacher had crept upon them, behind his awful veil, and discovered their hoarded iniquity of deed or thought. Many spread their clasped hands on their bosoms. There was nothing terrible in what Mr. Hooper said, at least, no violence; and yet, with every tremor of his melancholy voice, the hearers quaked. An unsought pathos came hand in hand with awe. So sensible were the audience of some unwonted attribute in their minister, that they longed for a breath of wind to blow aside the veil, almost believing that a stranger's visage would be discovered, though the form, gesture, and voice were those of Mr. Hooper.

At the close of the services, the people hurried out with indecorous confusion, eager to communicate their pent-up amazement, and conscious of lighter spirits the moment they lost sight of the black veil. Some gathered in little circles, huddled closely together, with their mouths all whispering in the centre; some went homeward alone, wrapt in silent meditation; some talked loudly, and profaned the Sabbath-day with ostentatious laughter. A few shook their sagacious heads, intimating that they could penetrate the mystery; while one or two affirmed that there was no mystery at all, but only that Mr. Hooper's eyes were so weakened by the midnight lamp, as to require a shade. After a brief interval, forth came good Mr. Hooper also, in the rear of his flock. Turning his veiled face from one group to another, he paid due reverence to the hoary heads, saluted the middle aged, with kind dignity as their friend and spiritual guide, greeted the young with mingled authority and love, and laid his hands on the little children's heads to bless them. Such was always his custom on the Sabbath-day. Strange and bewildered looks repaid him for his courtesy. None, as on former occasions, aspired to the honor of walking by their pastor's side. Old Squire Saunders, doubtless by an accidental lapse of memory, neglected to invite Mr. Hooper to his table, where the good clergyman had been wont to bless the food, almost every Sunday since his settlement. He returned, therefore to the parsonage, and, at the moment of closing the door, was observed to look back upon the people, all of whom had their eyes fixed upon the minister. A sad smile gleamed faintly from beneath the black veil, and flickered about his mouth, glimmering as he disappeared.

"How strange," said a lady, "that a simple black veil, such as any woman might wear on her bonnet, should become such a terrible thing on Mr. Hooper's face!"

"Something must surely be amiss with Mr. Hooper's intellects," observed her husband, the physician of the village. "But the strangest part of the affair is the effect of this vagary, even on a sober-minded man like myself. The black veil, though it covers only our pastor's face, throws its influence over his whole person, and makes him ghostlike from head to foot. Do you not feel it so?"

"Truly do I," replied the lady; "and I would not be alone

with him for the world. I wonder he is not afraid to be alone with himself!"

"Men sometimes are so," said her husband.

The afternoon service was attended with similar circumstances. At its conclusion, the bell tolled for the funeral of a young lady. The relatives and friends were assembled in the house, and the more distant acquaintances stood about the door, speaking of the good qualities of the deceased, when their talk was interrupted by the appearance of Mr. Hooper, still covered with his black veil. It was now an appropriate emblem. The clergyman stepped into the room where the corpse was laid, and bent over the coffin, to take a last farewell of his deceased parishioner. As he stooped, the veil hung straight from his forehead, so that, if her eyelids had not been closed forever, the dead maiden might have seen his face. Could Mr. Hooper be fearful of her glance, that he so hastily caught back the black veil? A person who watched the interview between the dead and living, scrupled not to affirm, that, at the instant when the clergyman's features were disclosed, the corpse had slightly shuddered, rustling the shroud and muslin cap, though the countenance retained the composure of death. A superstitious old woman was the only witness of this prodigy. From the coffin Mr. Hooper passed into the chamber of the mourners, and thence to the head of the staircase, to make the funeral prayer. It was a tender and heart-dissolving prayer, full of sorrow, yet so imbued with celestial hopes, that the music of a heavenly harp, swept by the fingers of the dead, seemed faintly to be heard among the saddest accents of the minister. The people trembled, though they but darkly understood him, when he prayed that they, and himself, and all of mortal race, might be ready, as he trusted this young maiden had been, for the dreadful hour that should snatch the veil from their faces. The bearers went heavily forth, and the mourners followed, saddening all the street, with the dead before them, and Mr. Hooper in his black veil behind.

"Why do you look back?" said one in the procession to his partner.

"I had a fancy," replied she, "that the minister and the maiden's spirit were walking hand in hand."

"And so had I, at the same moment," said the other.

That night, the handsomest couple in Milford village were to be joined in wedlock. Though reckoned a melancholy man, Mr. Hooper had a placid cheerfulness for such occasions, which often excited a sympathetic smile where livelier merriment would have been thrown away. There was no quality of his disposition which made him more beloved than this. The company at the wedding awaited his arrival with impatience, trusting that the strange awe, which had gathered over him throughout the day, would now be dispelled. But such was not the result. When Mr. Hooper came, the first thing that their eyes rested on was the same horrible black veil, which had added deeper gloom to the funeral, and could portend nothing but evil to the wedding. Such was its immediate effect on the guests that a cloud seemed to have rolled duskily from beneath the black crape, and dimmed the light of the candles. The bridal pair stood up before the minister. But the bride's cold fingers quivered in the tremulous hand of the bridegroom, and her deathlike paleness caused a whisper that the maiden who had been buried a few hours before was come from her grave to be married. If ever another wedding were so dismal, it was that famous one where they tolled the wedding knell. After performing the ceremony, Mr. Hooper raised a glass of wine to his lips, wishing happiness to the new-married couple in a strain of mild pleasantry that ought to have brightened the features of the guests, like a cheerful gleam from the heart. At that instant, catching a glimpse of his figure in the looking glass, the black veil involved his own spirit in the horror with which it overwhelmed all others. His frame shuddered, his lips grew pale, he spilt the untasted wine upon the carpet, and rushed forth into the darkness. For the Earth, too, had on her Black Veil.

The next day, the whole village of Milford talked of little else than Parson Hooper's black veil. That, and the mystery concealed behind it, supplied a topic for discussion between acquaintances meeting in the street, and good women gossiping at their open windows. It was the first item of news that the tavern-keeper told to his guests. The children babbled of it on their way to school. One imitative little imp covered his face with an old black handkerchief, thereby so affrighting his playmates that the panic seized himself, and he wellnigh lost his wits by his own waggery.

It was remarkable that of all the busybodies and impertinent people in the parish, not one ventured to put the plain question to Mr. Hooper, wherefore he did this thing. Hitherto, whenever there appeared the slightest call for such interference, he had never lacked advisers, nor shown himself averse to be guided by their judgment. If he erred at all, it was by so painful a degree of self-distrust, that even the mildest censure would lead him to consider an indifferent action as a crime. Yet, though so well acquainted with this amiable weakness, no individual among his parishioners chose to make the black veil a subject of friendly remonstrance. There was a feeling of dread, neither plainly confessed nor carefully concealed, which caused each to shift the responsibility upon another, till at length it was found expedient to send a deputation of the church, in order to deal with Mr. Hooper about the mystery, before it should grow into a scandal. Never did an embassy so ill discharge its duties. The minister received them with friendly courtesy, but became silent, after they were seated, leaving to his visitors the whole burden of introducing their important business. The topic, it might be supposed, was obvious enough. There was the black veil swathed round Mr. Hooper's forehead, and concealing every feature above his placid mouth, on which, at times, they could perceive the glimmering of a melancholy smile. But that piece of crape, to their imagination, seemed to hang down before his heart, the symbol of a fearful secret between him and them. Were the veil but cast aside, they might speak freely of it, but not till then. Thus they sat a considerable time, speechless, confused, and shrinking uneasily from Mr. Hooper's eye, which they felt to be fixed upon them with an invisible glance. Finally, the deputies returned abashed to their constituents, pronouncing the matter too weighty to be handled, except by a council of the churches, if, indeed, it might not require a general synod.

But there was one person in the village unappalled by the awe with which the black veil had impressed all beside herself. When the deputies returned without an explanation, or even venturing to demand one, she, with the calm energy of her character, determined to chase away the strange cloud that appeared to be settling round Mr. Hooper, every moment more darkly than before. As his plighted wife, it should be her privilege to know what the black veil concealed. At the minister's first visit, therefore, she entered upon the subject, with a direct simplicity, which made the task easier both for him and her. After he had seated himself, she fixed her eyes steadfastly upon the veil, but could discern nothing of the dreadful gloom that had so overawed the multitude; it was but a double fold of crape, hanging down from his forehead to his mouth, and slightly stirring with his breath.

"No," said she aloud, and smiling, "there is nothing terrible in this piece of crape, except that it hides a face which I am always glad to look upon. Come, good sir, let the sun shine from behind the cloud. First lay aside your black veil: then tell me why you put it on."

Mr. Hooper's smile glimmered faintly.

"There is an hour to come," said he, "when all of us shall cast aside our veils. Take it not amiss, beloved friend, if I wear this piece of crape till then."

"Your words are a mystery, too," returned the young lady. "Take away the veil from them, at least."

"Elizabeth, I will," said he, "so far as my vow may suffer me. Know, then, this veil is a type and a symbol, and I am bound to wear it ever, both in light and darkness, in solitude and before the gaze of multitudes, and as with strangers, so with my familiar friends. No mortal eye will see it withdrawn. This dismal shade must separate me from the world: even you, Elizabeth, can never come behind it!"

"What grievous affliction hath befallen you," she earnestly inquired, "that you should thus darken your eyes forever?"

"If it be a sign of mourning," replied Mr. Hooper, "I perhaps, like most other mortals, have sorrows dark enough to be typified by a black veil."

"But what if the world will not believe that it is the type of an innocent sorrow?" urged Elizabeth. "Beloved and respected as you are, there may be whispers, that you hide your face under the consciousness of secret sin. For the sake of your holy office, do away this scandal!"

The color rose into her cheeks as she intimated the nature of the rumors that were already abroad in the village. But Mr. Hooper's mildness did not forsake him. He even smiled again—that same sad smile, which always appeared like a faint glimmering of light, proceeding from the obscurity beneath the veil.

"If I hide my face for sorrow, there is cause enough," he merely replied; "and if I cover it for secret sin, what mortal might not do the same?"

And with this gentle, but unconquerable obstinacy did he resist all her entreaties. At length Elizabeth sat silent. For a few moments she appeared lost in thought, considering, probably, what new methods might be tried to withdraw her lover from so dark a fantasy, which, if it had no other meaning, was perhaps a symptom of mental disease. Though of a firmer character than his own, the tears rolled down her cheeks. But, in an instant, as if it were, a new feeling took the place of sorrow: her eyes were fixed insensibly on the black veil, when, like a sudden twilight in the air, its terrors fell around her. She arose, and stood trembling before him.

"And do you feel it then, at last?" said he mournfully.

She made no reply, but covered her eyes with her hand, and turned to leave the room. He rushed forward and caught her arm.

"Have patience with me, Elizabeth!" cried he, passionately. "Do not desert me, though this veil must be between us here on earth. Be mine, and hereafter there shall be no veil over my face, no darkness between our souls! It is but a mortal veil—it is not for eternity! O! you know not how lonely I am, and how frightened, to be alone behind my black veil. Do not leave me in this miserable obscurity forever!"

"Lift the veil but once, and look me in the face," said she.

"Never! It cannot be!" replied Mr. Hooper.

"Then farewell!" said Elizabeth.

She withdrew her arm from his grasp, and slowly departed, pausing at the door, to give one long, shuddering gaze, that seemed almost to penetrate the mystery of the black veil. But, even amid his grief, Mr. Hooper smiled to think that only a material emblem had separated him from happiness, though the horrors, which it shadowed forth, must be drawn darkly between the fondest of lovers.

From that time no attempts were made to remove Mr. Hooper's black veil, or, by a direct appeal, to discover the secret which it was supposed to hide. By persons who claimed a superiority to popular prejudice, it was reckoned merely an eccentric whim, such as often mingles with the sober actions of men otherwise rational, and tinges them all with its own semblance of insanity. But with the multitude good Mr. Hooper was irreparably a bugbear. He could not walk the street with any peace of mind, so conscious was he that the gentle and timid would turn aside to avoid him, and that others would make it a point of hardihood to throw themselves in his way. The impertinence of the latter class compelled him to give up his customary walk at sunset to the burial ground; for when he leaned pensively over the gate, there would always be faces behind the gravestones, peeping at his black veil. A fable went the rounds that the stare of the dead people drove him thence. It grieved him, to the very depth of his kind heart, to observe how the children fled from his approach, breaking up their merriest sports, while his melancholy figure was yet afar off. Their instinctive dread caused him to feel more strongly than aught else, that a preter-natural horror was interwoven with the threads of the black crape. In truth, his own antipathy to the veil was known to be so great, that he never willingly passed before a mirror, nor stooped to drink at a still fountain, lest, in its peaceful bosom, he should be affrighted by himself. This was what gave plausibility to the whispers, that Mr.

Hooper's conscience tortured him for some great crime too horrible to be entirely concealed, or otherwise than so obscurely intimated. Thus, from beneath the black veil, there rolled a cloud into the sunshine, an ambiguity of sin or sorrow, which enveloped the poor minister, so that love or sympathy could never reach him. It was said, that ghost and fiend consorted with him there. With self-shudderings and outward terrors, he walked continually in its shadow, groping darkly within his own soul, or gazing through a medium that saddened the whole world. Even the lawless wind, it was believed, respected his dreadful secret, and never blew aside the veil. But still good Mr. Hooper sadly smiled at the pale visages of the worldly throng as he passed by.

Among all its bad influences, the black veil had the one desirable effect, of making its wearer a very efficient clergyman. By the aid of his mysterious emblem—for there was no other apparent cause—he became a man of awful power, over souls that were in agony for sin. His converts always regarded him with a dread peculiar to themselves, affirming, though but figuratively, that, before he brought them to celestial light, they had been with him behind the black veil. Its gloom, indeed, enabled him to sympathize with all dark affections. Dying sinners cried aloud for Mr. Hooper, and would not yield their breath till he appeared; though ever, as he stooped to whisper consolation, they shuddered at the veiled face so near their own. Such were the terrors of the black veil, even when Death had bared his visage! Strangers came long distances to attend service at his church, with the mere idle purpose of gazing at his figure, because it was forbidden them to behold his face. But many were made to quake ere they departed! Once, during Governor Belcher's administration, Mr. Hooper was appointed to preach the election sermon. Covered with his black veil, he stood before the chief magistrate, the council, and the representatives, and wrought so deep an impression, that the legislative measures of that year were characterized by all the gloom and piety of our earliest ancestral sway.

In this manner Mr. Hooper spent a long life, irreproachable in outward act, yet shrouded in dismal suspicions; kind and loving, though unloved, and dimly feared; man apart from men, shunned in their health and joy, but ever summoned to their aid in mortal anguish. As years wore on, shedding their snows above his sable veil, he acquired a name throughout the New England churches, and they called him Father Hooper. Nearly all his parishioners, who were of mature age when he was settled, had been borne away by many a funeral: he had one congregation in the church, and a more crowded one in the churchyard; and having wrought so late into the evening, and done his work so well, it was now good Father Hooper's turn to rest.

Several persons were visible by the shaded candlelight, in the death chamber of the old clergyman. Natural connections he had none. But there was the decorously grave, though unmoved physician, seeking only to mitigate the last pangs of the patient whom he could not save. There were the deacons, and other eminently pious members of his church. There, also, was the Reverend Mr. Clark, of Westbury, a young and zealous divine, who had ridden in haste to pray by the bedside of the expiring minister. There was the nurse, no hired hand-maiden of death, but one whose calm affection had endured thus long in secrecy, in solitude, amid the chill of age, and would not perish, even at the dying hour. Who, but Elizabeth! And there lay the hoary head of good Father Hooper upon the death pillow, with the black veil still swathed about his brow, and reaching down over his face, so that each more difficult gasp of his faint breath caused it to stir. All through life that piece of crape had hung between him and the world; it had separated him from cheerful brotherhood and woman's love, and kept him in that saddest of all prisons, his own heart; and still it lay upon his face, as if to deepen the gloom of his darksome chamber, and shade him from the sunshine of eternity.

For some time previous, his mind had been confused, wavering doubtfully between the past and the present, and hovering forward, as it were, at intervals, into the indistinctness of the world to come. There had been feverish turns, which tossed him from side to side, and wore away what little strength he had. But in his most convulsive struggles, and in the wildest vagaries of his intellect, when no other thought retains its sober influence, he still showed an awful solicitude lest the black veil should slip aside. Even if his bewildered soul could have forgotten, there was a faithful woman at his pillow, who, with averted eyes, would have covered that aged face, which she had last beheld in the comeliness of manhood. At length the death-stricken old man lay quietly in the torpor of mental and bodily exhaustion, with an imperceptible pulse, and breath that grew fainter and fainter, except when a long, deep, and irregular inspiration seemed to prelude the flight of his spirit.

The minister of Westbury approached the bedside.

"Venerable Father Hooper," said he, "the moment of your release is at hand. Are you ready for the lifting of the veil that shuts in time from eternity?"

Father Hooper at first replied merely by a feeble motion of his head; then, apprehensive, perhaps, that his meaning might be doubtful, he exerted himself to speak.

"Yea," said he, in faint accents, "my soul hath a patient weariness until that veil be lifted."

"And is it fitting," resumed the Reverend Mr. Clark, "that a man so given to prayer, of such a blameless example, holy in deed and thought, so far as mortal judgment may pronounce; is it fitting that a father in the church should leave a shadow in his memory, that may seem to blacken a life so pure? I pray you, my venerable brother, let not this thing be! Suffer us to be gladdened by your triumphant aspect, as you go to your reward. Before the veil of eternity be lifted, let me cast aside this black veil from your face!"

And thus speaking, the Reverend Mr. Clark bent forward to reveal the mystery of so many years. But, exerting a sudden energy, that made all the beholders stand aghast, Father Hooper snatched both his hands from beneath the bedclothes, and pressed them strongly on the black veil, resolute to struggle, if the minister of Westbury would contend with a dying man.

"Never!" cried the veiled clergyman. "On earth, never!"

"Dark old man!" exclaimed the affrighted minister, "with

what horrible crime upon your soul are you now passing to the judgment?"

Father Hooper's breath heaved; it rattled in his throat but, with a mighty effort, grasping forward with his hands, he caught hold of life, and held it back till he should speak. He even raised himself in bed; and there he sat, shivering with the arms of death around him, while the black veil hung down, awful, at that last moment, in the gathered terrors of a lifetime. And yet the faint, sad smile, so often there, now seemed to glimmer from its obscurity, and linger on Father Hooper's lips.

"Why do you tremble at me alone?" cried he, turning his veiled face round the circle of pale spectators. "Tremble also at each other! Have men avoided me, and women shown no pity, and children screamed and fled, only for my black veil? What, but the mystery which it obscurely typifies, has made this piece of crape so awful? When the friend shows his inmost heart to his friend; the lover to his best beloved; when man does not vainly shrink from the eye of the Creator, loathsomely treasuring up the secret of his sin; then deem me a monster; for the symbol beneath which I have lived, and die! I look around me, and, lo! on every visage a Black Veil!"

While his auditors shrank from one another, in mutual affright, Father Hooper fell back upon his pillow, a veiled corpse with a faint smile lingering on the lips. Still veiled, they laid him in his coffin, and a veiled corpse they bore him to the grave. The grass of many years has sprung up and withered on that grave, the burial stone is moss-grown, and good Mr. Hooper's face is dust; but awful is still the thought that it mouldered beneath the Black Veil!

THE MINISTER'S BLACK VEIL

1. What kind of atmosphere is created by the first paragraph?
2. How does this compare with the first paragraph of "The Tell-Tale Heart"? Is there any indication here that this is to be a tragic story?
3. Do you feel, at the start of the story, as does Goodman Gray, that the parson "has gone mad"?
4. Note the various types of people in the congregation. Does Hawthorne have a reason to include all ages? How does this accord with our contention that there should be a "single group of characters"?
5. Why might the pale-faced congregation be "almost as fearful a sight to the minister as the black veil to them"? Do we know this at the first reading? Why does Hawthorne make this suggestion now?
6. Where does Hawthorne suggest what the veil might symbolize?
7. When are men afraid to be alone with themselves?
8. What two occasions, opposite in mood, are presided over by Hooper while wearing his veil? Why does Hawthorne give us these two examples?

9. What figure of speech do you recognize in "For the Earth, too, had on her Black Veil"? What does the earth's black veil symbolize here?

10. Hawthorne makes much of the fact that one person after the other fails to ask Hooper the meaning of the veil. Why does he do this? Who does finally ask him? With what result?

11. Once again, about half way through the story, we get a hint as to the significance of the veil. How does Hawthorne keep us interested after twice "tipping his hand"?

12. Although there are hints that Hooper may wear the veil because of his own secret sin, Hawthorne keeps us from condemning Hooper for wrongdoing. By the use of what adjective does he do this?

13. Why might the veil make him a more effective clergyman?

14. Why should the heart be the "saddest of all prisons"?

15. What does the veil symbolize?

16. Why do you think Hooper was, or was not, mad?

17. In what way is this story akin to "The Tell-Tale Heart"?

ERNEST HEMINGWAY

1898–1961

In Another Country

ONE OF *the most widely read and discussed American writers, Ernest Hemingway wrote short stories, novels, and travel books. An outdoor man, Hemingway was interested in bullfighting, hunting, and fishing. During World War I he was a volunteer ambulance driver in France and Italy; later he became a newspaper foreign correspondent. In the late Twenties and early Thirties, he was interested in the Spanish Civil War, and his novel* For Whom the Bell Tolls *reflects that interest.*

Ernest Hemingway won both the Pulitzer Prize and the Nobel Prize for literature. His deceptively simple and effective style has been an inspiration to a generation of younger writers.

In the fall the war was always there, but we did not go to it any more. It was cold in the fall in Milan and the dark came very early. Then the electric lights came on, and it was pleasant along the streets looking in the windows. There was much game hanging outside the shops, and the snow powdered in the fur of the foxes and the wind blew their tails. The deer hung stiff and heavy and empty, and small birds blew in the wind and the wind turned their feathers. It was a cold fall and the wind came down from the mountains.

We were all at the hospital every afternoon, and there

were different ways of walking across the town through the dusk to the hospital. Two of the ways were alongside canals, but they were long. Always, though, you crossed a bridge across a canal to enter the hospital. There was a choice of three bridges. On one of them a woman sold roasted chestnuts. It was warm, standing in front of her charcoal fire, and the chestnuts were warm afterward in your pocket. The hospital was very old and very beautiful, and you entered through a gate and walked across a courtyard and out a gate on the other side. There were usually funerals starting from the courtyard. Beyond the old hospital were the new brick pavilions, and there we met every afternoon and were all very polite and interested in what was the matter, and sat in the machines that were to make so much difference.

The doctor came up to the machine where I was sitting and said: "What did you like best to do before the war? Did you practise a sport?"

I said: "Yes, football."

"Good," he said. "You will be able to play football again better than ever."

My knee did not bend and the leg dropped straight from the knee to the ankle without a calf, and the machine was to bend the knee and make it move as in riding a tricycle. But it did not bend yet, and instead the machine lurched when it came to the bending part. The doctor said: "That will all pass. You are a fortunate young man. You will play football again like a champion."

In the next machine was a major who had a little hand like a baby's. He winked at me when the doctor examined his hand, which was between two leather straps that bounced up and down and flapped the stiff fingers, and said: "And will I too play football, captain-doctor?" He had been a very great fencer, and before the war the greatest fencer in Italy.

The doctor went to his office in a back room and brought a photograph which showed a hand that had been withered almost as small as the major's, before it had taken a machine course, and after was a little larger. The major held the photograph with his good hand and looked at it very carefully. "A wound?" he asked.

"An industrial accident," the doctor said.

"Very interesting, very interesting," the major said, and handed it back to the doctor.

"You have confidence?"

"No," said the major.

There were three boys who came each day who were about the same age I was. They were all three from Milan, and one of them was to be a lawyer, and one was to be a painter, and one had intended to be a soldier, and after we were finished with the machines, sometimes we walked back together to the Café Cova, which was next door to the Scala. We walked the short way through the communist quarter because we were four together. The people hated us because we were officers, and from a wine-shop some one called out, "A basso gli ufficiali!" as we passed. Another boy who walked with us sometimes and made us five wore a black silk handkerchief across his face because he had no nose then and his face was to be rebuilt. He had gone out to the front from the military academy and been wounded within an hour after he had gone into the front line for the first time. They rebuilt his face, but he came from a very old family and they could never get the nose exactly right. He went to South America and worked in a bank. But this was a long time ago, and then we did not any of us know how it was going to be afterward. We only knew then that there was always the war, but that we were not going to it any more.

We all had the same medals, except the boy with the black silk bandage across his face, and he had not been at the front long enough to get any medals. The tall boy with a very pale face who was to be a lawyer had been a lieutenant of Arditi and had three medals of the sort we each had only one of. He had lived a very long time with death and was a little detached. We were all a little detached, and there was nothing that held us together except that we met every afternoon at the hospital. Although, as we walked to the Cova through the tough part of town, walking in the dark, with light and singing coming out of the wine-shops, and sometimes having to walk into the street when the men and women would crowd together on the sidewalk so that we would have had to jostle them to get by, we felt held together by there being something that had happened that they, the people who disliked us, did not understand.

We ourselves all understood the Cova, where it was rich and warm and not too brightly lighted, and noisy and smoky at certain hours, and there were always girls at the tables and the illustrated papers on a rack on the wall. The girls at the Cova were very patriotic, and I found that the most patriotic people in Italy were the café girls—and I believe they are still patriotic.

The boys at first were very polite about my medals and asked me what I had done to get them. I showed them the papers, which were written in very beautiful language and full of *fratellanza* and *abnegazione*, but which really said, with the adjectives removed, that I had been given the medals because I was an American. After that their manner changed a little toward me, although I was their friend against outsiders. I was a friend, but I was never really one of them after they had read the citations, because it had been different with them and they had done very different things to get their medals. I had been wounded, it was true; but we all knew that being wounded, after all, was really an accident. I was never ashamed of the ribbons, though, and sometimes, after the cocktail hour, I would imagine myself having done all the things they had done to get their medals; but walking home at night through the empty streets with the cold wind and all the shops closed, trying to keep near the street lights, I knew that I would never have done such things, and I was very much afraid to die, and often lay in bed at night by myself, afraid to die and wondering how I would be when I went back to the front again.

The three with the medals were like hunting-hawks; and I was not a hawk, although I might seem a hawk to those who had never hunted; they, the three, knew better and so we drifted apart. But I stayed good friends with the boy who had been wounded his first day at the front, because he would never know now how he would have turned out; so he could never be accepted either, and I liked him because I thought perhaps he would not have turned out to be a hawk either.

The major, who had been the great fencer, did not believe in bravery, and spent much time while we sat in the machines correcting my grammar. He had complimented me on how I spoke Italian, and we talked together very easily. One day I had said that Italian seemed such an easy language to me that I could not take a great interest in it; everything was so easy to say. "Ah, yes," the major said. "Why, then, do you not take up the use of grammar?" So we took up the use of grammar, and soon Italian was such a difficult language that I was afraid to talk to him until I had the grammar straight in my mind.

The major came very regularly to the hospital. I do not think he ever missed a day, although I am sure he did not believe in the machines. There was a time when none of us believed in the machines, and one day the major said it was all nonsense. The machines were new then and it was we who were to prove them. It was an idiotic idea, he said, "a theory, like another." I had not learned my grammar, and he said I was a stupid impossible disgrace, and he was a fool to have bothered with me. He was a small man and he sat straight up in his chair with his right hand thrust into the machine and looked straight ahead at the wall while the straps thumped up and down with his fingers in them.

"What will you do when the war is over if it is over?" he asked me. "Speak grammatically!"

"I will go to the States."

"Are you married?"

"No, but I hope to be."

"The more of a fool you are," he said. He seemed very angry. "A man must not marry."

"Why, Signor Maggiore?"

"Don't call me 'Signor Maggiore.' "

"Why must not a man marry?"

"He cannot marry. He cannot marry," he said angrily. "If he is to lose everything, he should not place himself in a position to lose that. He should find things he cannot lose."

He spoke very angrily and bitterly, and looked straight ahead while he talked.

"But why should he necessarily lose it?"

"He'll lose it," the major said. He was looking at the wall. Then he looked down at the machine and jerked his little hand out from between the straps and slapped it hard against his thigh. "He'll lose it," he almost shouted. "Don't argue with me!" Then he called to the attendant who ran the machines. "Come and turn this damned thing off."

He went back into the other room for the light treatment and the massage. Then I heard him ask the doctor if he might use his telephone and he shut the door. When he came back into the room, I was sitting in another machine. He was wearing his cape and had his cap on, and he came directly toward my machine and put his arm on my shoulder.

"I am so sorry," he said, and patted me on the shoulder with his good hand. "I would not be rude. My wife has just died. You must forgive me."

"Oh—" I said, feeling sick for him. "I am *so* sorry."

He stood there biting his lower lip. "It is very difficult," he said. "I cannot resign myself."

He looked straight past me and out through the window. Then he began to cry. "I am utterly unable to resign myself," he said and choked. And then crying, his head up looking at nothing, carrying himself straight and soldierly, with tears on both his cheeks and biting his lips, he walked past the machines and out the door.

The doctor told me that the major's wife, who was very young and whom he had not married until he was definitely invalided out of the war, had died of pneumonia. She had been sick only a few days. No one expected her to die. The major did not come to the hospital for three days. Then he came at the usual hour, wearing a black band on the sleeve of his uniform. When he came back, there were large framed photographs around the wall, of all sorts of wounds before and after they had been cured by the machines. In front of the machine the major used were three photographs of hands like his that were completely restored. I do not know where the doctor got them. I always understood we were the first to use the machines. The photographs did not make much difference to the major because he only looked out of the window.

IN ANOTHER COUNTRY

1. What is the setting?

2. Who is the narrator?

3. Which of the characters are important to the story?
4. Who experiences the major conflict?
5. In what line (or lines) of the dialogue do you find a likely statement of the theme?
6. Did the major ever "resign" himself? What evidence is there of this?
7. From examining the first page of the story, what qualities of style do you notice?
8. What is the significance of the title other than the fact that the narrator is not a native of Italy?
9. What kind of story is this? Which of the following terms apply: character, plot, adventure, psychological, atmosphere, local color, or dramatic incident?

RING LARDNER

1885–1933

Haircut

RING LARDNER *was born in Michigan and spent much of his early life in the Midwest. He served for a time as a police, sports, and movie reporter for the South Bend, Indiana,* Times *and then went to work for a newspaper in Chicago. The* Chicago Examiner *sent him to the South for spring training with the White Sox baseball team. Later he was editor of* Sporting News.

Lardner's work is characterized by colorful language. Joseph G. E. Hopkins wrote in The Scribner Treasury, *"It was his way, apparently, to let them [the characters] babble on in the words they themselves have used, so that the illusion of reality is complete."* "Haircut," *one of his most famous stories, shows his hatred for "the cheater, the bully, the mean of spirit," for whom he had no pity.*

I got another barber that comes over from Carterville and helps me out Saturdays, but the rest of the time I can get along all right alone. You can see for yourself that this ain't no New York City and besides that, the most of the boys works all day and don't have no leisure to drop in here and get themselves prettied up.

You're a newcomer, ain't you? I thought I hadn't seen you round before. I hope you like it good enough to stay. As I say, we ain't no New York City or Chicago, but we have pretty good times. Not as good, though, since Jim Kendall got killed. When he was alive, him and Hod Meyers used to keep this town in an uproar. I bet they was more laughin' done here than any town its size in America.

Jim was comical, and Hod was pretty near a match for him. Since Jim's gone, Hod tries to hold his end up just the same as ever, but it's tough goin' when you ain't got nobody to kind of work with.

They used to be plenty fun in here Saturdays. This place is jampacked Saturdays, from four o'clock on. Jim and Hod would show up right after their supper, round six o'clock. Jim would set himself down in that big chair, nearest the blue spittoon. Whoever had been settin' in that chair, why they'd get up when Jim come in and give it to him.

You'd of thought it was a reserved seat like they have sometimes in a theayter. Hod would generally always stand or walk up and down, or some Saturdays, of course, he'd be settin' in this chair part of the time, gettin' a haircut.

Well, Jim would set there a w'ile without openin' his mouth only to spit, and then finally he'd say to me, "Whitey,"—my right name, that is, my right first name, is Dick, but everybody round here calls me Whitey—Jim would say, "Whitey, your nose looks like a rosebud tonight. You must of been drinkin' some of your aw de cologne."

So I'd say, "No, Jim, but you look like you'd been drinkin' somethin' of that kind or somethin' worse."

Jim would have to laugh at that, but then he'd speak up and say, "No, I ain't had nothin' to drink, but that ain't sayin'

I wouldn't like somethin'. I wouldn't even mind if it was wood alcohol."

Then Hod Meyers would say, "Neither would your wife." That would set everybody to laughin' because Jim and his wife wasn't on very good terms. She'd of divorced him only they wasn't no chance to get alimony and she didn't have no way to take care of herself and the kids. She couldn't never understand Jim. He *was* kind of rough, but a good fella at heart.

Him and Hod had all kinds of sport with Milt Sheppard. I don't suppose you've seen Milt. Well, he's got an Adam's apple that looks more like a mushmelon. So I'd be shavin' Milt and when I'd start to shave down here on his neck, Hod would holler, "Hey, Whitey, wait a minute! Before you cut into it, let's make up a pool and see who can guess closest to the number of seeds."

And Jim would say, "If Milt hadn't of been so hoggish, he'd of ordered a half a cantaloupe instead of a whole one and it might not of stuck in his throat."

All the boys would roar at this and Milt himself would force a smile, though the joke was on him. Jim certainly was a card!

There's his shavin' mug, settin' on the shelf, right next to Charley Vail's. "Charles M. Vail." That's the druggist. He comes in regular for his shave, three times a week. And Jim's is the cup next to Charley's. "James H. Kendall." Jim won't need no shavin' mug no more, but I'll leave it there just the same for old time's sake. Jim certainly was a character!

Years ago, Jim used to travel for a canned goods concern

over in Carterville. They sold canned goods. Jim had the whole northern half of the State and was on the road five days out of every week. He'd drop in here Saturdays and tell his experiences for that week. It was rich.

I guess he paid more attention to playin' jokes than makin' sales. Finally the concern let him out and he come right home here and told everybody he'd been fired instead of sayin' he'd resigned like most fellas would of.

It was a Saturday and the shop was full and Jim got up out of that chair and says, "Gentlemen, I got an important announcement to make. I been fired from my job."

Well, they asked him if he was in earnest and he said he was and nobody could think of nothin' to say till Jim finally broke the ice himself. He says, "I been sellin' canned goods and now I'm canned goods myself."

You see, the concern he'd been workin' for was a factory that made canned goods. Over in Carterville. And now Jim said he was canned himself. He was certainly a card!

Jim had a great trick that he used to play w'ile he was travelin'. For instance, he'd be ridin' on a train and they'd come to some little town like, well, like, we'll say, like Benton. Jim would look out the train window and read the signs on the stores.

For instance, they'd be a sign, "Henry Smith, Dry Goods." Well, Jim would write down the name and the name of the town and when he got to wherever he was goin' he'd mail back a postal card to Henry Smith at Benton and not sign no name to it, but he'd write on the card, well, somethin' like "Ask your wife about that book agent that spent the afternoon last week," or "Ask your Missus who kept her from gettin' lonesome the last time you was in Carterville." And he'd sign the card, "A Friend."

Of course, he never knew what really come of none of these jokes, but he could picture what *probably* happened and that was enough.

Jim didn't work very steady after he lost his position with the Carterville people. What he did earn, doin' odd jobs round town, why he spent pretty near all of it on gin and his family might of starved if the stores hadn't of carried them along. Jim's wife tried her hand at dressmakin', but they ain't nobody goin' to get rich makin' dresses in this town.

As I say, she'd of divorced Jim, only she seen that she couldn't support herself and the kids and she was always hopin' that some day Jim would cut out his habits and give her more than two or three dollars a week.

They was a time when she would go to whoever he was workin' for and ask them to give her his wages, but after she done this once or twice, he beat her to it by borrowin' most of his pay in advance. He told it all round town, how he had outfoxed his Missus. He certainly was a caution!

But he wasn't satisfied with just outwittin' her. He was sore the way she had acted, tryin' to grab off his pay. And he made up his mind he'd get even. Well, he waited till Evans's Circus was advertised to come to town. Then he told his wife and two kiddies that he was goin' to take them to the circus. The day of the circus, he told them he would get the tickets and meet them outside the entrance to the tent.

Well, he didn't have no intentions of bein' there or buyin'

tickets or nothin'. He got full of gin and laid round Wright's poolroom all day. His wife and the kids waited and waited and of course he didn't show up. His wife didn't have a dime with her, or nowhere else, I guess. So she finally had to tell the kids it was all off and they cried like they wasn't never goin' to stop.

Well, it seems, w'ile they was cryin', Doc Stair came along and he asked what was the matter, but Mrs. Kendall was stubborn and wouldn't tell him, but the kids told him and he insisted on takin' them and their mother in the show. Jim found this out afterwards and it was one reason why he had it in for Doc Stair.

Doc Stair come here about a year and a half ago. He's a mighty handsome young fella and his clothes always look like he has them made to order. He goes to Detroit two or three times a year and w'ile he's there he must have a tailor take his measure and then make him a suit to order. They cost pretty near twice as much, but they fit a whole lot better than if you just bought them in a store.

For a w'ile everybody was wonderin' why a young doctor like Doc Stair should come to a town like this where we already got old Doc Gamble and Doc Foote that's both been here for years and all the practice in town was always divided between the two of them.

Then they was a story got round that Doc Stair's gal had throwed him over, a gal up in the Northern Peninsula somewheres, and the reason he come here was to hide himself away and forget it. He said himself that he thought they wasn't nothin' like general practice in a place like ours to fit a man to be a good all round doctor. And that's why he'd came.

Anyways, it wasn't long before he was makin' enough to live on, though they tell me that he never dunned nobody for what they owed him, and the folks here certainly has got the owin' habit, even in my business. If I had all that was comin' to me for just shaves alone, I could go to Carterville and put up at the Mercer for a week and see a different picture every night. For instance, they's old George Purdy —but I guess I shouldn't ought to be gossipin'.

Well, last year, our coroner died, died of the flu. Ken Beatty, that was his name. He was the coroner. So they had to choose another man to be coroner in his place and they picked Doc Stair. He laughed at first and said he didn't want it, but they made him take it. It ain't no job that anybody would fight for and what a man makes out of it in a year would just about buy seeds for their garden. Doc's the kind, though, that can't say no to nothin' if you keep at him long enough.

But I was goin' to tell you about a poor boy we got here in town—Paul Dickson. He fell out of a tree when he was about ten years old. Lit on his head and it done somethin' to him and he ain't never been right. No harm in him, but just silly. Jim Kendall used to call him cuckoo; that's a name Jim had for anybody that was off their head, only he called people's head their bean. That was another of his gags, callin' head bean and callin' crazy people cuckoo. Only poor Paul ain't crazy, but just silly.

You can imagine that Jim used to have all kinds of fun

with Paul. He'd send him to the White Front Garage for a left-handed monkey wrench. Of course they ain't no such a thing as a left-handed monkey wrench.

And once we had a kind of a fair here and they was a baseball game between the fats and the leans and before the game started Jim called Paul over and sent him way down to Schrader's hardware store to get a key for the pitcher's box.

They wasn't nothin' in the way of gags that Jim couldn't think up, when he put his mind to it.

Poor Paul was always kind of suspicious of people, maybe on account of how Jim had kept foolin' him. Paul wouldn't have much to do with anybody only his own mother and Doc Stair and a girl here in town named Julie Gregg. That is, she ain't a girl no more, but pretty near thirty or over.

When Doc first come to town, Paul seemed to feel like here was a real friend and he hung round Doc's office most of the w'ile; the only time he wasn't there was when he'd go home to eat or sleep or when he seen Julie Gregg doin' her shoppin'.

When he looked out Doc's window and seen her, he'd run downstairs and join her and tag along with her to the different stores. The poor boy was crazy about Julie and she always treated him mighty nice and made him feel like he was welcome, though of course it wasn't nothin' but pity on her side.

Doc done all he could to improve Paul's mind and he told me once that he really thought the boy was gettin' better, that they was times when he was as bright and sensible as anybody else.

But I was goin' to tell you about Julie Gregg. Old Man Gregg was in the lumber business, but got to drinkin' and lost the most of his money and when he died, he didn't leave nothin' but the house and just enough insurance for the girl to skimp along on.

Her mother was a kind of a half invalid and didn't hardly ever leave the house. Julie wanted to sell the place and move somewheres else after the old man died, but the mother said she was born here and would die here. It was tough on Julie, as the young people round this town—well, she's too good for them.

She's been away to school and Chicago and New York and different places and they ain't no subject she can't talk on, where you take the rest of the young folks here and you mention anything to them outside of Gloria Swanson or Tommy Meighan and they think you're delirious. Did you see Gloria in Wages of Virtue? You missed somethin'!

Well, Doc Stair hadn't been here more than a week when he come in one day to get shaved and I recognized who he was as he had been pointed out to me, so I told him about my old lady. She's been ailin' for a couple years and either Doc Gamble or Doc Foote, neither one, seemed to be helpin' her. So he said he would come out and see her, but if she was able to get out herself, it would be better to bring her to his office where he could make a completer examination.

So I took her to his office and w'ile I was waitin' for her in the reception room, in come Julie Gregg. When somebody comes in Doc Stair's office, they's a bell that rings in his inside office so as he can tell they's somebody to see him.

So he left my old lady inside and come out to the front office and that's the first time him and Julie met and I guess it was what they call love at first sight. But it wasn't fifty-fifty. This young fella was the slickest lookin' fella she'd ever seen in this town and she went wild over him. To him she was just a young lady that wanted to see the doctor.

She'd come on about the same business I had. Her mother had been doctorin' for years with Doc Gamble and Doc Foote and without no results. So she'd heard they was a new doc in town and decided to give him a try. He promised to call and see her mother that same day.

I said a minute ago that it was love at first sight on her part. I'm not only judgin' by how she acted afterward but how she looked at him that first day in his office. I ain't no mind reader, but it was wrote all over her face that she was gone.

Now Jim Kendall, besides bein' a jokesmith and a pretty good drinker, well, Jim was quite a lady-killer. I guess he run pretty wild durin' the time he was on the road for them Carterville people, and besides that, he'd had a couple little affairs of the heart right here in town. As I say, his wife could of divorced him, only she couldn't.

But Jim was like the majority of men, and women, too, I guess. He wanted what he couldn't get. He wanted Julie Gregg and worked his head off tryin' to land her. Only he'd of said bean instead of head.

Well, Jim's habits and his jokes didn't appeal to Julie and of course he was a married man, so he didn't have no more chance than, well, than a rabbit. That's an expression of

Jim's himself. When somebody didn't have no chance to get elected or somethin', Jim would always say they didn't have no more chance than a rabbit.

He didn't make no bones about how he felt. Right in here, more than once, in front of the whole crowd, he said he was stuck on Julie and anybody that could get her for him was welcome to his house and his wife and kids included. But she wouldn't have nothin' to do with him; wouldn't even speak to him on the street. He finally seen he wasn't gettin' nowheres with his usual line so he decided to try the rough stuff. He went right up to her house one evenin' and when she opened the door he forced his way in and grabbed her. But she broke loose and before he could stop her, she run in the next room and locked the door and phoned to Joe Barnes. Joe's the marshal. Jim could hear who she was phonin' to and he beat it before Joe got there.

Joe was an old friend of Julie's pa. Joe went to Jim the next day and told him what would happen if he ever done it again.

I don't know how the news of this little affair leaked out. Chances is that Joe Barnes told his wife and she told somebody else's wife and they told their husband. Anyways, it did leak out and Hod Meyers had the nerve to kid Jim about it, right here in this shop. Jim didn't deny nothin' and kind of laughed it off and said for us all to wait; that lots of people had tried to make a monkey out of him, but he always got even.

Meanw'ile everybody in town was wise to Julie's bein' wild mad over the Doc. I don't suppose she had any idear how her face changed when him and her was together; of course she couldn't of, or she'd of kept away from him. And she didn't know that we was all noticin' how many times she made excuses to go to his office or pass it on the other side of the street and look up in his window to see if he was there. I felt sorry for her and so did most other people.

Hod Meyers kept rubbin' it into Jim about how the Doc had cut him out. Jim didn't pay no attention to the kiddin' and you could see he was plannin' one of his jokes.

One trick Jim had was the knack of changin' his voice. He could make you think he was a girl talkin' and he could mimic any man's voice. To show you how good he was along this line, I'll tell you the joke he played on me once.

You know, in most towns of any size, when a man is dead and needs a shave, why the barber that shaves him soaks him five dollars for the job, that is, he don't soak *him,* but whoever ordered the shave. I just charge three dollars because personally I don't mind much shavin' a dead person. They lay a whole lot stiller than live customers. The only thing is that you don't feel like talkin' to them and you get kind of lonesome.

Well, about the coldest day we ever had here, two years ago last winter, the phone rung at the house w'ile I was home to dinner and I answered the phone and it was a woman's voice and she said she was Mrs. John Scott and her husband was dead and would I come out and shave him.

Old John had always been a good customer of mine. But they live seven miles out in the country, on the Streeter road. Still I didn't see how I could say no.

So I said I would be there, but would have to come in a jitney and it might cost three or four dollars besides the price of the shave. So she, or the voice, it said that was all right, so I got Frank Abbott to drive me out to the place and when I got there, who should open the door but old John himself! He wasn't no more dead than, well, than a rabbit.

It didn't take no private detective to figure out who had played me this little joke. Nobody could of thought it up but Jim Kendall. He certainly was a card!

I tell you this incident just to show you how he could disguise his voice and make you believe it was somebody else talkin'. I'd of swore it was Mrs. Scott had called me. Anyways, some woman.

Well, Jim waited till he had Doc Stair's voice down pat; then he went after revenge.

He called Julie up on a night when he knew Doc was over in Carterville. She never questioned but what it was Doc's voice. Jim said he must see her that night; he couldn't wait no longer to tell her somethin'. She was all excited and told him to come to the house. But he said he was expectin' an important long distance call and wouldn't she please forget her manners for once and come to his office. He said they couldn't nothin' hurt her and nobody would see her and he just *must* talk to her a little w'ile. Well, poor Julie fell for it.

Doc always keeps a night light in his office, so it looked to Julie like they was somebody there.

Meanw'ile Jim Kendall had went to Wright's poolroom, where they was a whole gang amusin' themselves. The most of them had drank plenty of gin, and they was a rough bunch even when sober. They was always strong for Jim's jokes and when he told them to come with him and see some fun they give up their card games and pool games and followed along.

Doc's office is on the second floor. Right outside his door they's a flight of stairs leadin' to the floor above. Jim and his gang hid in the dark behind these stairs.

Well, Julie come up to Doc's door and rung the bell and they was nothin' doin'. She rung it again and she rung it seven or eight times. Then she tried the door and found it locked. Then Jim made some kind of a noise and she heard it and waited a minute, and then she says, "Is that you, Ralph?" Ralph is Doc's first name.

They was no answer and it must of came to her all of a sudden that she'd been bunked. She pretty near fell downstairs and the whole gang after her. They chased her all the way home, hollerin', "Is that you, Ralph?" and "Oh, Ralphie, dear, is that you?" Jim says he couldn't holler it himself, as he was laughin' too hard.

Poor Julie! She didn't show up here on Main Street for a long, long time afterward.

And of course Jim and his gang told everybody in town, everybody but Doc Stair. They was scared to tell him, and he might of never knowed only for Paul Dickson. The poor cuckoo, as Jim called him, he was here in the shop one night when Jim was still gloatin' yet over what he'd done to Julie. And Paul took in as much of it as he could understand and he run to Doc with the story.

It's a cinch Doc went up in the air and swore he'd make Jim suffer. But it was a kind of a delicate thing, because if it got out that he had beat Jim up, Julie was bound to hear of it and then she'd know that Doc knew and of course knowin' that he knew would make it worse for her than ever. He was goin' to do somethin', but it took a lot of figurin'.

Well, it was a couple days later when Jim was here in the shop again, and so was the cuckoo. Jim was goin' duck-shootin' the next day and had came in lookin' for Hod Meyers to go with him. I happened to know that Hod had went over to Carterville and wouldn't be home till the end of the week. So Jim said he hated to go alone and he guessed he would call it off. Then poor Paul spoke up and said if Jim would take him he would go along. Jim thought a w'ile and then he said, well, he guessed a half-wit was better than nothin'.

I suppose he was plottin' to get Paul out in the boat and play some joke on him, like pushin' him in the water. Anyways, he said Paul could go. He asked him had he ever shot a duck and Paul said no, he'd never even had a gun in his hands. So Jim said he could set in the boat and watch him and if he behaved himself, he might lend him his gun for a couple of shots. They made a date to meet in the mornin' and that's the last I seen of Jim alive.

Next mornin', I hadn't been open more than ten minutes when Doc Stair come in. He looked kind of nervous. He asked me had I seen Paul Dickson. I said no, but I knew where he was, out duck-shootin' with Jim Kendall. So Doc says that's what he had heard, and he couldn't understand it because Paul had told him he wouldn't never have no more to do with Jim as long as he lived.

He said Paul had told him about the joke Jim had played on Julie. He said Paul had asked him what he thought of the joke and the Doc had told him that anybody that would do a thing like that ought not to be let live.

I said it had been a kind of a raw thing, but Jim just couldn't resist no kind of a joke, no matter how raw. I said I thought he was all right at heart, but just bubblin' over with mischief. Doc turned and walked out.

At noon he got a phone call from old John Scott. The lake where Jim and Paul had went shootin' is on John's place. Paul had come runnin' up to the house a few minutes before and said they'd been an accident. Jim had shot a few ducks and then give the gun to Paul and told him to try his luck. Paul hadn't never handled a gun and he was nervous. He was shakin' so hard that he couldn't control the gun. He let fire and Jim sunk back in the boat, dead.

Doc Stair, bein' the coroner, jumped in Frank Abbott's flivver and rushed out to Scott's farm. Paul and old John was down on the shore of the lake. Paul had rowed the boat to shore, but they'd left the body in it, waitin' for Doc to come.

Doc examined the body and said they might as well fetch it back to town. They was no use leavin' it there or callin' a jury, as it was a plain case of accidental shootin'.

Personally I wouldn't never leave a person shoot a gun in the same boat I was in unless I was sure they knew somethin' about guns. Jim was a sucker to leave a new beginner have his gun, let alone a half-wit. It probably served Jim right, what he got. But still we miss him round here. He certainly was a card!

Comb it wet or dry?

HAIRCUT

1. In paragraph one what setting does Lardner establish? What is the significance of each of the two clauses in sentence two?
2. How soon does Lardner introduce his principal character? Who is he?
3. How does Lardner, in the first few paragraphs, build up the importance of Jim Kendall to the story?
4. "He [Jim] *was* kind of rough, but a good fella at heart." How does the practice of sending postal cards illustrate or contradict the statement that Jim was kind of rough, but a good fellow at heart?
5. What is the significance of Jim's shaving mug?
6. Does Jim's dismissal by the canned goods company have any importance in building his character in the story?
7. Why should Jim be angry because Doc Stair paid the circus admission for Mrs. Kendall and the children?
8. What is the point of Whitey's statement, "—but I guess I shouldn't ought to be gossipin."
9. Is Doc Stair's appointment as coroner essential to the plot? Is anything gained by mentioning it this early in the story?

10. How does Lardner introduce Julie Gregg?

11. Note how Lardner ties together the references to Paul's two friends. What is the dramatic purpose of this?

12. Doc Stair is quoted as saying, ". . . they was times when he [Paul] was as bright and sensible as anybody else." Why does Lardner introduce this idea so early in the story?

13. Why did Julie turn to Doc Stair?

14. Does Lardner prepare you for Whitey's witnessing the first meeting of Julie and Doc? Are you satisfied with this preparation, or do you think Lardner is taking too much advantage of coincidence?

15. How does Jim's behavior toward Julie illustrate Whitey's defense of Jim?

16. Which details indicate the theme of the story, the size and nature of the place?

17. What is the effect of Doc's comment to Paul about Jim's joke on Julie? Does this make Doc responsible for Jim's death?

18. Did Jim die as a result of an accident? Try to justify your conclusion.

19. What is your theory about Jim's letting Paul have the gun?

20. For a better understanding of the plot of this Lardner story, make an outline of all details important to the denouement.

21. Is the barber merely a narrator, or do we get some concept of the kind of man he is? How would you characterize him?

BRYAN MacMAHON

1909–

The Lion-Tamer

ONE OF *the new voices among Ireland's great storytellers is that of Bryan MacMahon, who was born in Listowel, County Kerry. He attended the local schools and then St. Patrick's College in Dublin. As a boy he frequently visited the local market place where he listened to the language and stories of the smiths, the shoemakers, and the saddlers.*

Bryan MacMahon has written short stories, radio scripts, and ballads. He is also known as a dramatist, a poet, a reviewer, and as a teacher. At present, he is a master of Listowel's National School.

What a New York Herald Tribune *book review said of Mr. MacMahon is aptly illustrated by* "The Lion-Tamer": "*. . . Here in effect is a writer who possesses the sensitivity of a poet and the rich, hearty humor of a peasant, a compassion for his fellow-men plus a rollicking remembrance of things past.*"

As I entered the public-house I saw the man eyeing me through the meshes of froth on the side of his uptilted glass. He was seated by the fire. It is a characteristic of the older public-houses in the smaller villages that the bar itself is half bar, half kitchen. The fire was burning brightly in the old range and strata of underclothing were drying on the bars above it. The publican gave me the glare such persons reserve for strangers. I ordered a bottle of stout and threw him a casual remark about the weather. As he gave me the drink his face thawed into friendliness and he ordered me to pull over to the fire.

I did so and found myself opposite the man who had scrutinized me on my entrance; by this time he had placed his glass on the tiles at the side of the range and was balancing himself on the two hind legs of his chair. His prim eyes were on my every movement. I sat down opposite him and as his eyes dropped preparatory to taking up his drink, I appraised him as thoroughly as I could in the small span of time allowed me: he had a pale boyish face with the pimples of belated adolescence upon it; his nose was pointed to make his profile a shallow isosceles triangle with the vertex on the tip of his nose. A thing that struck me about him was his boyishness—his immaturity. I put his age at twenty-two or -three at the outside.

I am gregarious and convivial to a degree considered alarming by my friends. At that moment I was pining for company. The fact that my business in the village had been finished late in the afternoon necessitated my staying in the place overnight, and, according as one grows older, the prospect of spending a night out of one's home is by no means relished. I timed my imbibing so that the young man opposite me and myself should finish our drinks together. Then I was quick to offer to buy him a drink. His refusal came with the unexpectedness of a slap. "I prefer to buy my own drinks!" he said. This type of brusque unequivocal refusal is rare in country parts. I accepted defeat, rankling not a little under the brutal and un-Irish nature of it. Just as I had begun to spin myself a cocoon of outraged reserve, his explanation was offered, and I was impressed by the rare directness of it: "A custom I learned in England," he said. "Treating is abominable—neither fair to the treater nor the treated. When two are drinking together it is impossible to have an odd number of drinks, and that is a limitation I can never accept. Nevertheless I am grateful to you for having asked me." All this came with the aplomb of one three times his senior in age. I called for my own drink; he called for his. I paid for mine; he paid for his. It struck me as unusual that the publican seemed to consider this arrangement entirely normal.

I was tempted to hang some cloth on the conversational peg of England. When I did so he spoke fluently and authoritatively of the Midland cities. I had spent six months in Birmingham, and each observation of his regarding that city struck me as objective, terse and accurate. As he continued speaking I found myself compelled to renew my respect for him. Before long we were chatting brightly but restrainedly. Putting a man at his job is an old trick of conversation; so I indicated vaguely the nature of my business in the village. He rose to the bait with alacrity. Taking a sip out of his glass he sucked in his lips and laid down his drink with a good deal of ceremony. Then he said: "What would you say my occupation was?" Followed the usual chit-chat and mock-surprise. First, "You a native of this place?" ("Yes.") "Hmmm! Teacher?" ("No.") "Insurance Agent? Machinist?

Student? Home Assistance Officer?" (We both laughed.) "Sacristan? Clerk of Works? Engineer?" The answer was always no.

"I give up," I said.

He sipped his drink with quiet triumph. "As a matter of fact I don't blame you in the least. I could have given you a thousand guesses and you'd never have got it."

"But that isn't telling me what you are!"

"I'm a lion-tamer," he said, "the only Irish-born lion-tamer there is."

I lifted my drink to my mouth and threw him a glance which must have spelled incredulity with a capital I.

He was quick to resent the fact that, in my own mind, I was calling him a liar. "If you doubt my word," he snapped, "I shall ask our friend O'Donoghue." He swivelled in his chair to ask the publican to bear witness for him, but Mr. O'Donoghue had vanished into the back premises from whence the clinking of bottles came to our ears.

I hastened to reassure him that I fully believed him. "You look so young," I said in extenuation of my fault.

"Young as I am, I've seen a good deal of life and have travelled more than my share."

There came a slight hiatus in the flow of our speech. I thought he seemed inclined to bear away from the absorbing subject of lion-taming. I hurried after him and, conversationally speaking, caught him by the coat-tails.

"How on earth, I ask, did you manage to become a lion-tamer?"

In lieu of response he took a packet of cigarettes from his

pocket, extracted one and tamped it deftly on his knee. He did not offer me a cigarette.

"The story does me little credit," he began. "For my part of it I have always wanted to be a doctor. But my black friend here on the hob" (here he indicated his drink) "and his wee yellow brother said no to my dreams of medicine." I noted his lapse into the vernacular.

A pause. A smile flickered on his lips—it was distressing to see one so young smile so bitterly. "I ran away with the circus one night after a row with the stepmother. Ever hear of Vaughan's? Not a top-notcher, but a good, honest little show as shows go. Vaughan's wife would have made a good sub. for the Fat Lady, only the old man never featured freaks. I remember a guy trying to sell the Boss a calf with six legs, but the Boss told him take the thing away. 'You'll gain two on the quarters of veal if you kill it,' the old man said.

"I found the tober hard graft. Taking down the Big Top of a wet night with your soaked pants clinging to your thighs was no picnic. I remember driving a wagon in the procession through the town—dressed as a cowboy I was—and my belly was back to my back with the hunger. Aye, and I had to turn every second minute to take a bite out of a raw turnip. I used chew it as strongly as I could to make the crowd believe I was chewing tobacco. Yes, and driving all night and trying to sleep on a pile of junk with the wind cutting through the slats in the wagon and every rut in the road rattling a panful of marbles on the floor of your skull. Right hard graft it was. But, by hell, I stuck it!

"The Boss saw I was frailer and finer than the ordinary run, aye, and that I had one hell of a tooth for the milk of the black cow. So he put me in charge of the cat—cleaning out from her and so on. The cat had four kittens, and this was the act: the cage was divided into two compartments and at every performance the trainer—he was an Edinburgh man—went into the cage and put them through their paces. First he went into the empty box. Then the four kittens were poked or coaxed out a small hole and McIvor put them up on four little stools—one in each corner of the box. When they were sitting pretty her ladyship was let out through a bigger slide and the tamer's job was to get her sitting on a big stool in the middle as if the whole cat family were posing for their photograph. The old lady was a sour old strap. During the performance three or four of us had to stand guard outside the bars with crowbars and poles ready to prise herself and Andy apart if she should take it into her head to maul him.

"I spent a few months cleaning out from Minnie. At times she had all the tricks of a real cat. I used stop and laugh at the way she'd stretch herself out and scrape at the wood just like your own pussy scraping the table leg. Maybe she'd get humorous and play with the cubs with those quick flicks that we see so often in the household edition. A lioness is only a Tab seen through a telescope. But frost played Molly Bawn to her and when hard weather came she was like a red devil out of hell.

"Andy McIvor was a tyrant of tyrants. He had realized his indispensability. Lion-tamers aren't two a penny, you know. The trade isn't listed in 'Careers for Your Children.' Most of the tamers come from European zoos and a few from England and Scotland. Whenever Andy had a row with the Boss, the Boss would be the first to pipe down. If he didn't do this the Missus would send for Andy and palaver him. Andy was inclined to go on the booze—not with me though: he considered me his inferior. The first portent of Andy's intention of hitting the bottle was his donning of a gold signet ring. The sight of that ring on his finger early in the morning was enough to set the whole show on edge. He commemorated obscure festivals and obscurer anniversaries. On a few occasions he went into the cage paralytic drunk and called the cat a cowardly old so-and-so. Except for one rip on his arm he always got away with it. The others believed that he was immune because he carried a certain kind of herb in his pocket, the smell of which the cat loved. But I doubt it. I've watched him hundreds of times and he had only the four legs of a chair and a whip between him and the Jordan-box. His prat was a kind of continual hissing, the rhythm of which I was never able to pick up, no matter how hard I tried.

"Things went from bad to worse with Andy. The man became insufferable. 'Three lion-tamers in this blasted country,' he'd say, 'one tied up with—(here he named a rival circus), one crippled with arthritis in Derry City, and the third is mysel'. Three of us in this blasted country. Pss. . . . Which of you fellows is willin' to go in to the cat? Eh?'

One night just before a show was due to commence Andy was brought back stone dead corpsed drunk. The Boss was fit to be tied. The wife began to cry. When the time came for Andy to go on, the Boss pulled a fast one on the audience. He pitched a big yarn about the lion-tamer's arm being mauled and turning septic and that he craved the indulgence of his patrons. The country boys didn't like it a bit. They had planked their good money on the offchance of seeing a man mangled. They boohed, hooted and blackguarded. Country boys are like greyhounds: they get all their courage when they are in the pack, especially if the pack happens to meet in darkness. But the Boss had all this mapped out. He made himself heard above the noise and offered £100 to any man who would go into the cage and stay there with the cat for two minutes. That corked their bottle. No one stirred. We had one of our own lads placed in the crowd. He was there to size up the situation and was to get in first if any country fellow made a move. Suddenly there was a jostling match among the crowd around the door of the tent. Then we saw that a big fellow who seemed to be half drunk was being pushed forward into the ring. Our man waited for a split second to see if the country boy was in earnest about going in. Then he jumped in and beat the yokel to the draw. The country boy looked nowhere and was pushed back into the people.

"The Boss began his patter. First he asked our man if he was willing to go in, and receiving a good gulp in reply he disclaimed all responsibility on behalf of the management of the Circus. Then 'Are you married? Address of your nearest relative?' and a word of advice, 'Young man, in the cage make every move deliberate, nothing hasty, you understand?' The Boss took out his wallet, smacked it with the palm of his hand and stated that it contained £100 in £5 notes. After which he extracted his watch and bade the challenger to move in. Our man took off his cap, wiped the sweat off his face with it, swallowed his Adam's apple a few times, looked around wildly and finally moved towards the cage. There was a deadly silence. But the Boss had his head well screwed on. He had it all squared up with the two Civic Guards at the flap that if any country boy was idiot enough to risk going into the cage he was to be prevented from doing so. So at the tensest moment of the fake drama, the local Sergeant stepped forward, clicked his fingers and raised a legal hand at the sham adventurer. Immediately the pantomime warmed up; the Boss shrugged his shoulders in a gesture of impotence; the crowd went wild, our man grew truculent and was inclined to assert his constitutional rights to commit suicide if he so wished. Then at the height of the hubbub the Boss held up his hand for silence, drew a fiver from his wallet and handed it to the challenger, shook hands with him and made a magnificent speech congratulating him on his indomitable courage. The crowd liked this better than ever and cheered the hero as he resumed his seat. It was a first-class stunt thought up on the spur of the moment without any rehearsal. It worked so well that the Boss was inclined to keep it up and work it now and again— once, say, in each county, but when it was broached to a sober Andy he spurned the suggestion and said, 'By hell he'd be made a monkey of by no mon!'

"It was in Ennistymon in Clare that Andy McIvor

walked out of the show for good and glory. When the Missus came out of the living-wagon after the evening performance she saw the Boss and Andy rolling over on the ground. Vaughan was no daw in a rough-and-tumble and he chawed a neat semicircle out of Andy's ear. It's surprising all the blood that can come out of a man's ear. Like a tap spouting red ink it was. The Missus started to holler like hell. Gathering her breath she'd shriek down to nothing. Then again she'd swell like an insulted hatching-hen—all with the dint of gathering her screech. The ponies grew restive in the long tent. We closed in to separate the pair of them. Andy was frothing at the mouth and his ear was a show to God and the world. The Boss had a big beard of blood after the bite. Andy bucked about with three of us clinging to his back; the Boss stripped his red teeth like a butcher's dog; the Missus went off in a dead weakness. The village lads watched us from a huge stupefied circle. As Andy calmed down he shrieked perdition and punishment on us all. He called us all Irish this and Irish that and Irish th' other thing. He said we were for the Boss. Indeed that was no lie for him; it was the Boss who was paying us, not Andy.

"Finally Vaughan was dragged into his wagon, and his Missus, who was prone on the grass, was slapped back to consciousness. Soon the Boss and the Missus were at it hot and heavy. In the heel of the hunt Mrs. Vaughan broke down and began to cry. In the meantime Andy had packed his bag and put on his signet ring; he cursed us all squarely as he departed. A bus was going the road—Andy hailed it and went away. The Circus was minus its lion-tamer.

"About six o'clock that evening I was in the harness-wagon when the Missus came up. 'Is he gone, Tim?' she asked. 'Aye, ma'am, gone by bus,' I answered. 'Good riddance!' she says. 'There's as good fish in the sea as was ever caught.' With that she eyed me shrewdly. Then, 'Come down, Tim, I want to talk to you.' I came down. Then, 'Take me down to the town, Tim. I want a drink.' With that she took my arm. The woman was huge and would persist in wearing a fur coat. Going out the gate I could feel the eyes of all the other chaps burning holes in my back. The vision of the Missus waltzing out arm-in-arm with a circus hand had no precedent in circus etiquette.

"When we got to a pub the Missus started to drink gin while I stuck to honest porter. But after a while she started to throw whiskey down me. 'You're out of the ordinary run, Tim,' she said, 'and I've been on to the Boss to give you your chance.'

" 'My chance, ma'am?'

" 'Aye, your chance, Tim.'

"Fuddled as I was, I started to put two and two together. I narrowed my eyes on her pneumatic side-face. 'This fat ould heap,' says I to myself, 'is aimin' to get me chawed up by the cat.' But she kept feeding me whiskey till she blunted the edge of my bitterness. Then I considered, 'Maybe I'm wrongin' the decent woman: maybe she *does* want me to go ahead in the world.'

" 'Three of them in all Ireland,' she primed, 'one with th' other crowd, a good man—even though he's on the wrong side of the fence—one in the City of Derry an' he crippled with rheumatism . . .'

" 'Arthritis, ma'am,' says I.

" 'Arthritis,' says she. 'And the third you know. A beast! A sot! A toper! A swiller! He'll never hold a job as long as he lives. None of the three are Irishmen,' she added regretfully.

"I sang dumb.

" 'Ah,' says she with an authentic Genevan sigh, 'Ireland produced a great poet in Tommy Moore, a great greyhound in Master Magrath and a great boxer in John L. But Ireland never produced a lion-tamer. Ah, the pity of it!'

"There wasn't a sinner in the bar but the two of us, yet she leaned across to me conspiratorially and gave me the biggest wink I have ever seen. 'Dave got a letter from Ringling,' she whispers. 'Ringling and Dave are just like that,' with this she put one fat finger on top of the other. ' "Dave," says he in the letter, "I could do with a first-class cat-man. Can you help me?" ' After she had let this sink home in me, 'I like you, Tim. I like everything about you. I like the way you clean out the cat's cage. I'm going to see you get your chance!'

"When we got back, the band—our moth-eaten band—was playing in the Big Top. I was drunk but I was well able to put my legs under me. Dimly I saw a knot of people around the ticket wagon. The slide hadn't gone up as yet. The Boss came against us with question-mark written all over his face. 'Dave,' says the Missus, 'did I ever in my life cross you?'

" 'Never!' says he.

" 'Well,' says she, 'don't deny me my request. You've got to give Timmy Moran here his chance to see what he's able to do with the cats!'

" 'I'm a man of quick decisions,' says the Boss. 'We'll bill you as Moranni. Wash your face in cold water. Get into that fellow's wagon. Pull up the duds on you and lie down until I call you.'

"Jacko and Drumshanbo came from nowhere and took me in hand. They led me to the lion-tamer's wagon, dragged the togs on me, then heaved me into the bunk and left me.

"When I awoke I was perished with the cold. The two boys were pummelling hell out of me. I heard the band playing and listened to the machine-gun fire of hand-clapping breaking across the music. When the applause ceased the stentorian voice of the Boss boomed out in a build-up for the acrobats Vivo and Vivienne.

"Jacko and Drumshanbo were working on me with a sponge and cold water. 'Snap out of it, Timothy,' they said, and slapped and splashed me as seconds pummel a fighter who is all but out on his feet. Then a voice spoke from the misty oblong of the caravan door: through gritted eyes I saw what looked like an up-ended sperm whale standing on the steps of the wagon. 'Twas the Missus, and whatever it was she was wearing it gave her the genuine sheen of something huge out of the ocean. She kept whispering 'Tim, Tim,' in a quavering voice. I fuddled out under the stars. The Boss bustled around from the back-flap. At first he was agitated, but on appreciating that I was actually erect, his agitation subsided. 'Come on,' says he, then, 'Don't let the cat see your face—and keep crouched. 'Tis a living cinch, I tell you! And always remember that we're there with the crowbars. And as soon as ever you see the cat and the four kittens sitting pretty, give your bow and get out. Above all, don't forget to make your bow!'

"When, with my trembling retinue, I got inside the tent, Vivienne was down on the strip waiting for Vivo to come down out of the air. I saw her sequins glittering though my eyes were the eyes of a dullard. There she stood with her Little Jack Horner pose until eventually Vivo thudded to the mat beside her.

"I put my nose sideways and upwards and searched the air for the odour of lion. Receiving it, I felt my face grow haggard. Hitherto that smell had connoted but a repugnant chore; now for me it had become charged with a novel deadliness.

" 'The Great Moranni . . . jaws of death . . . dangers of this amazing feat . . . accentuated (the Boss always pivoted on this word) . . . by the fact . . . female of the species . . . cubs . . . defensive instincts of the lioness . . . African home . . . movement not wholly in harmony . . . intrepid Moranni . . . limb from limb . . . Ladies . . . gentlemen . . . privilege and pride . . . the Great Moranni!'

"All the small noises of the circus ceased. I felt myself being propelled forward to make my bow. God forgive me, I did my level best to bounce out gaily with my hands up at 'Ou-la-la-la' and my crop flashing down to slap commandingly on my high boots. Uppermost in my mind was an access of retrospective appreciation of Andy McIvor. Roar after roar came from a circle that was studded with a thousand smoky blobs.

"The cage had been moved up to the verge of the outer

ring. I turned to it. Jacko gave me a short, light iron bar and Drumshanbo held out the chair. '’Tis as easy as pie,' said Jacko. Dirty Dan was there with a long iron pole. 'You poor so-and-so,' he said. Dirty Dan and I were old foes. I got up those steps, bent and went into the empty compartment. The Boss began to bark: now and again he gave an agonized look across his shoulder at me. I found the apprehension in his voice contagious. I got a squint at the Missus who was quivering like a bladder of lard in a hot corner. When the Boss had finished, the drummer picked up the thread of the tension and began to send his eerie peas hopping on the skin of the kettle-drum. This was designed to get the customers down, but, God's truth, it affected no one more than it did the Great Moranni. Iron poles clanged on the cage-bars as the men poked out the cubs through the smaller opening. It seemed to me that the cubs' heads had come together on the rim of a wheel and that the wheel had begun to spin violently. I blinked my way out of that spasm. I was fairly familiar with this routine, and after a good deal of tugging and hauling I got the four of them on their stools. The band pleaded for applause, got it, nourished it, fattened it, then killed it abruptly.

"Two things had begun to bother me: Number one, which of the poles clattering on the bars belonged to Dirty Dan? Number two, what was the jabber Andy carried on to Minnie when she came out? All I could think of was 'Allez-oop!' and that would have been acro-jabber, only any acros I knew said 'Huppie!' or 'Hup!' Still, in a pinch I reckoned 'Allez-oop' better than nothing.

"As the big slide came across—in pardon to you—I

began to retch off my stomach. But I had the presence of mind of half turning my back on the people who at this moment must have been closely watching the cat. The whiskey—subtly altered by my stomach-juices—began to dribble down my chin and neck. Some of it leaked out of my nose as out of a poteen-still. I felt so weak and banjaxed that I didn't give two hoots in hell whether it was on my leg or my hand that the lioness began to chew. Minnie came stalking out. Once again my tongue filled my mouth and I was racked by the second spasm of vomit. Through my tears I saw the four cubs eyeing their Ma's dinner. I grew conscious of voices nursing and cursing me alternately. I palmed away my dribbles and feebly raised the chair to shield me from the cat. She came padding towards me. I backed away from her. She put her nose to the retched whiskey and turned away without appearing to register any reaction except an ominous boredom. She looked at the kittens; then yawped ill-temperedly in my direction. The iron poles poked in through the bars. Which was Dirty Dan's?—that was the one that would let her in to me. I woke up, gathered my courage, crept towards her and started saying 'Hiss!' and 'Allez-oop!' in an endeavour to get her up on the centre stool. First she backed away from me; then she stopped and walked towards me. All the while I was hissing like a goose. I peeped from behind the chair at her face and I knew by it that she was itching to maul me. Just then one of the cubs put a trial paw towards the floor of the cage. I put down my hand and bundled her up again. The movement, simple as it was, made me sweat like a bull. As I was straightening myself my knees began to knock. Up to this I had thought that one's knees knocking was a figure of speech, but if anyone tells you that it's not a physical fact, you can call him a liar and quote me as your authority. Then I got a brainwave. I began to scrape the seat of the perch with one leg of my chair. The lioness put her nose to the point of scraping, so I brought my scraping to the offside of the seat from her and her inquisitive nose pursued it. I lowered the chair and scraped on the floor on my side of the seat. I'm blessed to God if she didn't jump up on the stool to view the situation as a whole. Immediately I pronged her with all four legs of the chair and put her sitting down.

"The deed was done! The kettle-drums rattled up and up and on and on. In barged the trumpets and brought the crowd to the peak of the huzza. The place swirled around me—cubs and lionesses and stools in that infernal wheel. My nostrils were assaulted by the fumes of whiskey and the unconquerable odour of lion-dung. Somebody called on me to bow. I backed against the side of the cage; my knees buckled while I gave the crowd as much of my profile as I could afford without even once taking my eyes off her ladyship. Again the applause backed up like a suddenly dammed river. I heard the gate clang open behind me. Inch by precious inch I retreated until my buttocks found the aperture: then the lads dragged me to the ground. I can't remember whether I took a second bow or not. Then the clowns spun out in cartwheels of colour and the feed banged in with his bright patter.

"The Boss and the Missus were there to congratulate me.

Pride was flowing down off the pair of them. 'Leave it there!' said himself, extending his hand. 'At last Ireland can boast that she has a lion-tamer.'

"I stayed with Vaughan's for two seasons and, believe you me, before I was finished I could cuff that old cat across the ear. Like all women, she was contrary now and again: once she gave me the hooks in a little place in North Tipp., nothing worth talking about, but still . . ." Here the young man made as if to tug his shirt over the back of his belt and show me scars and weals, but on my counterfeiting squeamishness he desisted.

"I left Vaughan's to start on my own—on a small scale, you know. I picked up a performing bear dirt-cheap from a chap in Dublin and ran a Pick-and-Win joint for three months, making as much money in that time at that racket as I had made in my whole circus career."

A clock struck. "Oho!" said my friend, glancing up. He finished his drink hurriedly and bade good-night to myself and the publican. I ordered a nightcap. The publican put his elbows on the counter and nodded towards the door through which the story-teller had gone. I saw pride lighting in his eyes.

"Isn't he good?" he asked.

"Damn good!" I agreed.

"What was it?"

"Eh?"

"It wasn't the Lizard in the Cardinal's Pocket?" The man's eyes pipped in anticipation of tiny triumph.

"Eh? No no."

"Nor the time he operated on his mother for appendicitis?"

"No no."

"Let me think. Don't tell me. Was it the Litter of Elk-Hounds he sold in Cruft's?"

"He said he was a lion-tamer," I faltered.

The publican grew solemn; then wan. Suddenly he brightened in parochial pride. "Blast me if I ever heard that one before." Then, ominously, "Isn't he able to put them together well?"

"Never heard better," I said.

The publican cupped his face in his palms. "What gave him the lead to that one?" He ruminated for a moment. Then his face splintered into the joy of discovery. "Blast me if it isn't Miss Evans's cats!"

"Miss Evans's cats?"

"Aye! he's feeding them while she's away. He must have a lead. Cats—lions, see? The Lizard story—he got the lead of that from a kid who brought a frog to school in his handkerchief. Once they took him as far as the Falls of Doonass on a Confraternity excursion and he came back with a grand story about Niagara. I'd say the Niagara story is his best. That's all we have in this place, him and the Caves": here he dismissed the hamlet with a gesture. "The caves are about a mile up the hill—spikes comin' up out of the floor and more hanging down from the ceiling. There's a big name for them. Would you remember what it is?"

"Stalagmites and stalactites," I said.

He repeated the words, savouring them. Then, "The

Caves are damn good, too." I pondered on the shade of meaning latent in the addendum "too."

I finished my drink, bade the publican good-night and walked up the village towards the tiny hotel. The night was still and frosty with a wealth of stars above. I heard the crunch-crunch of two Guards' boots on the gravelled path a hundred yards behind me. Lemon lamp-light glowed in a few houses, on the side of the street. On my right-hand side the bulk of the hill was clear against the northern sky. The place where the hotel stood was at the higher end of the street, and when I got to the top of the little eminence I looked back on the twenty or thirty mongrel houses in the village. Odd to consider, I pondered, that after all these years it is in this shabby insignificant hollow in Ireland the reincarnated spirit of Munchausen has found flesh fit to cover its shade.

THE LION-TAMER

1. In establishing the character of The Lion-Tamer what is the importance of his explanation about not accepting a drink?
2. What do you conclude is meant by "the milk of the black cow"?
3. What is the meaning of "Uppermost in my mind was an access of retrospective appreciation of Andy McIvor"?
4. What examples of humor do you find?
5. Why is it important to the story that the new lion-tamer be showing the effects of drink?

6. Why are repeated references made to the music?

7. What is the significance of "too" when the barkeep refers to the caves as being good?

8. Who was Munchausen? Explain the referencc in the last paragraph.

9. How would you classify this story: character, humor, local color, a tale?

BERNARD MALAMUD

1914–

The First Seven Years

THIS WRITER *was born in Brooklyn, New York, where he has lived most of his life. He attended Erasmus High School in that borough and later received degrees from the College of the City of New York and from Columbia University. His first writings were published in the Erasmus High School literary magazine. Subsequently, he taught at Oregon State College.*

Although he is also a novelist, Mr. Malamud is perhaps best known for his short stories, and his collection of stories, The Magic Barrel, *won wide acclaim. He is most concerned with the problems of the Jews in the modern world.*

"The First Seven Years" *illustrates Mr. Malamud's belief that fiction ". . . should be filled with love and beauty and hope."*

Feld, the shoemaker, was annoyed that his helper, Sobel, was so insensitive to his reverie that he wouldn't for a minute cease his fanatic pounding at the other bench. He gave him a look, but Sobel's bald head was bent over the last as he worked and he didn't notice. The shoemaker shrugged and continued to peer through the partly frosted window at the near-sighted haze of falling February snow. Neither the shifting white blur outside, nor the sudden deep remembrance of the snowy Polish village where he had wasted his youth could turn his thoughts from Max the college boy (a constant visitor in the mind since early that morning when Feld saw him trudging through the snowdrifts on his way to school), whom he so much respected because of the sacrifices he had made throughout the years—in winter or direst heat—to further his education. An old wish returned to haunt the shoemaker: that he had had a son instead of a daughter, but this blew away in the snow for Feld, if anything, was a practical man. Yet he could not help but contrast the diligence of the boy, who was a peddler's son, with Miriam's unconcern for an education. True, she was always with a book in her hand, yet when the opportunity arose for a college education, she had said no she would rather find a job. He had begged her to go, pointing out how many fathers could not afford to send their children to college, but she said she wanted to be independent. As for education, what was it, she asked, but books, which Sobel, who diligently read the classics, would as usual advise her on. Her answer greatly grieved her father.

A figure emerged from the snow and the door opened. At the counter the man withdrew from a wet paper bag a pair of battered shoes for repair. Who he was the shoemaker for a moment had no idea, then his heart trembled as he realized, before he had thoroughly discerned the face, that Max himself was standing there, embarrassedly explaining what he wanted done to his old shoes. Though Feld listened eagerly, he couldn't hear a word, for the opportunity that had burst upon him was deafening.

He couldn't exactly recall when the thought had occurred to him, because it was clear he had more than once considered suggesting to the boy that he go out with Miriam. But he had not dared speak, for if Max said no, how would he face him again? Or suppose Miriam, who harped so often on independence, blew up in anger and shouted at him for his meddling? Still, the chance was too good to let by: all it meant was an introduction. They might long ago have become friends had they happened to meet somewhere, therefore was it not his duty—an obligation—to bring them together, nothing more, a harmless connivance to replace an accidental encounter in the subway, let's say, or a mutual friend's introduction in the street? Just let him once see and talk to her and he would for sure be interested. As for Miriam, what possible harm for a working girl in an office, who met only loud-mouthed salesmen and illiterate shipping clerks, to make the acquaintance of a fine scholarly boy? Maybe he would awaken in her a desire to go to college; if not—the shoemaker's mind at last came to grips with the truth—let her marry an educated man and live a better life.

When Max finished describing what he wanted done to his shoes, Feld marked them, both with enormous holes in the soles which he pretended not to notice, with large white-chalk x's, and the rubber heels, thinned to the nails, he marked with o's, though it troubled him he might have mixed up the letters. Max inquired the price, and the shoemaker cleared his throat and asked the boy, above Sobel's insistent hammering, would he please step through the side door there into the hall. Though surprised, Max did as the shoemaker requested, and Feld went in after him. For a minute they were both silent, because Sobel had stopped banging, and it seemed they understood neither was to say anything until the noise began again. When it did, loudly, the shoemaker quickly told Max why he had asked to talk to him.

"Ever since you went to high school," hc said, in the dimly-lit hallway, "I watched you in the morning go to the subway to school, and I said always to myself, this is a fine boy that he wants so much an education."

"Thanks," Max said, nervously alert. He was tall and grotesquely thin, with sharply cut features, particularly a beak-like nose. He was wearing a loose, long slushy overcoat that hung down to his ankles, looking like a rug draped over his bony shoulders, and a soggy, old brown hat, as battered as the shoes he had brought in.

"I am a business man," the shoemaker abruptly said to conceal his embarrassment, "so I will explain you right away why I talk to you. I have a girl, my daughter Miriam—she is nineteen—a very nice girl and also so pretty that everybody looks on her when she passes by in the street. She is smart, always with a book, and I thought to myself that a boy like you, an educated boy—I thought maybe you will be interested sometime to meet a girl like this." He laughed a bit when he had finished and was tempted to say more but had the good sense not to.

Max stared down like a hawk. For an uncomfortable second he was silent, then he asked, "Did you say nineteen?"

"Yes."

"Would it be all right to inquire if you have a picture of her?"

"Just a minute." The shoemaker went into the store and

hastily returned with a snapshot that Max held up to the light.

"She's all right," he said.

Feld waited.

"And is she sensible—not the flighty kind?"

"She is very sensible."

After another short pause, Max said it was okay with him if he met her.

"Here is my telephone," said the shoemaker, hurriedly handing him a slip of paper. "Call her up. She comes home from work six o'clock."

Max folded the paper and tucked it away into his worn leather wallet.

"About the shoes," he said. "How much did you say they will cost me?"

"Don't worry about the price."

"I just like to have an idea."

"A dollar—dollar fifty. A dollar fifty," the shoemaker said.

At once he felt bad, for he usually charged two twenty-five for this kind of job. Either he should have asked the regular price or done the work for nothing.

Later, as he entered the store, he was startled by a violent clanging and looked up to see Sobel pounding with all his might upon the naked last. It broke, the iron striking the floor and jumping with a thump against the wall, but before the enraged shoemaker could cry out, the assistant had torn his hat and coat from the hook and rushed out into the snow.

So Feld, who had looked forward to anticipating how it would go with his daughter and Max, instead had a great worry on his mind. Without his temperamental helper he was a lost man, especially since it was years now that he had carried the store alone. The shoemaker had for an age suffered from a heart condition that threatened collapse if he dared exert himself. Five years ago, after an attack, it had appeared as though he would have either to sacrifice his business upon the auction block and live on a pittance thereafter, or put himself at the mercy of some unscrupulous employee who would in the end probably ruin him. But just at the moment of his darkest despair, this Polish refugee, Sobel, appeared one night from the street and begged for work. He was a stocky man, poorly dressed, with a bald head that had once been blond, a severely plain face and soft blue eyes prone to tears over the sad books he read, a young man but old—no one would have guessed thirty. Though he confessed he knew nothing of shoemaking, he said he was apt and would work for a very little if Feld taught him the trade. Thinking that with, after all, a landsman, he would have less to fear than from a complete stranger, Feld took him on and within six weeks the refugee rebuilt as good a shoe as he, and not long thereafter expertly ran the business for the thoroughly relieved shoemaker.

Feld could trust him with anything and did, frequently going home after an hour or two at the store, leaving all the money in the till, knowing Sobel would guard every cent of it. The amazing thing was that he demanded so little. His wants were few; in money he wasn't interested—in nothing but books, it seemed—which he one by one lent to Miriam, together with his profuse, queer written comments, manufactured during his lonely rooming house evenings, thick pads of commentary which the shoemaker peered at and twitched his shoulders over as his daughter, from her fourteenth year, read page by sanctified page, as if the word of God were inscribed on them. To protect Sobel, Feld himself had to see that he received more than he asked for. Yet his conscience bothered him for not insisting that the assistant accept a better wage than he was getting, though Feld had honestly told him he could earn a handsome salary if he worked elsewhere, or maybe opened a place of his own. But the assistant answered, somewhat ungraciously, that he was not interested in going elsewhere, and though Feld frequently asked himself what keeps him here? why does he stay? he finally answered it that the man, no doubt because of his terrible experiences as a refugee, was afraid of the world.

After the incident with the broken last, angered by Sobel's behavior, the shoemaker decided to let him stew for a week in the rooming house, although his own strength was taxed dangerously and the business suffered. However, after several sharp nagging warnings from both his wife and daughter, he went finally in search of Sobel, as he had once before, quite recently, when over some fancied slight—Feld had merely asked him not to give Miriam so many books to read because her eyes were strained and red—the assistant had left the place in a huff, an incident which, as usual, came to nothing for he had returned after the shoemaker had talked to him, and taken his seat at the bench. But this time, after Feld had plodded through the snow to Sobel's house—he had thought of sending Miriam but the idea became repugnant to him—the burly landlady at the door informed him in a nasal voice that Sobel was not at home, and though Feld knew this was a nasty lie, for where had the refugee to go? still for some reason he was not completely sure of—it may have been the cold and his fatigue—he decided not to insist on seeing him. Instead he went home and hired a new helper.

Having settled the matter, though not entirely to his satisfaction, for he had much more to do than before, and so, for example, could no longer lie late in bed mornings because he had to get up to open the store for the new assistant, a speechless, dark man with an irritating rasp as he worked, whom he would not trust with the key as he had Sobel. Furthermore, this one, though able to do a fair repair job, knew nothing of grades of leather or prices, so Feld had to make his own purchases; and every night at closing time it was necessary to count the money in the till and lock up. However, he was not dissatisfied, for he lived much in his thoughts of Max and Miriam. The college boy had called her, and they had arranged a meeting for this coming Friday night. The shoemaker would personally have preferred Saturday, which he felt would make it a date of the first magnitude, but he learned Friday was Miriam's choice, so he said nothing. The day of the week did not matter. What mattered was the aftermath. Would they like each other and want to be friends? He sighed at all the time that would have to go by before he knew for sure. Often he was tempted to talk to Miriam about the boy, to ask whether she thought she would like his type—he had told her only that he considered Max a nice boy and had suggested he call her—but the one time he tried she snapped at him—justly—how should she know?

At last Friday came. Feld was not feeling particularly well so he stayed in bed, and Mrs. Feld thought it better to remain in the bedroom with him when Max called. Miriam received the boy, and her parents could hear their voices, his throaty one, as they talked. Just before leaving, Miriam brought Max to the bedroom door and he stood there a minute, a tall, slightly hunched figure wearing a thick, droopy suit, and apparently at ease as he greeted the shoemaker and his wife, which was surely a good sign. And Miriam, although she had worked all day, looked fresh and pretty. She was a large-framed girl with a well-shaped body, and she had a fine open face and soft hair. They made, Feld thought, a first-class couple.

Miriam returned after 11:30. Her mother was already asleep, but the shoemaker got out of bed and after locating his bathrobe went into the kitchen, where Miriam, to his surprise, sat at the table, reading.

"So where did you go?" Feld asked pleasantly.

"For a walk," she said, not looking up.

"I advised him," Feld said, clearing his throat, "he shouldn't spend so much money."

"I didn't care."

The shoemaker boiled up some water for tea and sat

down at the table with a cupful and a thick slice of lemon.

"So how," he sighed after a sip, "did you enjoy?"

"It was all right."

He was silent. She must have sensed his disappointment, for she added, "You can't really tell much the first time."

"You will see him again?"

Turning a page, she said that Max had asked for another date.

"For when?"

"Saturday."

"So what did you say?"

"What did I say?" she asked, delaying for a moment—"I said yes."

Afterwards she inquired about Sobel, and Feld, without exactly knowing why, said the assistant had got another job. Miriam said nothing more and began to read. The shoemaker's conscience did not trouble him; he was satisfied with the Saturday date.

During the week, by placing here and there a deft question, he managed to get from Miriam some information about Max. It surprised him to learn that the boy was not studying to be either a doctor or lawyer but was taking a business course leading to a degree in accountancy. Feld was a little disappointed because he thought of accountants as bookkeepers and would have preferred "a higher profession." However, it was not long before he had investigated the subject and discovered that Certified Public Accountants were highly respected people, so he was thoroughly content as Saturday approached. But because Saturday was a busy day, he was much in the store and therefore did not see Max when he came to call for Miriam. From his wife he learned there had been nothing especially revealing about their meeting. Max had rung the bell and Miriam had got her coat and left with him—nothing more. Feld did not probe, for his wife was not particularly observant. Instead, he waited up for Miriam with a newspaper on his lap, which he scarcely looked at so lost was he in thinking of the future. He awoke to find her in the room with him, tiredly removing her hat. Greeting her, he was suddenly inexplicably afraid to ask anything about the evening. But since she volunteered nothing he was at last forced to inquire how she had enjoyed herself. Miriam began something non-committal but apparently changed her mind, for she said after a minute, "I was bored."

When Feld had sufficiently recovered from his anguished disappointment to ask why, she answered without hesitation, "Because he's nothing more than a materialist."

"What means this word?"

"He has no soul. He's only interested in things."

He considered her statement for a long time but then asked, "Will you see him again?"

"He didn't ask."

"Suppose he will ask you?"

"I won't see him."

He did not argue; however, as the days went by he hoped increasingly she would change her mind. He wished the boy would telephone, because he was sure there was more to him than Miriam, with her inexperienced eye, could discern. But Max didn't call. As a matter of fact he took a different route to school, no longer passing the shoemaker's store and Feld was deeply hurt.

Then one afternoon Max came in and asked for his shoes. The shoemaker took them down from the shelf where he had placed them, apart from the other pairs. He had done the work himself and the soles and heels were well built and firm. The shoes had been highly polished and somehow looked better than new. Max's Adam's apple went up once when he saw them, and his eyes had little lights in them.

"How much?" he asked, without directly looking at the shoemaker.

"Like I told you before," Feld answered sadly. "One dollar fifty cents."

Max handed him two crumpled bills and received in return a newly-minted silver half dollar.

He left. Miriam had not been mentioned. That night the shoemaker discovered that his new assistant had been all the while stealing from him, and he suffered a heart attack.

Though the attack was very mild, he lay in bed for three weeks. Miriam spoke of going for Sobel, but sick as he was Feld rose in wrath against the idea. Yet in his heart he knew there was no other way, and the first weary day back in the shop thoroughly convinced him, so that night after supper he dragged himself to Sobel's rooming house.

He toiled up the stairs, though he knew it was bad for him, and at the top knocked at the door. Sobel opened it and the shoemaker entered. The room was a small, poor one, with a single window facing the street. It contained a narrow cot, a low table and several stacks of books piled haphazardly around on the floor along the wall, which made him think how queer Sobel was, to be uneducated and read so much. He had once asked him, Sobel, why you read so much? and the assistant could not answer him. Did you ever study in a college someplace? he had asked, but Sobel shook his head. He read, he said, to know. But to know what, the shoemaker demanded, and to know, why? Sobel never explained, which proved he read much because he was queer.

Feld sat down to recover his breath. The assistant was resting on his bed with his heavy back to the wall. His shirt and trousers were clean, and his stubby fingers, away from the shoemaker's bench, were strangely pallid. His face was thin and pale, as if he had been shut in this room since the day he had bolted from the store.

"So when you will come back to work?" Feld asked him.

To his surprise, Sobel burst out, "Never."

Jumping up, he strode over to the window that looked out upon the miserable street. "Why should I come back?" he cried.

"I will raise your wages."

"Who cares for your wages!"

The shoemaker, knowing he didn't care, was at a loss what else to say.

"What do you want from me, Sobel?"

"Nothing."

"I always treated you like you was my son."

Sobel vehemently denied it. "So why you look for strange boys in the street they should go out with Miriam? Why you don't think of me?"

The shoemaker's hands and feet turned freezing cold. His voice became so hoarse he couldn't speak. At last he cleared his throat and croaked. "So what has my daughter got to do with a shoemaker thirty-five years old who works for me?"

"Why do you think I worked so long for you?" Sobel cried out. "For the stingy wages I sacrificed five years of my life so you could have to eat and drink and where to sleep?"

"Then for what?" shouted the shoemaker.

"For Miriam," he blurted—"for her."

The shoemaker, after a time, managed to say, "I pay wages in cash, Sobel," and lapsed into silence. Though he was seething with excitement, his mind was coldly clear, and he had to admit to himself he had sensed all along that Sobel felt this way. He had never so much as thought it consciously, but he had felt it and was afraid.

"Miriam knows?" he muttered hoarsely.

"She knows."

"You told her?"

"No."

"Then how does she know?"

"How does she know?" Sobel said, "because she knows. She knows who I am and what is in my heart."

Feld had a sudden insight. In some devious way, with his books and commentary, Sobel had given Miriam to understand that he loved her. The shoemaker felt a terrible anger at him for his deceit.

"Sobel, you are crazy," he said bitterly. "She will never marry a man so old and ugly like you."

Sobel turned black with rage. He cursed the shoemaker,

but then, though he trembled to hold it in, his eyes filled with tears and he broke into deep sobs. With his back to Feld, he stood at the window, fists clenched, and his shoulders shook with his choked sobbing.

Watching him, the shoemaker's anger diminished. His teeth were on edge with pity for the man, and his eyes grew moist. How strange and sad that a refugee, a grown man, bald and old with his miseries, who had by the skin of his teeth escaped Hitler's incinerators, should fall in love, when he had got to America, with a girl less than half his age. Day after day, for five years he had sat at his bench, cutting and hammering away, waiting for the girl to become a woman, unable to ease his heart with speech, knowing no protest but desperation.

"Ugly I didn't mean," he said half aloud.

Then he realized that what he had called ugly was not Sobel but Miriam's life if she married him. He felt for his daughter a strange and gripping sorrow, as if she were already Sobel's bride, the wife, after all, of a shoemaker, and had in her life no more than her mother had had. And all his dreams for her—why he had slaved and destroyed his heart with anxiety and labor—all these dreams of a better life were dead.

The room was quiet. Sobel was standing by the window reading, and it was curious that when he read he looked young.

"She is only nineteen," Feld said brokenly. "This is too young yet to get married. Don't ask her for two years more, till she is twenty-one, then you can talk to her."

Sobel didn't answer. Feld rose and left. He went slowly down the stairs but once outside, though it was an icy night and the crisp falling snow whitened the street, he walked with a stronger stride.

But the next morning, when the shoemaker arrived, heavy-hearted, to open the store, he saw he needn't have come, for his assistant was already seated at the last, pounding leather for his love.

THE FIRST SEVEN YEARS

1. What are the themes of Feld's reveries?
2. How did the thought that he had "wasted his youth" affect Feld's ambition for his daughter?
3. How is Feld's love for his daughter revealed?
4. Which adjectives does the author use that are particularly descriptive about Feld's visit to Sobel?
5. Is the dialogue intended to provoke laughter, or is it designed to describe the characters? What differences do you see in the speech of Miriam and her father and his helper? How do you account for these differences?
6. What was Sobel's reason for working so long at minimum wages?
7. What is the climax or turning point of this story?
8. Do you understand the significance of the title? If not, see the *Holy Bible,* book of *Genesis,* chapter 29, verses 9 to 20.

KATHERINE MANSFIELD

1888–1923

The Garden Party

Miss Mansfield *was born in New Zealand, the daughter of a banker. Because of ill health, she lived abroad in Italy, Switzerland, and France. Her first short story was published when she was nine. Miss Mansfield was a capable musician as well as a writer.*

In Miss Mansfield's stories you will note a care for detail, a sympathy for man and his living, and a precision in choice of word or phrase.

And after all the weather was ideal. They could not have had a more perfect day for a garden-party if they had ordered it. Windless, warm, the sky without a cloud. Only the blue was veiled with a haze of light gold, as it is sometimes in early summer. The gardener had been up since dawn, mowing the lawns and sweeping them, until the grass and the dark flat rosettes where the daisy plants had been seemed to shine. As for the roses, you could not help feeling they understood that roses are the only flowers that impress people at garden-parties; the only flowers that everybody is certain of knowing. Hundreds, yes, literally hundreds, had come out in a single night; the green bushes bowed down as though they had been visited by archangels.

Breakfast was not yet over before men came to put up the marquee.

"Where do you want the marquee put, mother?"

"My dear child, it's no use asking me. I'm determined to leave everything to you children this year. Forget I am your mother. Treat me as an honoured guest."

But Meg could not possibly go and supervise the men. She had washed her hair before breakfast, and she sat drinking her coffee in a green turban, with a dark wet curl stamped on each cheek. Jose, the butterfly, always came down in a silk petticoat and a kimono jacket.

"You'll have to go, Laura; you're the artistic one."

Away Laura flew, still holding her piece of bread-and-butter. It's so delicious to have an excuse for eating out of doors and besides, she loved to arrange things; she always felt she could do it so much better than anybody else.

Four men in their shirt-sleeves stood grouped together on the garden path. They carried staves covered with rolls of canvas, and they had big tool-bags slung on their backs. They looked impressive. Laura wished now that she had not got the bread-and-butter, but there was nowhere to put it, and she couldn't possibly throw it away. She blushed and tried to look severe and even a little bit short-sighted as she came up to them.

"Good morning," she said, copying her mother's voice. But that sounded so fearfully affected that she was ashamed, and stammered like a little girl, "Oh—or—have you come—is it about the marquee?"

"That's right, miss," said the tallest of the men, a lanky

freckled fellow, and he shifted his tool-bag, knocked back his straw hat and smiled down at her.

"That's about it."

His smile was so easy, so friendly that Laura recovered. What nice eyes he had, small, but such a dark blue! And now she looked at the others, they were smiling too. "Cheer up, we won't bite," their smile seemed to say. How very nice workmen were! And what a beautiful morning! She mustn't mention the morning; she must be business-like. The marquee.

"Well, what about the lily-lawn? Would that do?"

And she pointed to the lily-lawn with the hand that didn't hold the bread-and-butter. They turned, they stared in the direction. A little fat chap thrust out his under-lip, and the tall fellow frowned.

"I don't fancy it," said he. "Not conspicuous enough. You see, with a thing like a marquee," and he turned to Laura in his easy way, "you want to put it somewhere where it'll give you a bang slap in the eye, if you follow me."

Laura's upbringing made her wonder for a moment whether it was quite respectful of a workman to talk to her of bangs slap in the eye. But she did quite follow him.

"A corner of the tennis-court," she suggested. "But the band's going to be in one corner."

"H'm, going to have a band, are you?" said another of the workmen. He was pale. He had a haggard look as his dark eyes scanned the tennis-court. What was he thinking?

"Only a very small band," said Laura gently. Perhaps he wouldn't mind so much if the band was quite small. But the tall fellow interrupted.

"Look here, miss, that's the place. Against those trees. Over there. That'll do fine."

Against the karakas. Then the karaka-trees would be hidden. And they were so lovely, with their broad, gleaming leaves, and their clusters of yellow fruit. They were like trees you imagined growing on a desert island, proud, solitary, lifting their leaves and fruits to the sun in a kind of silent splendour. Must they be hidden by a marquee?

They must. Already the men had shouldered their staves and were making for the place. Only the tall fellow was left. He bent down, pinched a sprig of lavender, put his thumb and forefinger to his nose and snuffed up the smell. When Laura saw that gesture she forgot all about the karakas in her wonder at him caring for things like that—caring for the smell of lavender. How many men that she knew would have done such a thing? Oh, how extraordinarily nice workmen were, she thought. Why couldn't she have workmen for friends rather than the silly boys she danced with and who came to Sunday night supper? She would get on much better with men like these.

It's all the fault, she decided, as the tall fellow drew something on the back of an envelope, something that was to be looped up or left to hang, of these absurd class distinctions. Well, for her part, she didn't feel them. Not a bit, not an atom. . . . And now there came the chock-chock of wooden hammers. Some one whistled, some one sang out, "Are you right there, matey?" "Matey!" The friendliness of it, the—the— Just to prove how happy she was, just to show the tall fellow how at home she felt, and how she despised stupid conventions, Laura took a big bite of her bread-and-butter as she stared at the little drawing. She felt just like a work-girl.

"Laura, Laura, where are you? Telephone, Laura!" a voice cried from the house.

"Coming!" Away she skimmed, over the lawn, up the path, up the steps, across the veranda, and into the porch. In the hall her father and Laurie were brushing their hats ready to go to the office.

"I say, Laura," said Laurie very fast, "you might just give a squiz at my coat before this afternoon. See if it wants pressing."

"I will," said she. Suddenly she couldn't stop herself. She ran at Laurie and gave him a small, quick squeeze. "Oh, I do love parties, don't you?" gasped Laura.

"Ra-ther," said Laurie's warm, boyish voice, and he squeezed his sister too, and gave her a gentle push. "Dash off to the telephone, old girl."

The telephone. "Yes, yes; oh yes. Kitty? Good morning, dear. Come to lunch? Do, dear. Delighted of course. It will only be a very scratch meal—just the sandwich crusts and broken meringue-shells and what's left over. Yes, isn't it a perfect morning? Your white? Oh, I certainly should. One moment—hold the line. Mother's calling." And Laura sat back. "What, mother? Can't hear."

Mrs. Sheridan's voice floated down the stairs. "Tell her to wear that sweet hat she had on last Sunday."

"Mother says you're to wear that *sweet* hat you had on last Sunday. Good. One o'clock. Bye-bye."

Laura put back the receiver, flung her arms over her

head, took a deep breath, stretched and let them fall. "Huh," she sighed, and the moment after the sigh she sat up quickly. She was still, listening. All the doors in the house seemed to be open. The house was alive with soft, quick steps and running voices. The green baize door that led to the kitchen regions swung open and shut with a muffled thud. And now there came a long, chuckling absurd sound. It was the heavy piano being moved on its stiff castors. But the air! If you stopped to notice, was the air always like this? Little faint winds were playing chase, in at the tops of the windows, out at the doors. And there were two tiny spots of sun, one on the inkpot, one on a silver photograph frame, playing too. Darling little spots. Especially the one on the inkpot lid. It was quite warm. A warm little silver star. She could have kissed it.

The front door bell pealed, and there sounded the rustle of Sadie's print skirt on the stairs. A man's voice murmured; Sadie answered, careless, "I'm sure I don't know. Wait. I'll ask Mrs. Sheridan."

"What is it, Sadie?" Laura came into the hall.

"It's the florist, Miss Laura."

It was, indeed. There, just inside the door, stood a wide, shallow tray full of pots of pink lilies. No other kind. Nothing but lilies—canna lilies, big pink flowers, wide open, radiant, almost frighteningly alive on bright crimson stems.

"O-oh, Sadie!" said Laura, and the sound was like a little moan. She crouched down as if to warm herself at that blaze of lilies; she felt they were in her fingers, on her lips, growing in her breast.

"It's some mistake," she said faintly. "Nobody ever ordered so many. Sadie, go and find mother."

But at that moment Mrs. Sheridan joined them.

"It's quite right," she said calmly. "Yes, I ordered them. Aren't they lovely?" She pressed Laura's arm. "I was passing the shop yesterday, and I saw them in the window. And I suddenly thought for once in my life I shall have enough canna lilies. The garden-party will be a good excuse."

"But I thought you said you didn't mean to interfere," said Laura. Sadie had gone. The florist's man was still outside at his van. She put her arm round her mother's neck and gently, very gently, she bit her mother's ear.

"My darling child, you wouldn't like a logical mother, would you? Don't do that. Here's the man."

He carried more lilies still, another whole tray.

"Bank them up, just inside the door, on both sides of the porch, please," said Mrs. Sheridan. "Don't you agree, Laura?"

"Oh, I *do*, mother."

In the drawing-room Meg, Jose and good little Hans had at last succeeded in moving the piano.

"Now, if we put this chesterfield against the wall and move everything out of the room except the chairs, don't you think?"

"Quite."

"Hans, move these tables into the smoking-room, and bring a sweeper to take these marks off the carpet and—one moment, Hans—" Jose loved giving orders to the servants, and they loved obeying her. She always made them feel they were taking part in some drama. "Tell mother and Miss Laura to come here at once."

"Very good, Miss Jose."

She turned to Meg. "I want to hear what the piano sounds like, just in case I'm asked to sing this afternoon. Let's try over 'This Life is Weary.' "

Pom! Ta-ta-ta *Tee*-ta! The piano burst out so passionately that Jose's face changed. She clasped her hands. She looked mournfully and enigmatically at her mother and Laura as they came in.

> This Life is *Wee*-ary,
> A Tear—a Sigh.
> A Love that *Chan*-ges,
> This Life is *Wee*-ary,
> A Tear—a Sigh.
> A Love that *Chan*-ges,
> And then . . . Goodbye!

But at the word "Good-bye," and although the piano sounded more desperate than ever, her face broke into a brilliant, dreadfully unsympathetic smile.

"Aren't I in good voice, mummy?" she beamed.

> This Life is *Wee*-ary,
> Hope comes to Die.
> A Dream—a *Wa*-kening.

But now Sadie interrupted them. "What is it, Sadie?"

"If you please, m'm, cook says have you got the flags for the sandwiches?"

"The flags for the sandwiches, Sadie?" echoed Mrs.

Sheridan dreamily. And the children knew by her face that she hadn't got them. "Let me see." And she said to Sadie firmly, "Tell cook I'll let her have them in ten minutes."

Sadie went.

"Now, Laura," said her mother quickly. "Come with me into the smoking-room. I've got the names somewhere on the back of an envelope. You'll have to write them out for me. Meg, go upstairs this minute and take that wet thing off your head. Jose, run and finish dressing this instant. Do you hear me, children, or shall I have to tell your father when he comes home to-night? And—and, Jose, pacify cook if you do go into the kitchen, will you? I'm terrified of her this morning."

The envelope was found at last behind the dining-room clock, though how it had got there Mrs. Sheridan could not imagine.

"One of you children must have stolen it out of my bag, because I remember vividly—cream cheese and lemon-curd. Have you done that?"

"Yes."

"Egg and—" Mrs. Sheridan held the envelope away from her. "It looks like mice. It can't be mice, can it?"

"Olive, pet," said Laura, looking over her shoulder.

"Yes, of course, olive. What a horrible combination it sounds. Egg and olive."

They were finished at last, and Laura took them off to the kitchen. She found Jose there pacifying the cook, who did not look at all terrifying.

"I have never seen such exquisite sandwiches," said Jose's rapturous voice. "How many kinds did you say there were, cook? Fifteen?"

"Fifteen, Miss Jose."

"Well, cook, I congratulate you."

Cook swept up crusts with the long sandwich knife, and smiled broadly.

"Godber's has come," announced Sadie, issuing out of the pantry. She had seen the man pass the window.

That meant the cream puffs had come. Godber's were famous for their cream puffs. Nobody ever thought of making them at home.

"Bring them in and put them on the table, my girl," ordered cook.

Sadie brought them in and went back to the door. Of course Laura and Jose were far too grown-up to really care about such things. All the same, they couldn't help agreeing that the puffs looked very attractive. Very. Cook began arranging them, shaking off the extra icing sugar.

"Don't they carry one back to all one's parties?" said Laura.

"I suppose they do," said practical Jose, who never liked to be carried back. "They look beautifully light and feathery, I must say."

"Have one each, my dears," said cook in her comfortable voice. "Yer ma won't know."

Oh, impossible. Fancy cream puffs so soon after breakfast. The very idea made one shudder. All the same, two minutes later Jose and Laura were licking their fingers with that absorbed inward look that only comes from whipped cream.

"Let's go into the garden, out by the back way," suggested Laura. "I want to see how the men are getting on with the marquee. They're such awfully nice men."

But the back door was blocked by cook, Sadie, Godber's man and Hans.

Something had happened.

"Tuk-tuk-tuk," clucked cook like an agitated hen. Sadie had her hand clapped to her cheek as though she had toothache. Hans's face was screwed up in the effort to understand. Only Godber's man seemed to be enjoying himself; it was his story.

"What's the matter? What's happened?"

"There's been a horrible accident," said cook. "A man killed."

"A man killed! Where? How? When?"

But Godber's man wasn't going to have his story snatched from under his very nose.

"Know those little cottages just below here, miss?" Know them? Of course, she knew them. "Well, there's a young chap living there, name of Scott, a carter. His horse shied at a traction-engine, corner of Hawke Street this morning, and he was thrown out on the back of his head. Killed."

"Dead!" Laura stared at Godber's man.

"Dead when they picked him up," said Godber's man with relish. "They were taking the body home as I come up here." And he said to the cook, "He's left a wife and five little ones."

"Jose, come here." Laura caught hold of her sister's sleeve and dragged her through the kitchen to the other side of the green baize door. There she paused and leaned against it. "Jose!" she said, horrified, "however are we going to stop everything?"

"Stop everything, Laura!" cried Jose in astonishment. "What do you mean?"

"Stop the garden-party, of course." Why did Jose pretend?

But Jose was still more amazed. "Stop the garden-party? My dear Laura, don't be so absurd. Of course we can't do anything of the kind. Nobody expects us to. Don't be so extravagant."

"But we can't possibly have a garden-party with a man dead just outside the front gate."

That really was extravagant, for the little cottages were in a lane to themselves at the very bottom of a steep rise that led up to the house. A broad road ran between. True, they were far too near. They were the greatest possible eyesore, and they had no right to be in that neighbourhood at all. They were little mean dwellings painted a chocolate brown. In the garden patches there was nothing but cabbage stalks, sick hens and tomato cans. The very smoke coming out of their chimneys was poverty-stricken. Little rags and shreds of smoke, so unlike the great silvery plumes that uncurled from the Sheridans' chimneys. Washer-women lived in the lane and sweeps and a cobbler, and a man whose house-front was studded all over with minute bird-cages. Children swarmed. When the Sheridans were little they were forbidden to set foot there because of the revolting language and of what they might catch. But since they were grown up, Laura and Laurie on the prowls sometimes walked through. It was disgusting and sordid. They came out with a shudder. But still one must go everywhere; one must see everything. So through they went.

"And just think of what the band would sound like to that poor woman," said Laura.

"Oh, Laura!" Jose began to be seriously annoyed. "If you're going to stop a band playing every time some one has an accident, you'll lead a very strenuous life. I'm every bit as sorry about it as you. I feel just as sympathetic." Her eyes hardened. She looked at her sister just as she used to when they were little and fighting together. "You won't bring a drunken workman back to life by being sentimental," she said softly.

"Drunk! Who said he was drunk?" Laura turned furiously on Jose. She said, just as they had used to say on those occasions, "I'm going straight up to tell mother."

"Do, dear," cooed Jose.

"Mother, can I come into your room?" Laura turned the big glass doorknob.

"Of course, child. Why, what's the matter? What's given you such a colour?" And Mrs. Sheridan turned round from her dressing-table. She was trying on a new hat.

"Mother, a man's been killed," began Laura.

"Not in the garden?" interrupted her mother.

"No, no!"

"Oh, what a fright you gave me!" Mrs. Sheridan sighed with relief, and took off the big hat and held it on her knees.

"But listen, mother," said Laura. Breathless, half-choking, she told the dreadful story. "Of course, we can't have our party, can we?" she pleaded. "The band and every-body arriving. They'd hear us, mother; they're nearly neigh-bours!"

To Laura's astonishment her mother behaved just like Jose; it was harder to bear because she seemed amused. She refused to take Laura seriously.

"But, my dear child, use your common sense. It's only by accident we've heard of it. If some one had died there normally—and I can't understand how they keep alive in those poky little holes—we should still be having our party, shouldn't we?"

Laura had to say "yes" to that, but she felt it was all wrong. She sat down on her mother's sofa and pinched the cushion frill.

"Mother, isn't it really terribly heartless of us?" she asked.

"Darling!" Mrs. Sheridan got up and came over to her, carrying the hat. Before Laura could stop her she had popped it on. "My child!" said her mother, "the hat is yours. It's made for you. It's much too young for me. I have never seen you look such a picture. Look at yourself!" And she held up her hand-mirror.

"But, mother," Laura began again. She couldn't look at herself; she turned aside.

This time Mrs. Sheridan lost patience just as Jose had done.

"You are being very absurd, Laura," she said coldly. "People like that don't expect sacrifices from us. And it's not very sympathetic to spoil everybody's enjoyment as you're doing now."

"I don't understand," said Laura, and she walked quickly out of the room into her own bedroom. There, quite by chance, the first thing she saw was this charming girl in the mirror, in her black hat trimmed with gold daisies, and a long black velvet ribbon. Never had she imagined she could look like that. Is mother right? she thought. And now she hoped her mother was right. Am I being extravagant? Perhaps it was extravagant. Just for a moment she had another glimpse of that poor woman and those little children, and the body being carried into the house. But it all seemed blurred, unreal, like a picture in the newspaper. I'll remember it again after the party's over, she decided. And somehow that seemed quite the best plan . . .

Lunch was over by half-past one. By half-past two they were all ready for the fray. The green-coated band had arrived and was established in a corner of the tennis-court.

"My dear!" trilled Kitty Maitland, "aren't they too like frogs for words? You ought to have arranged them round the pond with the conductor in the middle on a leaf."

Laurie arrived and hailed them on his way to dress. At

the sight of him Laura remembered the accident again. She wanted to tell him. If Laurie agreed with the others, then it was bound to be all right. And she followed him into the hall.

"Laurie!"

"Hallo!" He was half-way upstairs, but when he turned round and saw Laura he suddenly puffed out his cheeks and goggled his eyes at her. "My word, Laura! You do look stunning," said Laurie. "What an absolutely topping hat!"

Laura said faintly "Is it?" and smiled up at Laurie, and didn't tell him after all.

Soon after that people began coming in streams. The band struck up; the hired waiters ran from the house to the marquee. Wherever you looked there were couples strolling, bending to the flowers, greeting, moving on over the lawn. They were like bright birds that had alighted in the Sheridans' garden for this one afternoon, on their way to where? Ah, what happiness it is to be with people who all are happy, to press hands, press cheeks, smile into eyes.

"Darling Laura, how well you look!"

"What a becoming hat, child!"

"Laura, you look quite Spanish. I've never seen you look so striking."

And Laura, glowing, answered softly, "Have you had tea? Won't you have an ice? The passion-fruit ices really are rather special." She ran to her father and begged him. "Daddy darling, can't the band have something to drink?"

And the perfect afternoon slowly ripened, slowly faded, slowly its petals closed.

"Never a more delightful garden party . . ." "The greatest success . . ." "Quite the most . . ."

Laura helped her mother with good-byes. They stood side by side in the porch till it was all over.

"All over, all over, thank heaven," said Mrs. Sheridan. "Round up the others, Laura. Let's go and have some fresh coffee. I'm exhausted. Yes, it's been very successful. But oh, these parties, these parties! Why will you children insist on giving parties!" And they all of them sat down in the deserted marquee.

"Have a sandwich, daddy dear. I wrote the flag."

"Thanks." Mr. Sheridan took a bite and the sandwich was gone. He took another. "I suppose you didn't hear of a beastly accident that happened to-day?" he said.

"My dear," said Mrs. Sheridan, holding up her hand, "we did. It nearly ruined the party. Laura insisted we should put it off."

"Oh, mother!" Laura didn't want to be teased about it.

"It was a horrible affair all the same," said Mr. Sheridan. "The chap was married too. Lived just below in the lane, and leaves a wife and half a dozen kiddies, so they say."

An awkward little silence fell. Mrs. Sheridan fidgeted with her cup. Really, it was very tactless of father . . .

Suddenly she looked up. There on the table were all those sandwiches, cakes, puffs, all uneaten, all going to be wasted. She had one of her brilliant ideas.

"I know," she said. "Let's make up a basket. Let's send that poor creature some of this perfectly good food. At any rate, it will be the greatest treat for the children. Don't you agree? And she's sure to have neighbours calling in and so on. What a point to have it all ready prepared. Laura!" She jumped up. "Get me the big basket out of the stairs cupboard."

"But, mother, do you really think it's a good idea?" said Laura.

Again, how curious, she seemed to be different from them all. To take scraps from their party. Would the poor woman really like that?

"Of course! What's the matter with you to-day? An hour or two ago you were insisting on us being sympathetic, and now—"

Oh, well! Laura ran for the basket. It was filled, it was heaped by her mother.

"Take it yourself, darling," said she. "Run down just as you are. No, wait, take the arum lilies too. People of that class are so impressed by arum lilies."

"The stems will ruin her lace frock," said practical Jose.

So they would. Just in time. "Only the basket, then. And, Laura!"—her mother followed her out of the marquee—"don't on any account—"

"What, mother?"

No, better not put such ideas into the child's head! "Nothing! Run along."

It was just growing dusky as Laura shut their garden gates. A big dog ran by like a shadow. The road gleamed white, and down below in the hollow the little cottages were in deep shade. How quiet it seemed after the afternoon. Here she was going down the hill to somewhere where a man lay dead, and she couldn't realize it. Why couldn't she? She stopped a minute. And it seemed to her that kisses, voices, tinkling spoons, laughter, the smell of crushed grass were somehow inside her. She had no room for anything else. How strange! She looked up at the pale sky, and all she thought was, "Yes, it was the most successful party."

Now the broad road was crossed. The lane began, smoky and dark. Women in shawls and men's tweed caps hurried by. Men hung over the palings; the children played in the doorways. A low hum came from the mean little cottages. In some of them there was a flicker of light, and a shadow, crab-like, moved across the window. Laura bent her head and hurried on. She wished now she had put on a coat. How her frock shone! And the big hat with the velvet streamer—if only it was another hat! Were the people looking at her? They must be. It was a mistake to have come; she knew all along it was a mistake. Should she go back even now?

No, too late. This was the house. It must be. A dark knot of people stood outside. Beside the gate an old, old woman with a crutch sat in a chair, watching. She had her feet on a newspaper. The voices stopped as Laura drew near. The group parted. It was as though she was expected, as though they had known she was coming here.

Laura was terribly nervous. Tossing the velvet ribbon over her shoulder, she said to a woman standing by, "Is this Mrs. Scott's house?" and the woman, smiling queerly, said, "It is, my lass."

Oh, to be away from this! She actually said, "Help me,

God," as she walked up the tiny path and knocked. To be away from these staring eyes, or to be covered up in anything, one of those women's shawls even. I'll just leave the basket and go, she decided. I shan't even wait for it to be emptied.

Then the door opened. A little woman in black showed in the gloom.

Laura said, "Are you Mrs. Scott?" But to her horror the woman answered, "Walk in please, miss," and she was shut in the passage.

"No," said Laura, "I don't want to come in. I only want to leave this basket. Mother sent—"

The little woman in the gloomy passage seemed not to have heard her. "Step this way, please, miss," she said in an oily voice, and Laura followed her.

She found herself in a wretched little low kitchen, lighted by a smoky lamp. There was a woman sitting before the fire.

"Em," said the little creature who had led her in. "Em! It's young lady." She turned to Laura. She said meaningly, "I'm 'er sister, miss. You'll excuse 'er, won't you?"

"Oh, but of course!" said Laura. "Please, please don't disturb her. I—I only want to leave—"

But at that moment the woman at the fire turned round. Her face, puffed up, red, with swollen eyes and swollen lips, looked terrible. She seemed as though she couldn't understand why Laura was there. What did it mean? Why was this stranger standing in the kitchen with a basket? What was it all about? And the poor face puckered up again.

"All right, my dear," said the other. "I'll thenk the young lady."

And again she began. "You'll excuse her, miss, I'm sure," and her face, swollen too, tried an oily smile.

Laura only wanted to get out, to get away. She was back in the passage. The door opened. She walked straight through into the bedroom, where the dead man was lying.

"You'd like a look at 'im, wouldn't you?" said Em's sister, and she brushed past Laura over to the bed. "Don't be afraid, my lass,—" and now her voice sounded fond and sly, and fondly she drew down the sheet—" 'e looks a picture. There's nothing to show. Come along, my dear."

Laura came.

There lay a young man, fast asleep—sleeping so soundly, so deeply, that he was far, far away from them both. Oh, so remote, so peaceful. He was dreaming. Never wake him up again. His head was sunk in the pillow, his eyes were closed; they were blind under the closed eyelids. He was given up to his dream. What did garden-parties and baskets and lace frocks matter to him? He was far from all those things. He was wonderful, beautiful. While they were laughing and while the band was playing, this marvel had come to the lane. Happy . . . happy. . . . All is well, said that sleeping face. This is just as it should be. I am content.

But all the same you had to cry, and she couldn't go out of the room without saying something to him. Laura gave a loud childish sob.

"Forgive my hat," she said.

And this time she didn't wait for Em's sister. She found her way out of the door, down the path, past all those dark people. At the corner of the lane she met Laurie.

He stepped out of the shadow. "Is that you, Laura?"

"Yes."

"Mother was getting anxious. Was it all right?"

"Yes, quite. Oh, Laurie!" She took his arm, she pressed up against him.

"I say, you're not crying, are you?" asked her brother.

Laura shook her head. She was.

Laurie put his arm round her shoulder. "Don't cry," he said in his warm, loving voice. "Was it awful?"

"No," sobbed Laura. "It was simply marvellous. But, Laurie—" She stopped, she looked at her brother. "Isn't life," she stammered, "isn't life—" But what life was she couldn't explain. No matter. He quite understood.

"*Isn't* it, darling?" said Laurie.

THE GARDEN PARTY

1. How does the first paragraph provide a setting for the contrast which occurs toward the end of the story?
2. How does Miss Mansfield in a single phrase or sentence point out the differences in the three girls in the first half page?
3. What detail quickly establishes Laura's approximate age?
4. What is the significance of the remark made by the "little fat chap" that a marquee should be conspicuous? Why does Miss

Mansfield introduce the workman who was pale and who had a haggard look as his dark eyes scanned the tennis court?

5. What is the dramatic purpose of the song Jose sings?
6. What was Laura's first impulse when she heard of the death of the carter?
7. After her conversation with her mother in which Laura proposed canceling the party, she said, "I don't understand." What couldn't she understand?
8. Explain the poignancy of "Excuse my hat."
9. What happens to Laura throughout the day of the party?

FRANK O'CONNOR
(MICHAEL O'DONOVAN)
1903–

The Idealist

THIS AUTHOR *was born in County Cork, Ireland, and attended a Christian Brothers school in Cork. By the time he was twelve he had written poems, biographies, and essays on Irish history. He worked for a while as a librarian because he thought it would give him time to write. His first American publication was a short story in* The Atlantic Monthly.

Frank O'Connor's stories are notable not only for their mellow humor, but also for the genuineness of his characters. In addition to story writing, he has written verse, literary criticism, and biography.

I don't know how it is about education, but it never seemed to do anything for me but get me into trouble.

Adventure stories weren't so bad, but as a kid I was very serious and preferred realism to romance. School stories were what I liked best, and, judged by our standards, these were romantic enough for anyone. The schools were English, so I suppose you couldn't expect anything else. They were always called "the venerable pile," and there was usually a ghost in them; they were built in a square that was called "the quad," and, according to the pictures, they were all clock-towers, spires, and pinnacles, like the lunatic asylum with us. The fellows in the stories were all good climbers, and got in and out of school at night on ropes made of knotted sheets. They dressed queerly; they wore long trousers, short, black jackets, and top hats. Whenever they did anything wrong they were given "lines" in Latin. When it was a bad case, they were flogged and never showed any sign of pain; only the bad fellows, and they always said: "Ow! Ow!"

Most of them were grand chaps who always stuck together and were great at football and cricket. They never told lies and wouldn't talk to anyone who did. If they were caught out and asked a point-blank question, they always told the truth, unless someone else was with them, and then even if they were to be expelled for it they wouldn't give his name, even if he was a thief, which, as a matter of fact, he frequently was. It was surprising in such good schools, with fathers who never gave less than five quid, the number of thieves there were. The fellows in our school hardly ever stole, though they only got a penny a week, and sometimes not even that, as when their fathers were on the booze and their mothers had to go to the pawn.

I worked hard at the football and cricket, though of course we never had a proper football and the cricket we played was with a hurley stick against a wicket chalked on some wall. The officers in the barrack played proper cricket, and on summer evenings I used to go and watch them, like one of the souls in Purgatory watching the joys of Paradise.

Even so, I couldn't help being disgusted at the bad way things were run in our school. Our "venerable pile" was a red brick building without tower or pinnacle a fellow could climb, and no ghost at all: we had no team, so a fellow, no matter how hard he worked, could never play for the school, and, instead of giving you "lines," Latin or any other sort, Murderer Moloney either lifted you by the ears or bashed you with a cane. When he got tired of bashing you on the hands he bashed you on the legs.

But these were only superficial things. What was really wrong was ourselves. The fellows sucked up to the masters and told them all that went on. If they were caught out in anything they tried to put the blame on someone else, even if it meant telling lies. When they were caned they snivelled and said it wasn't fair; drew back their hands as if they were terrified, so that the cane caught only the tips of their fingers, and then screamed and stood on one leg, shaking out their fingers in the hope of getting it counted as one. Finally they roared that their wrist was broken and crawled back to their desks with their hands squeezed under their armpits, howling. I mean you couldn't help feeling ashamed, imagining what chaps from a decent school would think if they saw it.

My own way to school led me past the barrack gate. In those peaceful days sentries never minded you going past the guard-room to have a look at the chaps drilling in the barrack square; if you came at dinnertime they even called you in and gave you plumduff and tea. Naturally, with such temptations I was often late. The only excuse, short of a letter from your mother, was to say you were at early Mass. The Murderer would never know whether you were or not, and if he did anything to you you could easily get him into trouble with the parish priest. Even as kids we knew who the real boss of the school was.

But after I started reading those confounded school stories I was never happy about saying I had been to Mass. It was a lie, and I knew that the chaps in the stories would have died sooner than tell it. They were all round me like invisible presences, and I hated to do anything which I felt they might disapprove of.

One morning I came in very late and rather frightened.

"What kept you till this hour, Delaney?" Murderer Moloney asked, looking at the clock.

I wanted to say I had been at Mass, but I couldn't. The invisible presences were all about me.

"I was delayed at the barrack, sir," I replied in panic.

There was a faint titter from the class, and Moloney raised his brows in mild surprise. He was a big powerful man with fair hair and blue eyes and a manner that at times was deceptively mild.

"Oh, indeed," he said, politely enough. "And what delayed you?"

"I was watching the soldiers drilling, sir," I said.

The class tittered again. This was a new line entirely for them.

"Oh," Moloney said casually, "I never knew you were such a military man. Hold out your hand!"

Compared with the laughter the slaps were nothing, and besides, I had the example of the invisible presences to sustain me. I did not flinch. I returned to my desk slowly and quietly without snivelling or squeezing my hands, and the Murderer looked after me, raising his brows again as though to indicate that this was a new line for him, too. But the others gaped and whispered as if I were some strange animal. At playtime they gathered about me, full of curiosity and excitement.

"Delaney, why did you say that about the barrack?"

"Because 'twas true," I replied firmly. "I wasn't going to tell him a lie."

"What lie?"

"That I was at Mass."

"Then couldn't you say you had to go on a message?"

"That would be a lie too."

"Cripes, Delaney," they said, "you'd better mind yourself. The Murderer is in an awful wax. He'll massacre you."

I knew that. I knew only too well that the Murderer's professional pride had been deeply wounded, and for the rest of the day I was on my best behaviour. But my best wasn't enough, for I underrated the Murderer's guile. Though he pretended to be reading, he was watching me the whole time.

"Delaney," he said at last without raising his head from the book, "was that you talking?"

" 'Twas, sir," I replied in consternation.

The whole class laughed. They couldn't believe but that I was deliberately trailing my coat, and, of course, the laugh must have convinced him that I was. I suppose if people do tell you lies all day and every day, it soon becomes a sort of perquisite which you resent being deprived of.

"Oh," he said, throwing down his book, "we'll soon stop that."

This time it was a tougher job, because he was really on his mettle. But so was I. I knew this was the testing-point for me, and if only I could keep my head I should provide a model for the whole class. When I had got through the ordeal without moving a muscle, and returned to my desk with my hands by my sides, the invisible presences gave me a great clap. But the visible ones were nearly as annoyed as the Murderer himself. After school half a dozen of them followed me down the school yard.

"Go on!" they shouted truculently. "Shaping as usual!"

"I was not shaping."

"You were shaping. You're always showing off. Trying to pretend he didn't hurt you—a blooming crybaby like you!"

"I wasn't trying to pretend," I shouted, even then resisting the temptation to nurse my bruised hands. "Only decent fellows don't cry over every little pain like kids."

"Go on!" they bawled after me. "You ould idiot!" And, as I went down the school lane, still trying to keep what the stories called "a stiff upper lip," and consoling myself with the thought that my torment was over until next morning, I heard their mocking voices after me.

"Loony Larry! Yah, Loony Larry!"

I realized that if I was to keep on terms with the invisible presences I should have to watch my step at school.

So I did, all through that year. But one day an awful thing happened. I was coming in from the yard, and in the porch outside our schoolroom I saw a fellow called Gorman taking something from a coat on the rack. I always described Gorman to myself as "the black sheep of the school." He was a fellow I disliked and feared; a handsome, sulky, spoiled, and sneering lout. I paid no attention to him because I had escaped for a few moments into my dream-world in which fathers never gave less than fivers and the honour of the school was always saved by some quiet, unassuming fellow like myself—"a dark horse," as the stories called him.

"Who are you looking at?" Gorman asked threateningly.

"I wasn't looking at anyone," I replied with an indignant start.

"I was only getting a pencil out of my coat," he added, clenching his fists.

"Nobody said you weren't," I replied, thinking that this was a very queer subject to start a row about.

"You'd better not, either," he snarled. "You can mind your own business."

"You mind yours!" I retorted, purely for the purpose of saving face. "I never spoke to you at all."

And that, so far as I was concerned, was the end of it.

But after playtime the Murderer, looking exceptionally serious, stood before the class, balancing a pencil in both hands.

"Everyone who left the classroom this morning, stand out!" he called. Then he lowered his head and looked at us from under his brows. "Mind now, I said everyone!"

I stood out with the others, including Gorman. We were all very puzzled.

"Did you take anything from a coat on the rack this morning?" the Murderer asked, laying a heavy, hairy paw on Gorman's shoulder and staring menacingly into his eyes.

"Me, sir?" Gorman exclaimed innocently. "No, sir."

"Did you see anyone else doing it?"

"No, sir."

"You?" he asked another lad, but even before he reached me at all I realized why Gorman had told the lie and wondered frantically what I should do.

"You?" he asked me, and his big red face was close to mine, his blue eyes were only a few inches away, and the smell of his toilet soap was in my nostrils. My panic made me say the wrong thing as though I had planned it.

"I didn't take anything, sir," I said in a low voice.

"Did you see someone else do it?" he asked, raising his

brows and showing quite plainly that he had noticed my evasion. "Have you a tongue in your head?" he shouted suddenly, and the whole class, electrified, stared at me. "You?" he added curtly to the next boy as though he had lost interest in me.

"No, sir."

"Back to your desks, the rest of you!" he ordered. "Delancy, you stay here."

He waited till everyone was seated again before going on.

"Turn out your pockets."

I did, and a half-stifled giggle rose, which the Murderer quelled with a thunderous glance. Even for a small boy I had pockets that were museums in themselves: the purpose of half the things I brought to light I couldn't have explained myself. They were antiques, prehistoric and unlabelled. Among them was a school story borrowed the previous evening from a queer fellow who chewed paper as if it were gum. The Murderer reached out for it, and holding it at arm's length, shook it out with an expression of deepening disgust as he noticed the nibbled corners and margins.

"Oh," he said disdainfully, "so this is how you waste your time! What do you do with this rubbish—eat it?"

" 'Tisn't mine, sir," I said against the laugh that sprang up. "I borrowed it."

"Is that what you did with the money?" he asked quickly, his fat head on one side.

"Money?" I repeated in confusion. "What money?"

"The shilling that was stolen from Flanagan's overcoat this morning."

(Flanagan was a little hunchback whose people coddled him; no one else in the school would have possessed that much money.)

"I never took Flanagan's shilling." I said, beginning to cry, "and you have no right to say I did."

"I have the right to say you're the most impudent and defiant puppy in the school," he replied, his voice hoarse with rage, "and I wouldn't put it past you. What else can anyone expect and you reading this dirty, rotten, filthy rubbish?" And he tore my school story in halves and flung them to the furthest corner of the classroom. "Dirty, filthy, English rubbish! Now, hold out your hand."

This time the invisible presences deserted me. Hearing themselves described in these contemptuous terms, they fled. The Murderer went mad in the way people do whenever they're up against something they don't understand. Even the other fellows were shocked, and, heaven knows, they had little sympathy with me.

"You should put the police on him," they advised me later in the playground. "He lifted the cane over his shoulder. He could get the gaol for that."

"But why didn't you say you didn't see anyone?" asked the eldest, a fellow called Spillane.

"Because I did," I said, beginning to sob all over again at the memory of my wrongs. "I saw Gorman."

"Gorman?" Spillane echoed incredulously. "Was it Gorman took Flanagan's money? And why didn't you say so?"

"Because it wouldn't be right," I sobbed.

"Why wouldn't it be right?"

"Because Gorman should have told the truth himself," I said. "And if this was a proper school he'd be sent to Coventry."

"He'd be sent where?"

"Coventry. No one would ever speak to him again."

"But why would Gorman tell the truth if he took the money?" Spillane asked as you'd speak to a baby. "Jay, Delaney," he added pityingly, "you're getting madder and madder. Now, look at what you're after bringing on yourself!"

Suddenly Gorman came lumbering up, red and angry.

"Delaney," he shouted threateningly, "did you say I took Flanagan's money?"

Gorman, though I of course didn't realize it, was as much at sea as Moloney and the rest. Seeing me take all that punishment rather than give him away, he concluded that I must be more afraid of him than of Moloney, and that the proper thing to do was to make me more so. He couldn't have come at a time when I cared less for him. I didn't even bother to reply but lashed out with all my strength at his brutal face. This was the last thing he expected. He screamed, and his hand came away from his face, all blood. Then he threw off his satchel and came at me, but at the same moment a door opened behind us and a lame teacher called Murphy emerged. We all ran like mad and the fight was forgotten.

It didn't remain forgotten, though. Next morning after prayers the Murderer scowled at me.

"Delaney, were you fighting in the yard after school yesterday?"

For a second or two I didn't reply. I couldn't help feeling that it wasn't worth it. But before the invisible presences fled forever, I made another effort.

"I was, sir," I said, and this time there wasn't even a titter. I was out of my mind. The whole class knew it and was awe-stricken.

"Who were you fighting?"

"I'd sooner not say, sir," I replied, hysteria beginning to well up in me. It was all very well for the invisible presences, but they hadn't to deal with the Murderer.

"Who was he fighting with?" he asked lightly, resting his hands on the desk and studying the ceiling.

"Gorman, sir," replied three or four voices—as easy as that!

"Did Gorman hit him first?"

"No, sir. He hit Gorman first."

"Stand out," he said, taking up the cane. "Now," he added, going up to Gorman, "you take this and hit him. And make sure you hit him hard," he went on, giving Gorman's arm an encouraging squeeze. "He thinks he's a great fellow. You show him now what we think of him."

Gorman came towards me with a broad grin. He thought it a great joke. The class thought it a great joke. They began to roar with laughter. Even the Murderer permitted himself a modest grin at his own cleverness.

"Hold out your hand," he said to me.

I didn't. I began to feel trapped and a little crazy.

"Hold out your hand, I say," he shouted, beginning to lose his temper.

"I will not," I shouted back, losing all control of myself.

"You what?" he cried incredulously, dashing at me round the classroom with his hand raised as though to strike me. "What's that you said, you dirty little thief?"

"I'm not a thief, I'm not a thief," I screamed. "And if he comes near me I'll kick the shins off him. You have no right to give him that cane, and you have no right to call me a thief either. If you do it again, I'll go down to the police and then we'll see who the thief is."

"You refused to answer my questions," he roared, and if I had been in my right mind I should have known he had suddenly taken fright; probably the word "police" had frightened him.

"No," I said through my sobs, "and I won't answer them now either. I'm not a spy."

"Oh," he retorted with a sarcastic sniff, "so that's what you call a spy, Mr. Delaney?"

"Yes, and that's what they all are, all the fellows here—dirty spies!—but I'm not going to be a spy for you. You can do your own spying."

"That's enough now, that's enough!" he said, raising his fat hand almost beseechingly. "There's no need to lose control of yourself, my dear young fellow, and there's no need whatever to screech like that. 'Tis most unmanly. Go back to your seat now and I'll talk to you another time."

I obeyed, but I did no work. No one else did much either. The hysteria had spread to the class. I alternated between fits of exultation at my own successful defiance of the Murderer, and panic at the prospect of his revenge; and at each change of mood I put my face in my hands and sobbed again. The Murderer didn't even order me to stop. He didn't so much as look as me.

After that I was the hero of the school for the whole afternoon.

Gorman tried to resume the fight, but Spillane ordered him away contemptuously—a fellow who had taken the master's cane to another had no status. But that wasn't the sort of hero I wanted to be. I preferred something less sensational.

Next morning I was in such a state of panic that I didn't know how I should face school at all. I dawdled, between two minds as to whether or not I should mitch. The silence of the school lane and yard awed me. I had made myself late as well.

"What kept you, Delaney?" the Murderer asked quietly.

I knew it was no good.

"I was at Mass, sir."

"All right. Take your seat."

He seemed a bit surprised. What I had not realized was the incidental advantage of our system over the English one. By this time half a dozen of his pets had brought the

Murderer the true story of Flanagan's shilling, and if he didn't feel a monster he probably felt a fool.

But by that time I didn't care. In my school sack I had another story. Not a school story this time, though. School stories were a washout: "Bang! Bang!"—that was the only way to deal with men like the Murderer. "The only good teacher is a dead teacher."

THE IDEALIST

1. To what effect is the first paragraph used?
2. Why were school stories romantic "by our standards"?
3. How did the stories of English schools affect the boy?
4. Why, "compared with the laughter," were the slaps nothing?
5. Why did the "visible presences" turn against Delaney?
6. Should we consider the "invisible presences" characters in this story?
7. Why did Delaney lie to the Murderer the day after the fight? What change has taken place?

ALAN PATON

1903-

Ha'penny

ALAN PATON is a citizen of South Africa and has always been concerned with the problems of his "beloved country." For ten years he taught in a native Zulu school. He became interested in penal reform and became principal of Diepkloof Reformatory. He is known as the instigator of many humane practices in dealing with the several hundred young African inmates. Much of his sympathetic nature is evident in "Ha'penny," which appeared in his short story collection, Tales From a Troubled Land.

Mr. Paton's best-known novel, Cry, the Beloved Country, *has been translated into many foreign languages and was also made into a successful stage play and motion picture.*

Of the six hundred boys at the reformatory, about one hundred were from ten to fourteen years of age. My Department had from time to time expressed the intention of taking them away, and of establishing a special institution for them, more like an industrial school than a reformatory. This would have been a good thing, for their offences were very trivial, and they would have been better by themselves. Had such a school been established, I should have liked to have been Principal of it myself, for it would have been an easier job; small boys turn instinctively towards affection, and one controls them by it, naturally and easily.

Some of them, if I came near them, either on parade or in school or at football, would observe me watchfully, not directly or fully, but obliquely and secretly; sometimes I would surprise them at it, and make some small sign of recognition, which would satisfy them so that they would cease to observe me, and would give their full attention to the event of the moment. But I knew that my authority was thus confirmed and strengthened.

These secret relations with them were a source of continuous pleasure to me. Had they been my own children I would no doubt have given a greater expression to it. But often I would move through the silent and orderly parade, and stand by one of them. He would look straight in front of him with a little frown of concentration that expressed both childish awareness of and manly indifference to my nearness. Sometimes I would tweak his ear, and he would give me a brief smile of acknowledgment, or frown with still greater concentration. It was natural I suppose to confine these outward expressions to the very smallest, but they were taken as symbolic, and some older boys would observe them and take themselves to be included. It was a relief, when the reformatory was passing through times of turbulence and trouble, and when there was danger of estrangement between authority and boys, to make these simple and natural gestures, which were reassurances both to me and them that nothing important had changed.

On Sunday afternoons when I was on duty, I would take my car to the reformatory and watch the free boys being signed out at the gate. This simple operation was also watched by many boys not free, who would tell each other "in so many weeks I'll be signed out myself." Amongst the watchers were always some of the small boys, and these I would take by turns in the car. We would go out to the Potchefstroom Road with its ceaseless stream of traffic, and to the Baragwanath crossroads, and come back by the Van Wyksrus road to the reformatory. I would talk to them about their families, their parents, their sisters and brothers, and I would pretend to know nothing of Durban, Port Elizabeth, Potchefstroom, and Clocolan, and ask them if these places were bigger than Johannesburg.

One of the small boys was Ha'penny, and he was about twelve years old. He came from Bloemfontein and was the biggest talker of them all. His mother worked in a white person's house, and he had two brothers and two sisters. His brothers were Richard and Dickie and his sisters Anna and Mina.

"Richard and Dickie?" I asked.

"Yes, *meneer.*"

"In English," I said, "Richard and Dickie are the same name."

When we returned to the reformatory, I sent for Ha'penny's papers; there it was plainly set down, Ha'penny was a waif, with no relatives at all. He had been taken in from one home to another, but he was naughty and uncontrollable, and eventually had taken to pilfering at the market.

I then sent for the Letter Book, and found that Ha'penny wrote regularly, or rather that others wrote for him till he could write himself, to Mrs. Betty Maarman, of 48 Vlak Street, Bloemfontein. But Mrs. Maarman had never once replied to him. When questioned, he had said, perhaps she is sick. I sat down and wrote at once to the Social Welfare Officer at Bloemfontein, asking him to investigate.

The next time I had Ha'penny out in the car, I questioned him again about his family. And he told me the same as before, his mother, Richard and Dickie, Anna and Mina. But he softened the "D" of "Dickie," so that it sounded now like Tickie.

"I thought you said Dickie," I said.

"I said Tickie," he said.

He watched me with concealed apprehension, and I came to the conclusion that this waif of Bloemfontein was a clever boy, who had told me a story that was all imagination, and had changed one single letter of it to make it safe from any question. And I thought I understood it all too, that he was ashamed of being without a family, and had invented them all, so that no one might discover that he was fatherless and motherless, and that no one in the world cared whether he was alive or dead. This gave me a strong feeling for him, and I went out of my way to manifest towards him that fatherly care that the State, though not in those words, had enjoined upon me by giving me this job.

Then the letter came from the Social Welfare Officer

in Bloemfontein, saying that Mrs. Betty Maarman of 48 Vlak Street was a real person, and that she had four children, Richard and Dickie, Anna and Mina, but that Ha'penny was no child of hers, and she knew him only as a derelict of the streets. She had never answered his letters, because he wrote to her as *mother,* and she was no mother of his, nor did she wish to play any such role. She was a decent woman, a faithful member of the church, and she had no thought of corrupting her family by letting them have anything to do with such a child.

But Ha'penny seemed to me anything but the usual delinquent, his desire to have a family was so strong, and his reformatory record was so blameless, and his anxiety to please and obey so great, that I began to feel a great duty towards him. Therefore I asked him about his "mother."

He could not speak enough of her, nor with too high praise. She was loving, honest, and strict. Her home was clean. She had affection for all her children. It was clear that the homeless child, even as he had attached himself to me, would have attached himself to her; he had observed her even as he had observed me, but did not know the secret of how to open her heart, so that she would take him in, and save him from the lonely life that he led.

"Why did you steal when you had such a mother?" I asked.

He could not answer that; not all his brains nor his courage could find an answer to such a question, for he knew that with such a mother he would not have stolen at all.

"The boy's name is Dickie," I said, "not Tickie."

And then he knew the deception was revealed. Another boy might have said, "I told you it was Dickie," but he was too intelligent for that; he knew that if I had established that the boy's name was *Dickie,* I must have established other things too. I was shocked by the immediate and visible effect of my action. His whole brave assurance died within him, and he stood there exposed, not as a liar, but as a homeless child who had surrounded himself with mother, brothers, and sisters, who did not exist. I had shattered the very foundations of his pride, and his sense of human significance.

He fell sick at once, and the doctor said it was tuberculosis. I wrote at once to Mrs. Maarman, telling her the whole story, of how this small boy had observed her, and had decided that she was the person he desired for his mother. But she wrote back saying that she could take no responsibility for him. For one thing, Ha'penny was a Mosuto, and she was a coloured woman; for another, she had never had a child in trouble, and how could she take such a boy?

Tuberculosis is a strange thing; sometimes it manifests itself suddenly in the most unlikely host, and swiftly sweeps to the end. Ha'penny withdrew himself from the world, from all Principals and mothers, and the doctor said there was little hope. In desperation I sent money for Mrs. Maarman to come.

She was a decent homely woman, and seeing that the situation was serious, she, without fuss or embarrassment, adopted Ha'penny for her own. The whole reformatory accepted her as his mother. She sat the whole day with him, and talked to him of Richard and Dickie, Anna and Mina, and how they were all waiting for him to come home. She poured out her affection on him, and had no fear of his sickness, nor did she allow it to prevent her from satisfying his hunger to be owned. She talked to him of what they would do when he came back, and how he would go to the school, and what they would buy for Guy Fawkes night.

He in his turn gave his whole attention to her, and when I visited him he was grateful, but I had passed out of his world. I felt judged in that I had sensed only the existence and not the measure of his desire. I wished I had done something sooner, more wise, more prodigal.

We buried him on the reformatory farm, and Mrs. Maarman said to me, "when you put up the cross, put he was my son."

"I'm ashamed," she said, "that I wouldn't take him."

"The sickness," I said, "the sickness would have come."

"No," she said, shaking her head with certainty. "It wouldn't have come. And if it had come at home, it would have been different."

So she left for Bloemfontein, after her strange visit to a reformatory. And I was left too, with the resolve to be more prodigal in the task that the State, though not in so many words, had enjoined on me.

HA'PENNY

1. Would you describe this story as melodramatic? (See Glossary) What are the qualities of the story which substantiate your opinion?
2. What universal desire did Ha'penny have?
3. What elements in this character of Ha'penny help to lift this story out of the classification of sentimentality?
4. Was the principal wrong in telling the child that the brother's name was Dickie, not Tickie? Does this have any bearing on your answer to question one?
5. How does the author make plausible the change in behavior of Mrs. Maarman? Is this essential in helping to forestall a charge of sentimentality?
6. What is the meaning of the last sentence?
7. Why is this story told in the first person? Can you imagine the same story told throughout in the third person? What would be lost or gained by such a method?

EDGAR ALLAN POE

1809–1849

The Tell-Tale Heart

KNOWN EQUALLY WELL *as poet and short story writer, Poe has exerted a great influence on the writing of the short story. His theory of "oneness" or "single effect" is quoted in almost every discussion of the form of the short story.*

Frequently referred to as the originator of the detective story, Poe proved himself a master of the story of cipher analysis in "The Gold Bug." His tales of horror and imagination, such as "The Tell-Tale Heart," have fascinated readers for generations. Motion pictures and television programs made from these stories have chilled and thrilled millions of the present generation.

True! nervous, very, very dreadfully nervous I had been and am; but why *will* you say that I am mad? The disease had sharpened my senses, not destroyed, not dulled them. Above all was the sense of hearing acute. I heard all things in the heaven and in the earth. I heard many things in hell. How then am I mad? Hearken! and observe how healthily, how calmly, I can tell you the whole story.

It is impossible to say how first the idea entered my brain, but, once conceived, it haunted me day and night. Object there was none. Passion there was none. I loved the old man. He had never wronged me. He had never given me insult. For his gold I had no desire. I think it was his eye! Yes, it was this! One of his eyes resembled that of a vulture—a pale blue eye with a film over it. Whenever it fell upon me my blood ran cold, and so by degrees, very gradually, I made up my mind to take the life of the old man, and thus rid myself of the eye for ever.

Now this is the point. You fancy me mad. Madmen know nothing. But you should have seen *me*. You should have seen how wisely I proceeded—with what caution—with what foresight, with what dissimulation, I went to work! I was never kinder to the old man than during the whole week before I killed him. And every night about midnight I turned the latch of his door and opened it—oh, so gently! And then when I had made an opening sufficient for my head I put in a dark lantern all closed, closed so that no light shone out, and then I thrust in my head. Oh, you would have laughed to see how cunningly I thrust it in! I moved it slowly, very, very slowly, so that I might not disturb the old man's sleep. It took me an hour to place my whole head within the opening so far that I could see him as he lay upon his bed. Ha! would a madman have been so wise as this? And then when my head was well in the room I undid the lantern cautiously—oh, so cautiously—cautiously (for the hinges creaked), I undid it just so much that a single thin ray fell upon the vulture eye. And this I did for seven long nights, every night just at midnight, but I found the eye always closed, and so it was impossible to do the work, for it was not the old man who vexed me but his Evil Eye. And every morning, when the day broke, I went boldly into the chamber and spoke courageously to him, calling him by name in a hearty tone, and inquiring how he had passed the night. So you see he would have been a very profound old man, indeed, to suspect that every night, just at twelve, I looked in upon him while he slept.

Upon the eighth night I was more than usually cautious in opening the door. A watch's minute hand moves more quickly than did mine. Never before that night had I *felt* the extent of my own powers, of my sagacity. I could scarcely contain my feelings of triumph. To think that there I was opening the door little by little, and he not even to dream of my secret deeds or thoughts. I fairly chuckled at the idea, and perhaps he heard me, for he moved on the bed suddenly as if startled. Now you may think that I drew back—but no. His room was as black as pitch with the thick darkness (for the shutters were close fastened through fear of robbers), and so I knew that he could not see the opening of the door, and I kept pushing it on steadily, steadily.

I had my head in, and was about to open the lantern, when my thumb slipped upon the tin fastening, and the old man sprang up in the bed, crying out, "Who's there?"

I kept quite still and said nothing. For a whole hour I did not move a muscle, and in the meantime I did not hear him lie down. He was still sitting up in the bed, listening; just as I have done night after night hearkening to the death watches in the wall.

Presently I heard a slight groan, and I knew it was the groan of mortal terror. It was not a groan of pain or of grief—oh, no! it was the low stifled sound that arises from the bottom of the soul when overcharged with awe. I knew the sound well. Many a night, just at midnight, when all the world slept, it has welled up from my own bosom, deepening, with its dreadful echo, the terrors that distracted me. I say I knew it well. I knew what the old man felt, and pitied him although I chuckled at heart. I knew that he had been lying awake ever since the first slight noise when he had turned in the bed. His fears had been ever since growing upon him. He had been trying to fancy them causeless, but could not. He had been saying to himself, "It is nothing but the wind in the chimney, it is only a mouse crossing the floor," or "It is merely a cricket which has made a single chirp." Yes, he has been trying to comfort himself with these suppositions; but he had found all in vain. *All in vain*, because Death in approaching him had stalked with his black shadow before him and enveloped the victim. And is was the mournful influence of the unperceived shadow that caused him to feel, although he neither saw nor heard, to *feel* the presence of my head within the room.

When I had waited a long time very patiently without hearing him lie down, I resolved to open a little—a very, very little, crevice in the lantern. So I opened it—you cannot imagine how stealthily, stealthily—until at length a single dim ray like the thread of the spider shot out from the crevice and fell upon the vulture eye.

It was open, wide, wide open, and I grew furious as I gazed upon it. I saw it with perfect distinctness—all a dull blue with a hideous veil over it that chilled the very marrow in my bones, but I could see nothing else of the old man's face or person, for I had directed the ray as if by instinct precisely upon the damned spot.

And now have I not told you that what you mistake for madness is but over-acuteness of the senses? now, I say, there came to my ears a low, dull, quick sound, such as a watch makes when enveloped in cotton. I knew *that* sound well, too. It was the beating of the old man's heart. It increased my fury, as the beating of a drum stimulates the soldier into courage.

But even yet I refrained and kept still. I scarcely breathed. I held the lantern motionless. I tried how steadily I could maintain the ray upon the eye. Meantime the hellish tattoo of the heart increased. It grew quicker and quicker, and louder and louder, every instant. The old man's terror *must* have been extreme! It grew louder, I say, louder every moment!—do you mark me well? I have told you that I am nervous: so I am. And now at the dead hour of the night, amid the dreadful silence of that old house, so strange a noise as this excited me to uncontrollable terror. Yet, for some minutes longer I refrained and stood still. But the beating grew louder, louder! I thought the heart must burst. And now a new anxiety seized me—the sound would be heard by a neighbour! The old man's hour had come! With a loud yell, I threw open the lantern and leaped into the room. He shrieked once—once only. In an instant I dragged him to the floor, and pulled the heavy bed over him. I then smiled gaily, to find the deed so far done. But for many minutes the heart beat on with a muffled sound. This, however, did not vex me; it would not be heard through the wall. At length it ceased. The old man was dead. I removed the bed and examined the corpse. Yes, he was stone, stone dead. I placed my hand upon the heart and held it there many minutes. There was no pulsation. He was stone dead. His eye would trouble me no more.

If still you think me mad, you will think so no longer when I describe the wise precautions I took for the concealment of the body. The night waned, and I worked hastily, but in silence.

I took up three planks from the flooring of the chamber, and deposited all between the scantlings. I then replaced the boards so cleverly, so cunningly, that no human eye—not even *his*—could have detected anything wrong. There was nothing to wash out—no stain of any kind—no blood-spot whatever. I had been too wary for that.

When I had made an end of these labours, it was four o'clock—still dark as midnight. As the bell sounded the hour, there came a knocking at the street door. I went down to open it with a light heart,—for what had I *now* to fear? There entered three men, who introduced themselves, with perfect suavity, as officers of the police. A shriek had been heard by a neighbour during the night;

suspicion of foul play had been aroused; information had been lodged at the police office, and they (the officers) had been deputed to search the premises.

I smiled,—for *what* had I to fear? I bade the gentlemen welcome. The shriek, I said, was my own in a dream. The old man, I mentioned, was absent in the country. I took my visitors all over the house; bade them search—search *well.* I led them, at length, to *his* chamber. I showed them his treasures, secure, undisturbed. In the enthusiasm of my confidence, I brought chairs into the room, and desired them *here* to rest from their fatigues, while I myself, in the wild audacity of my perfect triumph, placed my own seat upon the very spot beneath which reposed the corpse of the victim.

The officers were satisfied. My *manner* had convinced them. I was singularly at ease. They sat, and while I answered cheerily, they chatted of familiar things. But ere long, I felt myself getting pale and wished them gone. My head ached, and I fancied a ringing in my ears; but still they sat, and still chatted. The ringing became more distinct;—it continued and became more distinct: I talked more freely to get rid of the feeling: but it continued and gained definitiveness—until, at length, I found that the noise was *not* within my ears.

No doubt I now grew *very* pale;—but I talked more fluently, and with a heightened voice. Yet the sound increased—and what could I do? It was *a low, dull, quick sound—much such a sound as a watch makes when enveloped in cotton.* I gasped for breath—and yet the officers heard it not. I talked more quickly—more vehemently; but the noise steadily increased. I arose and argued about trifles, in a high key and with violent gesticulations; but the noise steadily increased. Why *would* they not be gone? I paced the floor to and fro with heavy strides, as if excited to fury by the observations of the men—but the noise steadily increased. O God! what *could* I do? I foamed—I raved—I swore! I swung the chair upon which I had been sitting, and grated it upon the boards, but the noise arose over all and continually increased. It grew louder—louder—*louder!* And still the men chatted pleasantly, and smiled. Was it possible they heard not? Almighty God!—no, no! They heard!—they suspected!—they *knew!*—they were making a mockery of my horror!—this I thought, and this I think. But anything was better than this agony! Anything was more tolerable than this derision! I could bear those hypocritical smiles no longer! I felt that I must scream or die!—and now—again!—hark! louder! louder! louder! *louder!*—

"Villains!" I shrieked, "dissemble no more! I admit the deed!—tear up the planks!—here, here!—it is the beating of his hideous heart!"

THE TELL-TALE HEART

1. What is the conflict in this story? What are the two contending forces which come face to face?
2. Notice the last sentence in the first paragraph, "Hearken!

and observe how healthily, how calmly, I can tell you the whole story." Does this sentence have any ironic effect?

3. Notice the transition between paragraphs one and two. What one word in the first sentence of the second paragraph relates to the mental state suggested in the first?

4. What induces the character (who remains unnamed throughout the story) to kill the old man? Would a man of normal mentality react in the same fashion?

5. In paragraph four the man speaks of the Evil Eye. Is this used in its customary way? Why is it capitalized?

6. Note the nightly closing of the shutters. Why were they closed? What is ironical about this practice of the old man?

7. What were "the death watches in the wall" referred to in paragraph seven? What is the dramatic purpose in mentioning them at this time? What is the name given to this device of the storyteller?

8. Note the absence of light in the murder chamber throughout the first half of the story. What is the symbolic meaning of light in literature? What do we associate with darkness, with night?

9. In describing the effectiveness of his senses, which of the five did the man say had become particularly sensitive? Note very carefully the description of the old man's heartbeat. How is this related to the next-to-last paragraph of the story?

10. Is the death of the old man the climax, the turning point, of

this story? Note that the man says, "His eye would trouble me no more." Could Poe have said, "*He* would trouble me no more"?

11. What was the reason for the visit of the police? Did the neighbors really hear anything?
12. Why does the murderer place his chair "upon the very spot beneath which reposed the corpse of the victim"? What symbolic significance is there in the act?
13. The story ends with ". . . here, here!—it is the beating of his hideous heart!" What was the beating the murderer heard? Was there actually any noticeable sound?

J. F. POWERS

1917–

Jamesie

A NATIVE *of Illinois, J. F. Powers has made the Midwest his home except for a brief residence in Ireland. He worked for a time as a department store clerk, insurance salesman, and chauffeur. He has taught writing at St. John's University and at Marquette University.*

This author is the winner of a National Book Award for Morte d'Urban, *a novel, but is even better known for his short stories which have appeared in a great many anthologies.*

There it was, all about Lefty, in Ding Bell's Dope Box.

"We don't want to add coals to the fire, but it's common knowledge that the Local Pitcher Most Likely To Succeed is fed up with the home town. Well, well, the boy's good, which nobody can deny, and the scouts are on his trail, but it doesn't say a lot for his team spirit, not to mention his civic spirit, this high-hat attitude of his. And that fine record of his—has it been all a case of him and him alone? How about the team? The boys have backed him up, they've given him the runs, and that's what wins ball games. They don't pay off on strike-outs. There's one kind of player every scribe knows—and wishes he didn't—the lad who gets four for four with the willow, and yet, somehow, his team goes down to defeat—but does that worry this gent? Not a bit of it. He's too busy celebrating his own personal success, figuring his batting average, or, if he's a pitcher, his earned run average and strike-outs. The percentage player. We hope we aren't talking about Lefty. If we are, it's too bad, it is, and no matter where he goes from here, especially if it's up to the majors, it won't remain a secret very long, nor will he . . . See you at the game Sunday. Ding Bell."

"Here's a new one, Jamesie," his father said across the porch, holding up the rotogravure section.

With his father on Sunday it could be one of three things—a visit to the office, fixing up his mother's grave in Calvary, or just sitting on the porch with all the Chicago papers, as today.

Jamesie put down the *Courier* and went over to his father without curiosity. It was always Lindy or the *Spirit of St. Louis*, and now without understanding how this could so suddenly be, he was tired of them. His father, who seemed to feel that a growing boy could take an endless interest in these things, appeared to know the truth at last. He gave a page to the floor—that way he knew what he'd read and how far he had to go—and pulled the newspaper around his ears again. Before he went to dinner he would put the paper in order and wish out loud that other people would have the decency to do the same.

Jamesie, back in his chair, granted himself one more chapter of *Baseball Bill in the World Series*. The chapters were running out again, as they had so many times before, and he knew, with the despair of a narcotic, that his need had no end.

Baseball Bill, at fifty cents a volume and unavailable at the library, kept him nearly broke, and Francis Murgatroyd, his best friend . . . too stingy to go halves, confident he'd get to read them all as Jamesie bought them, and each time offering to exchange the old Tom Swifts and Don Sturdys he had got for Christmas—as though that were the same thing!

Jamesie owned all the Baseball Bills to be had for love or money in the world, and there was nothing in the back of this one about new titles being in preparation. Had the author died, as some of them did, and left his readers in the lurch? Or had the series been discontinued—for where, after *Fighting for the Pennant* and *In the World Series*, could Baseball Bill go? *Baseball Bill, Manager*, perhaps. But then what?

"A plot to *fix* the World Series! So that was it! Bill began to see it all. . . . The mysterious call in the night! The diamond necklace in the dressing room! The scribbled note under the door! With slow fury Bill realized that the peculiar odor on the note paper was the odor in his room now! It was the odor of strong drink and cigar smoke! And it came from his midnight visitor! The same! Did he represent the powerful gambling syndicate? Was *he* Blackie Humphrey himself? Bill held his towering rage in check and smiled at his visitor in his friendly, boyish fashion. His visitor must get no inkling of his true thoughts. Bill must play the game—play the very fool they took him for! Soon enough they would discover for themselves, but to their everlasting sorrow, the courage and daring of Baseball Bill . . ."

Jamesie put the book aside, consulted the batting averages in the *Courier,* and reread Ding Bell. Then, not waiting for dinner and certain to hear about it at supper, he ate a peanut butter sandwich with catsup on it, and left by the back door. He went down the alley calling for Francis Murgatroyd. He got up on the Murgatroyd gate and swung—the death-defying trapeze act at the circus —until Francis came down the walk.

"Hello, Blackie Humphrey," Jamesie said tantalizingly.

"Who's Blackie Humphrey?"

"You know who Blackie Humphrey is all right."

"Aw, Jamesie, cut it out."

"And you want me to throw the World Series!"

"Baseball Bill!"

"In the World Series. It came yesterday."

"Can I read it?"

Jamesie spoke in a hushed voice. "So you're Blackie Humphrey?"

"All right. But I get to read it next."

"So you want me to throw the World Series, Blackie. Is that it? Say you do."

"Yes, I do."

"Ask me again. Call me Bill."

"Bill, I want you to throw the World Series. Will you, Bill?"

"I might." But that was just to fool Blackie. Bill tried to keep his towering rage in check while feigning an interest in the nefarious plot. "Why do you want me to throw it, Blackie?"

"I don't know."

"Sure you know. You're a dirty crook and you've got a lot of dough bet on the other team."

"Uh, huh."

"Go ahead. Tell me that."

While Blackie unfolded the criminal plan Bill smiled at him in his friendly, boyish fashion.

"And who's behind this, Blackie?"

"I don't know."

"Say it's the powerful gambling syndicate."

"It's them."

"Ah, ha! Knock the ash off your cigar."

"Have I got one?"

"Yes, and you've got strong drink on your breath, too."

"Whew!"

Blackie should have fixed him with his small, piglike eyes.

"Fix me with your small, piglike eyes."

"Wait a minute, Jamesie!"

"Bill. Go ahead. Fix me."

"O.K. But you don't get to be Bill all the time."

"Now blow your foul breath in my face."

"There!"

"Now ask me to have a cigar. Go ahead."

Blackie was offering Bill a cigar, but Bill knew it was to get him to break training and refused it.

"I see through you, Blackie." No, that was wrong. He had to conceal his true thoughts and let Blackie play him for a fool. Soon enough his time would come and . . . "Thanks for the cigar, Blackie," he said. "I thought it was a cheap one. Thanks, I'll smoke it later."

"I paid a quarter for it."

"Hey, that's too much, Francis!"

"Well, if I'm the head of the powerful—"

Mr. Murgatroyd came to the back door and told Francis to get ready.

"I can't go to the game, Jamesie," Francis said. "I have to caddy for him."

Jamesie got a ride with the calliope when it had to stop at the corner for the light. The calliope was not playing now, but yesterday it had roamed the streets, all red and gold and glittering like a hussy among the pious, black Fords parked on the Square, blaring and showing off, with a sign, Jayvill vs. Beardstown.

The ball park fence was painted a swampy green except for an occasional new board. Over the single ticket window cut in the fence hung a sign done in the severe black and white railroad manner, "Home of the Jayville Independents," but everybody called them the "Indees."

Jamesie bought a bottle of Green River out of his savings and made the most of it, swallowing it in sips, calling upon his will power under the sun. He returned the bottle and stood for a while by the ticket window making designs in the dust with the corrugated soles of his new tennis shoes. Ding Bell, with a pretty lady on his arm and carrying the black official scorebook, passed inside without paying, and joked about it.

The Beardstown players arrived from sixty miles away with threatening cheers. Their chartered bus stood steaming and dusty from the trip. The players wore gray suits with "Barons" written across their chests and had the names of sponsors on their backs—Palms Café, Rusty's Wrecking, Coca-Cola.

Jamesie recognized some of the Barons but put down a desire to speak to them.

The last man to leave the bus, Jamesie thought, must be Guez, the new pitcher imported from East St. Louis for the game. Ding Bell had it in the Dope Box that "Saliva Joe" was one of the few spitters left in the business, had been up in the Three Eye a few years, was a full-blooded Cuban, and ate a bottle of aspirins a game, just like candy.

The dark pitcher's fame was too much for Jamesie. He walked alongside Guez. He smelled the salt and pepper of the gray uniform, saw the scarred plate on the right toe, saw the tears in the striped stockings—the marks of bravery or moths—heard the distant chomp of tobacco being chewed, felt—almost—the iron drape of the flannel, and was reduced to friendliness with the pitcher, the enemy.

"Are you a real Cuban?"

Guez looked down, rebuking Jamesie with a brief stare, and growled, "Go away."

Jamesie gazed after the pitcher. He told himself that he hated Guez—that's what he did, hated him! But it didn't do much good. He looked around to see if anybody had been watching, but nobody had, and he wanted somebody his size to vanquish—somebody who might think Guez was as good as Lefty. He wanted to bet a million dollars on Lefty against Guez, but there was nobody to take him up on it.

The Indees began to arrive in ones and twos, already in uniform but carrying their spikes in their hands. Jamesie spoke to all of them except J. G. Nickerson, the manager. J. G. always glared at kids. He thought they were stealing his baseballs and laughing about it behind his back. He was a great one for signaling with a score card from the bench, like Connie Mack, and Ding Bell had ventured to say that managers didn't come any brainier than Jayville's own J. G. Nickerson, even in the big time. But if there should be a foul ball, no matter how tight the game or critical the situation, J. G. would leap up, straining like a bird dog, and try to place it, waving the bat boy on without taking his eyes off the spot where it disappeared over the fence or in the weeds. That was why they called him the Foul Ball.

The Petersons—the old man at the wheel, a red handkerchief tied tight enough around his neck to keep his head on, and the sons, all players, Big Pete, Little Pete, Middle Pete, and Extra Pete—roared up with their legs hanging out the doorless Model T and the brass radiator boiling over.

The old man ran the Model T around in circles, damning it for a runaway horse, and finally got it parked by the gate.

"Hold 'er, Knute!" he cackled.

The boys dug him in the ribs, tickling him, and were like puppies that had been born bigger than their father, jollying him through the gate, calling him Barney Oldfield.

Lefty came.

"Hi, Lefty," Jamesie said.

"Hi, kid," Lefty said. He put his arm around Jamesie and took him past the ticket taker.

"It's all right, Mac," he said.

"Today's the day, Lefty," Mac said. "You can do it, Lefty."

Jamesie and Lefty passed behind the grandstand. Jamesie saw Lefty's father, a skinny, brown-faced man in a yellow straw katy.

"There's your dad, Lefty."

Lefty said, "Where?" but looked the wrong way and walked a little faster.

At the end of the grandstand Lefty stopped Jamesie. "My old man is out of town, kid. Got that?"

Jamesie did not see how this could be. He knew Lefty's father. Lefty's father had a brown face and orange gums. But Lefty ought to know his own father. "I guess it just looked like him, Lefty," Jamesie said.

Lefty took his hand off Jamesie's arm and smiled. "Yeah, that's right, kid. It just looked like him on account of he's out of town—in Peoria."

Jamesie could still feel the pressure of Lefty's fingers on his arm. They came out on the diamond at the Indees bench near first base. The talk quieted down when Lefty appeared. Everybody thought he had a big head, but nobody could say a thing against his pitching record, it was that good. The scout for the New York Yankees had invited him only last Sunday to train with them next spring. The idea haunted the others. J. G. had shut up about the beauties of teamwork.

J. G. was counting the balls when Jamesie went to the suitcase to get one for Lefty. J. G. snapped the lid down.

"It's for Lefty!"

"Huh!"

"He wants it for warm up."

"Did you tell this kid to get you a ball, Left?"

"Should I bring my own?" Lefty said.

J. G. dug into the suitcase for a ball, grunting, "I only asked him." He looked to Jamesie for sympathy. He considered the collection of balls and finally picked out a fairly new one.

"Lefty, he likes 'em brand new," Jamesie said.

"Who's running this club?" J. G. bawled. But he threw the ball back and broke a brand new one out of its box and tissue paper. He ignored Jamesie's ready hand and yelled to Lefty going out to the bull pen, "Coming at you, Left," and threw it wild.

Lefty let the ball bounce through his legs, not trying for it. "Nice throw," he said.

Jamesie retrieved the ball for Lefty. They tossed it back and forth, limbering up, and Jamesie aped Lefty's professional indolence.

When Bugs Bidwell, Lefty's battery mate, appeared with his big mitt, Jamesie stood aside and buttoned his glove back on his belt. Lefty shed his red blanket coat with the leather sleeves and gave it to Jamesie for safe-keeping. Jamesie folded it gently over his arm, with the white chenille "J" showing out. He took his stand behind Bugs to get a good look at Lefty's stuff.

Lefty had all his usual stuff—the fast one with the two little hops in it, no bigger than a pea; his slow knuckler that looked like a basketball, all the stitches standing still and staring you in the face; his sinker that started out high like a wild pitch, then dipped a good eight inches and straightened out for a called strike. But something was wrong—Lefty with nothing to say, no jokes, no sudden whoops, was not himself. Only once did he smile at a girl in the bleachers and say she was plenty . . . and sent a fast one smacking into Bug's mitt for what he meant.

That, for a moment, was the Lefty that Jamesie's older cousins knew about. They said a nice kid like Jamesie ought to be kept away from him, even at the ball park. Jamesie was always afraid it would get back to Lefty that the cousins thought he was poor white trash, or that he would know it in some other way, as when the cousins passed him on the street and looked the other way. He was worried, too, about what Lefty might think of his Sunday clothes, the snow-white blouse, the floppy sailor tie, the soft linen pants, the sissy clothes. His tennis shoes—sneakers, he ought to say—were all right, but not the golf stockings that left his knees bare, like a rich kid's. The tough guys, because they were tough or poor—he didn't know which—wore socks, not stockings, and they wore them rolled down slick to their ankles.

Bugs stuck his mitt with the ball in it under his arm and got out his Beechnut. He winked at Jamesie and said, "Chew?"

Jamesie giggled. He liked Bugs. Bugs, on loan from the crack State Hospital team, was all right—nothing crazy about him; he just liked it at the asylum, he said, the big grounds and lots of cool shade, and he was not required to work or take walks like the regular patients. He was the only Indee on speaking terms with Lefty.

Turning to Lefty, Bugs said, "Ever seen this Cuban work?"

"Naw."

"I guess he's got it when he's right."

"That so?" Lefty caught the ball with his bare hand and spun it back to Bugs. "Well, all I can promise you is a no-hit game. It's up to you clowns to get the runs."

"And me hitting a lousy .211."

"All you got to do is hold me. Anyhow what's the Foul Ball want for his five bucks—Mickey Cochrane?"

"Yeah, Left."

"I ought to quit him."

"Ain't you getting your regular fifteen?"

"Yeah, but I ought to quit. The Yankees want me. Is my curve breaking too soon?"

"It's right in there, Left."

It was a pitchers' battle until the seventh inning. Then the Indees pushed a run across.

The Barons got to Lefty for their first hit in the seventh, and when the next man bunted, Lefty tried to field it instead of letting Middle Pete at third have it, which put two on with none out. Little Pete threw the next man out at first, the only play possible, and the runners advanced to second and third. The next hitter hammered a line drive to Big Pete at first, and Big Pete tried to make it two by throwing to second, where the runner was off, but it was too late and the runner on third scored on the play. J. G. from the bench condemned Big Pete for a dumb Swede. The next man popped to short center.

Jamesie ran out with Lefty's jacket. "Don't let your arm get cold, Lefty."

"Some support I got," Lefty said.

"Whyn't you leave me have that bunt, Lefty?" Middle Pete said, and everybody knew he was right.

"Two of them pitches was hit solid," Big Pete said. "Good anywhere."

"Now, boys," J. G. said.

"Aw, dry up," Lefty said, grabbing a blade of grass to chew. "I ought to quit you bums."

Pid Kirby struck out for the Indees, but Little Pete walked, and Middle Pete advanced him to second on a long fly to left. Then Pete tripled to the weed patch in center, clear up against the Chevrolet sign, driving in Little Pete. Guez whiffed Kelly Larkin, retiring the side, and the Indees were leading the Barons 2 to 1.

The first Baron to bat in the eighth had J. G. frantic with fouls. The umpire was down to his last ball and calling for more. With trembling fingers J. G. unwrapped new balls. He had the bat boy and the bat boy's assistant hunting for them behind the grandstand. When one fell among the automobiles parked near first, he started to go and look for himself, but thought of Jamesie and sent him instead. "If anybody tries to hold out on you, come and tell me."

After Jamesie found the ball he crept up behind a familiar blue Hupmobile, dropping to his knees when he was right under Uncle Pat's elbow, and then popping up to scare him.

"Look who's here," his cousin said. It had not been Uncle Pat's elbow at all, but Gabriel's. Uncle Pat, who had never learned to drive, sat on the other side to be two feet closer to the game.

Jamesie stepped up on the running board, and Gabriel offered him some popcorn.

"So you're at the game, Jamesie," Uncle Pat said, grinning as though it were funny. "Gabriel said he thought that was you out there."

"Where'd you get the cap, Jamesie?" Gabriel said.

"Lefty. The whole team got new ones. And if they win today J. G. says they're getting whole new uniforms."

"Not from me," Uncle Pat said, looking out on the field. "Who the thunder's wearing my suit today?"

"Lee Coles, see?" Gabriel said, pointing to the player. Lee's back—Mallon's Grocery—was to them.

Uncle Pat, satisfied, slipped a bottle of near beer up from the floor to his lips and tipped it up straight, which explained to Jamesie the foam on his mustache.

"You went and missed me again this week," Uncle Pat said broodingly. "You know what I'm going to do, Jamesie?"

"What?"

"I'm going to stop taking your old *Liberty* magazine if you don't bring me one first thing tomorrow morning."

"I will." He would have to bring Uncle Pat his own free copy and erase the crossword puzzle. He never should have sold out on the street. That was how you lost your regular customers.

Uncle Pat said, "This makes the second time I started in to read a serial and had this happen to me."

"Is it all right if the one I bring you tomorrow has got 'Sample Copy' stamped on it?"

"That's all right with me, Jamesie, but I ought to get it for nothing." Uncle Pat swirled the last inch of beer in the bottle until it was all suds.

"I like the *Post,*" Gabriel said. "Why don't you handle the *Post?*"

"They don't need anybody now."

"What he ought to handle," Uncle Pat said, "is the *Country Gentleman.*"

"How's the Rosebud coming, Jamesie?" Gabriel asked. "But I don't want to buy any."

Uncle Pat and Gabriel laughed at him.

Why was that funny? He'd had to return eighteen boxes and tell them he guessed he was all through being the local representative. But why was that so funny?

"Did you sell enough to get the bicycle, Jamesie?"

"No." He had sold all the Rosebud salve he could, but not nearly enough to get the Ranger bicycle. He had to be satisfied with the Eveready flashlight.

"Well, I got enough of that Rosebud salve now to grease the Hup," Gabriel said. "Or to smear all over me the next time I swim the English Channel—with Gertrude Ederle. It ought to keep the fishes away."

"It smells nice," Uncle Pat said. "But I got plenty."

Jamesie felt that they were protecting themselves against him.

"I sent it all back anyway," he said, but that was not true; there were six boxes at home in his room that he had to keep in order to get the flashlight. Why was that the way it always worked out? Same way with the flower seeds. Why was it that whenever he got a new suit at Meyer Brothers they weren't giving out ball bats or compasses?

Why was it he only won a half pound of bacon at the carnival, never a Kewpie doll or an electric fan? Why did he always get tin whistles and crickets in the Crackerjack, never a puzzle, a ring, or a badge? And one time he had got nothing! Why was it that the five-dollar bill he found on South Diamond Street belonged to Mr. Hutchinson? But he *had* found a quarter in the dust at the circus that nobody claimed.

"Get your aunt Kate to take that cap up in the back," Uncle Pat said, smiling.

Vaguely embarrassed, Jamesie said, "Well, I got to get back."

"If that's Lefty's cap," Gabriel called after him, "you'd better send it to the cleaners."

When he got back to the bench and handed the ball over, J. G. seemed to forget all about the bases being crowded.

"Thank God," he said. "I thought you went home with it."

The Barons were all on Lefty now. Shorty Parker, their manager, coaching at third, chanted, "Take him out . . . Take him out . . . Take him out."

The Barons had started off the ninth with two clean blows. Then Bugs took a foul ball off the chicken wire in front of the grandstand for one out, and Big Pete speared a drive on the rise for another. Two down and runners on first and third. Lefty wound up—bad baseball—and the man on first started for second, the batter stepping into the pitch, not to hit it but to spoil the peg to second. The runner was safe; the man on third, threatening to come home after a false start, slid yelling back into the sack. It was close and J. G. flew off the bench to protest a little.

After getting two strikes on the next batter, Lefty threw four balls, so wide it looked like a deliberate pitch-out, and that loaded the bases.

J. G. called time. He went out to the mound to talk it over with Lefty, but Lefty waved him away. So J. G. consulted Bugs behind the plate. Jamesie, lying on the grass a few feet away, could hear them.

"That's the first windup I ever seen a pitcher take with a runner on first."

"It was pretty bad," Bugs said.

"And then walking that last one. He don't look wild to me, neither."

"He ain't wild, J. G.; I'll tell you that."

"I want your honest opinion, Bugs."

"I don't know what to say, J. G."

"Think I better jerk him?"

Bugs was silent, chewing it over.

"Guess I better leave him in, huh?"

"You're the boss, J. G. I don't know nothing for sure."

"I only got Extra Pete to put in. They'd murder him. I guess I got to leave Lefty in and take a chance."

"I guess so."

When J. G. had gone Bugs walked halfway out to the mound and spoke to Lefty. "You all right?"

"I had a little twinge before."

"A little what?"

Lefty touched his left shoulder.

"You mean your arm's gone sore?"

"Naw. I guess it's nothing."

Bugs took his place behind the plate again. He crouched, and Jamesie, from where he was lying, saw two fingers appear below the mitt—the signal. Lefty nodded, wound up, and tried to slip a medium-fast one down the middle. Guez, the batter, poled a long ball into left—foul by a few feet. Bugs shook his head in the mask, took a new ball from the umpire, and slammed it hard at Lefty.

Jamesie saw two fingers below the mitt again. What was Bugs doing? It wasn't smart baseball to give Guez another like the last one!

Guez swung and the ball fell against the left field fence—fair. Lee Coles, the left fielder, was having trouble locating it in the weeds. Kelly Larkin came over from center to help him hunt. When they found the ball, Guez had completed the circuit and the score was 5 to 2 in favor of the Barons.

Big Pete came running over to Lefty from first base, Little Pete from second, Pid Kirby from short, Middle Pete from third. J. G., calling time again, walked out to them.

"C'mere, Bugs," he said.

Bugs came slowly.

"What'd you call for on that last pitch?"

"Curve ball."

"And the one before that?"

"Same."

"And what'd Lefty give you?"

"It wasn't no curve. It wasn't much of anything."

"No," J. G. said. "It sure wasn't no curve ball. It was right in there, not too fast, not too slow, just right—for batting practice."

"It slipped," Lefty said.

"Slipped, huh!" Big Pete said. "How about the other one?"

"They both slipped. Ain't that never happened before?"

"Well, it ain't never going to happen again—not to me, it ain't," J. G. said. "I'm taking you out!"

He shouted to Extra Pete on the bench, "Warm up! You're going in!" He turned to Lefty.

"And I'm firing you. I just found out your old man was making bets under the grandstand—and they wasn't on us! I can put you in jail for this!"

"Try it," Lefty said, starting to walk away.

"If you knew it, J. G.," Big Pete said, "whyn't you let us know?"

"I just now found it out, is why."

"Then I'm going to make up for lost time," Big Pete said, following Lefty, "and punch this guy's nose."

Old man Peterson appeared among them—somebody must have told him what it was all about. "Give it to him, son!" he cackled.

Jamesie missed the fight. He was not tall enough to see over all the heads, and Gabriel, sent by Uncle Pat, was dragging him away from it all.

"I always knew that Lefty was a bad one," Gabriel said

on the way home. "I knew it from the time he used to hunch in marbles."

"It reminds me of the Black Sox scandal of 1919," Uncle Pat said. "I wonder if they'll hold the old man, too."

Jamesie, in tears, said, "Lefty hurt his arm and you don't like him just because he don't work, and his father owes you at the store! Let me out! I'd rather walk by myself than ride in the Hupmobile—with you!"

He stayed up in his room, feigning a combination stomach-ache and headache, and would not come down for supper. Uncle Pat and Gabriel were down there eating. His room was over the dining room, and the windows were open upstairs and down, but he could not quite hear what they said. Uncle Pat was laughing a lot—that was all for sure—but then he always did that. Pretty soon he heard no more from the dining room and he knew they had gone to sit on the front porch.

Somebody was coming up the stairs. Aunt Kate. He knew the wavering step at the top of the stairs to be hers, and the long pause she used to catch her breath—something wrong with her lungs? Now, as she began to move, he heard ice tinkling in a glass. Lemonade. She was bringing him some supper. She knocked. He lay heavier on the bed and with his head at a painful angle to make her think he was suffering. She knocked again. If he pinched his forehead it would look red and feverish. He did. Now.

"Come in," he said weakly.

She came in, gliding across the room in the twilight, tall and white as a sail in her organdy, serene before her patient. Not quite opening his eyes, he saw her through the lashes. She thought he was sick all right, but even if she didn't, she would never take advantage of him to make a joke, like Uncle Pat, prescribing, "A good dose of salts! That's the ticket!" Or Gabriel, who was even meaner, "An enema!"

He had Aunt Kate fooled completely. He could fool her every time. On Halloween she was the kind of person who went to the door every time the bell rang. She was the only grownup he knew with whom it was not always the teeter-totter game. She did not raise herself by lowering him. She did not say back to him the things he said, slightly changed, accented with a grin, so that they were funny. Uncle Pat did. Gabriel did. Sometimes, if there was company, his father did.

"Don't you want the shades up, Jamesie?"

She raised the shades, catching the last of that day's sun, bringing the ball players on the wall out of the shadows and into action. She put the tray on the table by his bed.

Jamesie sat up and began to eat. Aunt Kate was the best one. Even if she noticed it, she would say nothing about his sudden turn for the better.

She sat across from him in the rocker, the little red one he had been given three years ago, when he was just a kid in the first grade, but she did not look too big for it. She ran her hand over the front of his books, frowning at Baseball Bill, Don Sturdy, Tom Swift, Horatio Alger, Jr., and the *Sporting News.* They had come between him and her.

"Where are the books we used to read, Jamesie?"

"On the bottom shelf."

She bent to see them. There they were, his old friends and hers—hers still. Perseus. Theseus. All those old Greeks. Sir Lancelot. Merlin. Sir Tristram. King Arthur. Oliver Twist. Pinocchio. Gulliver. He wondered how he ever could have liked them, and why Aunt Kate still did. Perhaps he still did, a little. But they turned out wrong, most of them, with all the good guys dying or turning into fairies and the bad guys becoming dwarfs. The books he read now turned out right, if not until the very last page, and the bad guys died or got what was coming to them.

"Were they talking about the game, Aunt Kate?"

"Your uncle was, and Gabriel."

Jamesie waited a moment. "Did they say anything about Lefty?"

"I don't know. Is he the one who lost the game on purpose?"

"That's a lie, Aunt Kate! That's just what Uncle Pat and Gabriel say!"

"Well, I'm sure I don't know—"

"You *are* on their side!"

Aunt Kate reached for his hand, but he drew it back.

"Jamesie, I'm sure I'm not on anyone's side. How can I be? I don't know about baseball—and I don't care about it!"

"Well, I *do!* And I'm not one bit sick—and you thought I was!"

Jamesie rolled out of bed, ran to the door, turned, and said, "Why don't you get out of my room and go and be with them! You're on their side! And Uncle Pat drinks *near beer!*"

He could not be sure, but he thought he had her crying, and if he did it served her right. He went softly down the stairs, past the living room, out the back door, and crept along the house until he reached the front porch. He huddled under the spiraea bushes and listened to them talk. But it was not about the game. It was about President Coolidge. His father was for him. Uncle Pat was against him.

Jamesie crept back along the house until it was safe to stand up and walk. He went down the alley. He called for Francis.

But Francis was not home—still with his father, Mrs. Murgatroyd said.

Jamesie went downtown, taking his own special way, through alleys, across lots, so that he arrived on the Square without using a single street or walking on a single sidewalk. He weighed himself on the scales in front of Kresge's. He weighed eighty-three pounds, and the little card said, "You are the strong, silent type, and silence is golden." He weighed himself in front of Grant's. He weighed eighty-four pounds, and the card said, "Cultivate your good tastes and make the most of your business connections."

He bought a ball of gum from the machine in front of the Owl Drugstore. It looked like it was time for a black one to come out, and black was his favorite flavor, but it was a green one. Anyway he was glad it had not been white.

He coveted the Louisville Sluggers in the window of the D. & M. Hardware. He knew how much they cost. They were autographed by Paul Waner, Ty Cobb, Rogers Hornsby, all the big league stars, and if Lefty ever cracked his, a Paul Waner, he was going to give it to Jamesie, he said.

When Lefty was up with the Yankees—though they had not talked about it yet—he would send for Jamesie. He would make Jamesie the bat boy for the Yankees. He would say to Jake Ruppert, the owner of the Yankees, "Either you hire my friend, Jamesie, as bat boy or I quit." Jake Ruppert would want his own nephew or somebody to have the job, but what could he do? Jamesie would have a uniform like the regular players, and get to travel around the country with them, living in hotels, eating in restaurants, taking taxi-cabs, and would be known to everybody as Lefty's best friend, and they would both be Babe Ruth's best friends, the three of them going everywhere together. He would get all the Yankees to write their names on an Official American League ball and then send it home to Francis Murgatroyd, who would still be going to school back in Jayville—poor old Francis; and he would write to him on hotel stationery with his own fourteen-dollar fountain pen.

And then he was standing across the street from the jail. He wondered if they had Lefty locked up over there, if Uncle Pat and Gabriel had been right—not about Lefty throwing a game—that was a lie!—but about him being locked up. A policeman came out of the jail. Jamesie waited for him to cross the street. He was Officer Burkey. He was Phil Burkey's father, and Phil had shown Jamesie his father's gun and holster one time when he was sleeping. Around the house Mr. Burkey looked like anybody else, not a policeman.

"Mr. Burkey, is Lefty in there?"

Mr. Burkey, through for the day, did not stop to talk, only saying, "Ah, that he is, boy, and there's where he deserves to be."

Jamesie said "Oh yeah!" to himself and went around to the back side of the jail. It was a brick building, painted gray, and the windows were open, but not so you could see inside, and they had bars over them.

Jamesie decided he could do nothing if Mr. Burkey was off duty. The street lights came on; it was night. He began to wonder, too, if his father would miss him. Aunt Kate would not tell. But he would have to come in the back way and sneak up to his room. If it rained tomorrow he would stay in and make up with Aunt Kate. He hurried home, and did not remember that he had meant to stay out all night, maybe even run away forever.

The next morning Jamesie came to the jail early. Mr. Burkey, on duty, said he might see Lefty for three minutes, but it was a mystery to him why anyone, especially a nice boy like Jamesie, should want to see the bum. "And don't tell your father you was here."

Jamesie found Lefty lying on a narrow iron bed that was all springs and no covers or pillow.

"Lefty," he said, "I came to see you."

Lefty sat up. He blinked at Jamesie and had trouble getting his eyes to see.

Jamesie went closer. Lefty stood up. They faced each other. Jamesie could have put his hand through the bars and touched Lefty.

"Glad to see you, kid."

"Lefty," Jamesie said, "I brought you some reading." He handed Lefty Uncle Pat's copy of *Liberty* magazine.

"Thanks, kid."

He got the box of Rosebud salve out of his pocket for Lefty.

"Well, thanks, kid. But what do I do with it?"

"For your arm, Lefty. It says 'recommended for aches and pains.' "

"I'll try it."

"Do you like oranges, Lefty?"

"I can eat 'em."

He gave Lefty his breakfast orange.

A funny, sweet smell came off Lefty's breath, like perfume, only sour. Burnt matches and cigar butts lay on the cell floor. Did Lefty smoke? Did he? Didn't he realize what it would do to him?

"Lefty, how do you throw your sinker?"

Lefty held the orange and showed Jamesie how he gripped the ball along the seams, how he snapped his wrist before he let it fly.

"But be sure you don't telegraph it, kid. Throw 'em all the same—your fast one, your floater, your curve. Then they don't know where they're at."

Lefty tossed the orange through the bars to Jamesie.

"Try it."

Jamesie tried it, but he had it wrong at first, and Lefty had to reach through the bars and show him again. After that they were silent, and Jamesie thought Lefty did not seem very glad to see him after all, and remembered the last gift.

"And I brought you this, Lefty."

It was *Baseball Bill in the World Series.*

"Yeah?" Lefty said, momentarily angry, as though he thought Jamesie was trying to kid him. He accepted the book reluctantly.

"He's a pitcher, Lefty," Jamesie said. "Like you, only he's a right-hander."

The sour perfume on Lefty's breath came through the bars again, a little stronger on a sigh.

Wasn't that the odor of strong drink and cigar smoke —the odor of Blackie Humphrey? Jamesie talked fast to keep himself from thinking. "This book's all about Baseball Bill and the World Series," he gulped, "and Blackie Humphrey and some dirty crooks that try to get Bill to throw it, but . . ." He gave up; he knew now. And Lefty had turned his back.

After a moment, during which nothing happened inside him to explain what he knew now, Jamesie got his legs to take him away, out of the jail, around the corner, down the street—away. He did not go through alleys, across lots, between buildings, over fences—No. He used the streets and sidewalks, like anyone else, to get where he was going—away—and was not quite himself.

JAMESIE

1. What is the author's purpose in introducing Lefty in the first paragraph when he does not refer to him again for more than three pages?
2. How does the author depict Lefty's personality and character in the opening paragraph?
3. How does Mr. Powers establish the time of the story?
4. How old do you estimate Jamesie to be?
5. On which side does Jamesie align himself in the make-believe about the fixing of the World Series?
6. How does the author best demonstrate Jamesie's interest in baseball?
7. When do we get the first inkling that Lefty's father is to figure in the plot?
8. Why is Jamesie angry at Uncle Pat after the fight?
9. What is meant by the statement that Aunt Kate "did not raise herself by lowering him"?
10. What is typical about Jamesie's turning against Aunt Kate?
11. What finally convinces Jamesie of Lefty's guilt?
12. What does the final paragraph establish about Jamesie as a result of the total experience?

LEONARD Q. ROSS
(LEE CALVIN ROSTEN)
1908–

Mr. Kaplan's Hobo

BORN IN POLAND, *Leonard Q. Ross became an American economist and humorist. He was a Phi Beta Kappa scholar at the University of Chicago, where he received a Ph.D. degree. During the years of the great American depression, he worked at many jobs as a bus boy, salesman, and camp counselor. While engaged in part-time teaching of English to adults, he conceived the idea for his famous* Education of H*y*m*a*n K*a*p*l*a*n *stories.*

During World War II he worked for the government in many posts. Some of his writing has found its way to Hollywood and has been made into movies. This author uses the name Rosten *for his serious writing and* Ross *for his humor.*

Perhaps Mr. Parkhill should have known better. Perhaps he should have known Mr. Kaplan better. And yet, in Mr. Parkhill's conscientious concern for *every* student in the beginners' grade there could be no discrimination. Despite Mr. Kaplan's distressing class record, despite his amazing renditions of the English language, Mr. Parkhill insisted on treating him as any other student. Just because Mr. Kaplan referred to rubber heels as "robber hills," or called a pencil-sharpener a "pantsil-chopner," was no reason he should not participate in the regular exercises of the class on an equal footing. (Mr. Parkhill had weakened a bit in this resolution when Mr. Kaplan had given the opposite of "new" as "second hand.")

And now Mr. Kaplan stood at the front of the room before the class, ready to speak for five minutes during the Recitation and Speech period.

"Speak slowly, Mr. Kaplan," said Mr. Parkhill. "Watch your pronunciation. Remember it isn't how—er—*fast* you talk, or how *much* you say. Try to be accurate. Speak distinctly."

Mr. Kaplan nodded with a great and confident smile.

"And do watch your 'e's and 'a's. You always confuse them in your speech."

Mr. Kaplan nodded again, beaming. "I'll be so careful, Mr. Pockhill, you'll be soprize," he said gallantly.

"And the class will feel free to interrupt with corrections at any time." Mr. Parkhill finished his instructions with an encouraging nod to the class. Allowing the students to interrupt with corrections had proved very successful. It kept them alert, and it made the student reciting particularly careful, since there was a certain stigma attached to being corrected by a fellow-student—much greater than if Mr. Parkhill did the correcting. It was natural for *him* to catch errors.

"Very well, Mr. Kaplan." Mr. Parkhill sighed, aware that he could do no more. Now it was in the hands of God. He took Mr. Kaplan's seat. (He always took the seat of the student reciting during Recitation and Speech period. It seemed to establish a comradely rapport in the class; besides, it was easier to hear and watch the student speaking.)

Mr. Kaplan took a deep breath. For a suspended moment he surveyed the class. There was pride in his glance. Mr. Kaplan loved to recite. He loved to write on the blackboard. In fact, he loved any activity in which he was the single center of attention. He laughed a strange, soft, rather meaningless laugh. Then he began:

"Ladies an' gantleman—I s'pose dat's how I should beginnink—an' also Mr. Pockheel an' faller-students—"

He cleared his throat, almost with a flourish.

"Eh—I'm spikking tonight becawss it's Rasitation an' Spitch time an'—"

"Sp*ee*ch, Mr. Kaplan," Mr. Parkhill interpolated gently. "Watch your 'e's."

"Becawss it's Rasitation an' Sp*eeee*ch time, so I'll talkink abot mine vaca—no—*my* vacation." Mr. Kaplan corrected himself, smiling, as he saw Mr. Parkhill frown. "So is de name fromm my leetle sp—sp*eeee*ch: My Vacation!"

Mr. Kaplan stopped sententiously. He had a keen sense of structure.

"Foist, I must tell abot my hobo."

The class, with the fervent intensity with which it listened to students reciting, looked puzzled. So did Mr. Parkhill.

"My hobo is—"

"Your—er—*what?*" asked Mr. Parkhill anxiously.

"My hobo."

"No soch woid!" cried Mr. Norman Bloom. Whenever Mr. Bloom suspected an error in vocabulary, he jumped to the conclusion that there was "no soch woid." It was the safest tactic.

"Oh, no?" asked Mr. Kaplan, smiling. "Maybe you *positif*?"

"Well, there is such a word," said Mr. Parkhill, quickly. "But—er—are you sure you *mean* 'hobo'?"

"Aha!" Mr. Kaplan cried triumphantly, looking at Mr. Bloom. "So *is* soch a void! Vell, I tink I minn 'hobo'. My hobo is hiking—hiking in de voods, or on de heels, or op de montains—all kinds hiking. Venever is a fine day, mit sonshinink, I go hiking in—"

"He means 'hobby,'" hissed Miss Rose Mitnick to Mrs. Rodriguez. Miss Mitnick was a shy girl. Ordinarily she did not volunteer corrections, although she was the best student in the class. But between Miss Mitnick and Mr. Kaplan there was something of a feud. Mr. Kaplan heard Miss Mitnick's hiss. So did everyone else.

"So I'm corracted by Mitnick," said Mr. Kaplan generously. "Is not my '*hobo*.' My *hobby*—Hau Kay! But Bloom shouldn't say dere's no void 'hobo.' It's only *annoder* void, dat's all."

Mr. Bloom was impotent against this sophistry. Mr. Kaplan smiled graciously at both Miss Mitnick and Mr. Bloom, with the faintest suggestion of irony. Suddenly he straightened up. His smile grew wider, almost beatific. An exalted look came into his eyes. With a sudden motion he stretched both hands outward and cried, "De sky! De son! De stoss! De clods. De frash air in de longs. All—all is pot fromm Netcher!"

A reverent hush fell over the class as Mr. Kaplan depicted the glories of Nature.

"An' do ve human fools taking edwantage? No!"

Miss Mitnick blushed as if she were personally responsible for man's indifference to the out-of-doors.

"But in hiking is all enjoymint fromm soch Netcher. Dat's vy I'm makink a hobby fromm hiking. Ladies an' gantleman, have you one an' all, or even saparate, falt *in de soul* de trees, de boids, de gress, de bloomers—all de scinnery?"

A swift titter from the ladies made Mr. Kaplan pause, his hands arrested in mid-air.

"Yas, de trees, de boids, de gress, de bloomers—"

"Er—pardon me," said Mr. Parkhill, clearly embarrassed. "But what word *are* you using, Mr. Kaplan?"

"All kinds," Mr. Kaplan said with sublime simplicity.

"But—er—you used one word—"

" 'Bloomers' ain't natural hobjects!" blurted Mrs. Moskowitz firmly. Mrs. Moskowitz was a straightforward, earthy soul. And, as a married woman, she could speak out where Mr. Parkhill or the class might hesitate. "You mean 'flowers,' Mr. Kaplan, so don't mix op two languages!"

Mr. Parkhill, who had thought that Mr. Kaplan's use of "bloomers" came from a misconstruction of the verb "to bloom," naïvely transformed into a noun, suddenly recalled that *Blumen* meant "flowers" in Mr. Kaplan's native tongue.

"Hau Kay!" said Mr. Kaplan, promptly. "So podden me an' denk you! Is de void batter 'flower.' So I love to smallink de flowers, like Moskovitz said. I love to breedink de frash air. Mostly, I love to hear de boids sinking."

"You *must* watch your 'k's and 'g's," said Mr. Parkhill earnestly. " 'Singing,' not 'sin*k*ing.' "

Mr. Kaplan lifted his eyebrows with a responsive "Ah!"

"An' ven de boids is singing, den is Netcher commink ot in all kinds gorgeous."

Mr. Parkhill looked at the floor; there was no point in being picayune.

"Vell, lest veek I took my vife ot to de contry. I told my vife, 'Sarah, you should have an absolutel vacation. Slip—eat—valk aron' in Netcher. Stay in de bad how late you vant in de mornink!' But my vife! *Ach!* Did she slapt late? No! Not my Sarah. Avery mornink she got op six o'clock, no matter vat time it vas!"

For a moment there was a stunned silence. Then Miss Mitnick interrupted with shy but firm determination. She did not look at Mr. Kaplan. She addressed her words to Mr. Parkhill—rather, to Mr. Parkhill's tie. "How can Mr. Kaplan say she got up every morning at six o'clock 'no matter what time it was?' A mistake."

The class nodded, the full meaning of Mr. Kaplan's paradox sinking in.

"Yes," said Mr. Parkhill. "I'm sure you didn't mean that, Mr. Kaplan."

Mr. Kaplan's great smile did not leave his face for

a moment. He looked at Miss Mitnick through half-closed eyes and, with infinite superiority, said, "I have a foistcless idea vat I'm minnink, Mitnick. My vife gats op so oily in de mornink dat *you* couldn't tell vat time it vas, *I* couldn't tell vat time it vas, even Mr. Pockheel couldn't tell. Avery day in de contry she vas gattink op six o'clock, *no matter vat time it vas.*"

Miss Mitnick's blush was heart-rending.

"Don' be like that, Kaplan!" exclaimed Mr. Bloom, jumping into the gap chivalrously. "If it's six o'clock, so you *do* know what time it was, no? So how you can say—"

"Aha!" Mr. Kaplan cried defiantly. "Dat's exactel de mistake you makink just like Mitnick. If I'm *slippink* an' it's six o'clock, so do *I* know vat time it is? Vould *you* know it was six o'clock if *you* vas slippink?"

It was a dazzling dialectical stroke. It silenced Mr. Kaplan's critics with instant and deadly accuracy. Mr. Bloom pursed his lips, a miserable man. Miss Mitnick frowned and flushed, such metaphysical reasoning quite beyond her. Mrs. Moskowitz's eyes held awe for Mr. Kaplan's devastating logic. It remained for Mr. Parkhill to break through the impasse.

"But—er—Mr. Kaplan, if one *states* the time as six o'clock, then it's incorrect to add 'no matter what time it was.' That's a contradiction."

The class sat breathless. Mr. Kaplan's smile seemed ossified for one long moment as he looked at Mr. Parkhill. Then it flowed into life and peace again. "Oh, vell. If it's a *conterdiction*"—he looked haughtily at Miss Mitnick and Mr. Bloom—"dat's difference!"

Mr. Bloom nodded in acquiescence, as if he understood this masterful denouement; he tried to achieve a profound expression. A bewildered look crept into Miss Mitnick's eyes.

Mr. Kaplan beamed. He put his hands out dramatically and exclaimed, "How many you fine city pipple ever saw de son commink op? How many you children fromm Netcher smalled de gress in de mornink all vet mit dues? How many—"

Just then the bell rang in the corridors of the American Night Preparatory School for Adults. Mr. Kaplan stopped, his hand in mid-air—like a gull coasting. The class seemed suspended, like the hand.

"I'm afraid the period's up," said Mr. Parkhill.

Mr. Kaplan sighed philosophically, took his handkerchief from his pocket, and wiped the perspiration from his brow. "Vell, denks Gott dat's de and fromm de spi-sp*ee*ch of—" he drew himself erect—"Hymen Keplen."

As Mr. Kaplan uttered his own name, as if he were referring to some celebrity known to them all, Mr. Parkhill, by some visual conditioned reflex, *saw* the name. He saw it just as Mr. Kaplan always wrote it. It seemed impossible, fantastic, yet Mr. Kaplan had *pronounced* his name in red and blue and green: H*Y*M*A*N K*A*P*-L*A*N.

Mr. Parkhill sat quite still, thinking, as the class filed out.

MR. KAPLAN'S HOBO

1. Characterize Mr. Kaplan at the beginning of the story. Does his self-confidence ever desert him? What is his state at the end of the lesson?
2. Between whom is the conflict in this story? Who wins out in the end?
3. What is the function of Mr. Parkhill in the story? Is he more than a mere intermediary?
4. As you read this story, did you take time to supply the proper equivalents for Mr. Kaplan's mispronounced words? Why is this important in a story of this kind?
5. What is our attitude toward Mr. Kaplan? Do we laugh *at* him, or *with* him? Why?

SAKI

(H. H. MUNRO)

1870–1916

The Story-Teller

ALTHOUGH *he was born in Burma, H. H. Munro was brought up in England. He later returned to Burma where he served in the Burma police. Although best known today as a writer of an unusual type of short stories, he was for a time a writer of political sketches and served as a foreign correspondent for British newspapers in the Balkans, Russia, and France.*

Saki, as he preferred to be known in his writing career, was offered a commission in the army during World War I, but he chose to serve as an enlisted man. He became a corporal, was sent to France, and was killed in action in November, 1916.

Saki, who was also a novelist, is best known as a writer of horror and humorous stories.

It was a hot afternoon, and the railway carriage was correspondingly sultry, and the next stop was at Templecombe, nearly an hour ahead. The occupants of the carriage were a small girl, and a smaller girl, and a small boy. An aunt belonging to the children occupied one corner seat, and the further corner seat on the opposite side was occupied by a bachelor who was a stranger to their party, but the small girls and the small boy emphatically occupied the compartment. Both the aunt and the children were conversational in a limited, persistent way, reminding one of the attentions of a housefly that refused to be discouraged. Most of the aunt's remarks seemed to begin with "Don't," and nearly all of the children's remarks began with "Why?" The bachelor said nothing out loud.

"Don't, Cyril, don't," exclaimed the aunt, as the small boy began smacking the cushions of the seat, producing a cloud of dust at each blow.

"Come and look out of the window," she added.

The child moved reluctantly to the window. "Why are those sheep being driven out of that field?" he asked.

"I expect they are being driven to another field where there is more grass," said the aunt weakly.

"But there is lots of grass in that field," protested the boy; "there's nothing else but grass there. Aunt, there's lots of grass in that field."

"Perhaps the grass in the other field is better," suggested the aunt fatuously.

"Why is it better?" came the swift, inevitable question.

"Oh, look at those cows!" exclaimed the aunt. Nearly every field along the line had contained cows or bullocks, but she spoke as though she were drawing attention to a rarity.

"Why is the grass in the other field better?" persisted Cyril.

The frown on the bachelor's face was deepening to a scowl. He was a hard, unsympathetic man, the aunt decided in her mind. She was utterly unable to come to any satisfactory decision about the grass in the other field.

The smaller girl created a diversion by beginning to recite "On the Road to Mandalay." She only knew the first line, but she put her limited knowledge to the fullest possible use. She repeated the line over and over again in a dreamy but resolute and very audible voice; it seemed to the bachelor as though some one had had a bet with her that she could not repeat the line aloud two thousand times without stopping. Whoever it was who had made the wager was likely to lose his bet.

"Come over here and listen to a story," said the aunt, when the bachelor had looked twice at her and once at the communication cord.

The children moved listlessly towards the aunt's end of the carriage. Evidently her reputation as a story-teller did not rank high in their estimation.

In a low, confidential voice, interrupted at frequent intervals by loud, petulant questions from her listeners, she began an unenterprising and deplorably uninteresting story about a little girl who was good, and made friends with every one on account of her goodness, and was finally saved from a mad bull by a number of rescuers who admired her moral character.

"Wouldn't they have saved her if she hadn't been good?" demanded the bigger of the small girls. It was exactly the question that the bachelor had wanted to ask.

"Well, yes," admitted the aunt lamely, "but I don't think they would have run quite so fast to her help if they had not liked her so much."

"It's the stupidest story I've ever heard," said the bigger of the small girls, with immense conviction.

"I didn't listen after the first bit, it was so stupid," said Cyril.

The smaller girl made no actual comment on the story, but she had long ago recommenced a murmured repetition of her favourite line.

"You don't seem to be a success as a story-teller," said the bachelor suddenly from his corner.

The aunt bristled in instant defence at this unexpected attack.

"It's a very difficult thing to tell stories that children can both understand and appreciate," she said stiffly.

"I don't agree with you," said the bachelor.

"Perhaps *you* would like to tell them a story," was the aunt's retort.

"Tell us a story," demanded the bigger of the small girls.

"Once upon a time," began the bachelor, "there was a little girl called Bertha, who was extraordinarily good."

The children's momentarily-aroused interest began at once to flicker; all stories seemed dreadfully alike, no matter who told them.

"She did all that she was told, she was always truthful, she kept her clothes clean, ate milk puddings as though they were jam tarts, learned her lessons perfectly, and was polite in her manners."

"Was she pretty?" asked the bigger of the small girls.

"Not as pretty as any of you," said the bachelor, "but she was horribly good."

There was a wave of reaction in favour of the story; the word horrible in connection with goodness was a novelty that commended itself. It seemed to introduce a ring of truth that was absent from the aunt's tales of infant life.

"She was so good," continued the bachelor, "that she won several medals for goodness, which she always wore, pinned on to her dress. There was a medal for obedience, another medal for punctuality, and a third for good behaviour. They were large metal medals and they clinked against one another as she walked. No other child in the town where she lived had as many as three medals, so everybody knew that she must be an extra good child."

"Horribly good," quoted Cyril.

"Everybody talked about her goodness, and the Prince of the country got to hear about it, and he said that as she was so very good she might be allowed once a week to walk in his park, which was just outside the town. It was a beautiful park, and no children were ever allowed in it, so it was a great honour for Bertha to be allowed to go there."

"Were there any sheep in the park?" demanded Cyril.

"No," said the bachelor, "there were no sheep."

"Why weren't there any sheep?" came the inevitable question arising out of that answer.

The aunt permitted herself a smile, which might almost have been described as a grin.

"There were no sheep in the park," said the bachelor, "because the Prince's mother had once had a dream that her son would either be killed by a sheep or else by a clock falling on him. For that reason the Prince never kept a sheep in his park or a clock in his palace."

The aunt suppressed a gasp of admiration.

"Was the Prince killed by a sheep or by a clock?" asked Cyril.

"He is still alive, so we can't tell whether the dream will come true," said the bachelor unconcernedly; "anyway, there were no sheep in the park, but there were lots of little pigs running all over the place."

"What colour were they?"

"Black with white faces, white with black spots, black all over, grey with white patches, and some were white all over."

The story-teller paused to let a full idea of the park's treasures sink into the children's imaginations; then he resumed:

"Bertha was rather sorry to find that there were no flowers in the park. She had promised her aunts, with tears in her eyes, that she would not pick any of the kind Prince's flowers, and she had meant to keep her promise, so of course it made her feel silly to find that there were no flowers to pick."

"Why weren't there any flowers?"

"Because the pigs had eaten them all," said the bachelor promptly. "The gardeners had told the Prince that you couldn't have pigs and flowers, so he decided to have pigs and no flowers."

There was a murmur of approval at the excellence of the Prince's decision; so many people would have decided the other way.

"There were lots of other delightful things in the park. There were ponds with gold and blue and green fish in them, and trees with beautiful parrots that said clever things at a moment's notice, and humming birds that hummed all the popular tunes of the day. Bertha walked up and down and enjoyed herself immensely, and thought to herself: 'If I were not so extraordinarily good I should not have been allowed to come into this beautiful park and enjoy all that there is to be seen in it,' and her three medals clinked against one another as she walked and helped to remind her how very good she really was. Just then an enormous wolf came prowling into the park to see if it could catch a fat little pig for its supper."

"What colour was it?" asked the children, amid an immediate quickening of interest.

"Mud-colour all over, with a black tongue and pale grey eyes that gleamed with unspeakable ferocity. The first thing that it saw in the park was Bertha; her pinafore was so spotlessly white and clean that it could be seen from a great distance. Bertha saw the wolf and saw that it was stealing towards her, and she began to wish that she had never been allowed to come into the park. She ran as hard as she could, and the wolf came after her with huge leaps and bounds. She managed to reach a shrubbery of myrtle bushes and she hid herself in one of the thickest of the bushes. The wolf came sniffing among the branches, its black tongue lolling out of its mouth and its pale-grey eyes glaring with rage. Bertha was terribly frightened, and thought to herself: 'If I had not been so extraordinarily good I should have been safe in the town at this moment.' However, the scent of the myrtle was so strong that the wolf could not sniff out where Bertha was hiding, and the bushes were so thick that he might have hunted about in them for a long time without catching sight of her, so he thought he might as well go off and catch a little pig instead. Bertha was trembling very much at having the wolf prowling and sniffing so near her, and as she trembled the medal for obedience clinked against the medals for good conduct and punctuality. The wolf was just moving away when he heard the sound of the medals clinking and stopped to listen; they clinked again in a bush quite near him. He dashed into the bush, his pale grey eyes gleaming with ferocity and triumph, and dragged Bertha out and devoured her to the last morsel. All that was left of her were her shoes, bits of clothing, and the three medals for goodness."

"Were any of the little pigs killed?"

"No, they all escaped."

"The story began badly," said the smaller of the small girls, "but it had a beautiful ending."

"It is the most beautiful story that I ever heard," said the bigger of the small girls, with immense decision.

"It is the *only* beautiful story I have ever heard," said Cyril.

A dissentient opinion came from the aunt.

"A most improper story to tell to young children! You have undermined the effect of years of careful teaching."

"At any rate," said the bachelor, collecting his belongings preparatory to leaving the carriage, "I kept them quiet for ten minutes, which was more than you were able to do."

"Unhappy woman!" he observed to himself as he walked down the platform of Templecombe station; "for the next six months or so these children will assail her in public with demands for an improper story!"

THE STORY-TELLER

1. What are the touches of humor in the first paragraph?
2. Why does the aunt "permit herself a smile, which might be described as a grin"?
3. Where do we find an example that shows the bachelor to have greater imagination and resourcefulness than the aunt?
4. What is the *paradox* of the bachelor's story?
5. What is the meaning of "unhappy" in his observation as he walked away from the train?

JESSE STUART

1907–

Rain on Tanyard Hollow

BORN IN W-HOLLOW, *Greenup County, Kentucky, Jesse Stuart, one of the editors of this book, taught in a country school as a very young man. He later became a high school principal and county superintendent of schools. During World War II he enlisted in the Navy and was a commissioned officer in the Naval Reserve.*

In 1954 Jesse Stuart suffered a near-fatal heart attack. After his recovery he returned to writing, lecturing, and farming. He has represented the United States State Department around the world.

Mr. Stuart's work includes twenty-six books, ranging from poetry through biography, autobiography, novels, and short stories.

"Don't kill that snake, Sweeter," Mammie said. "Leave it alone among the strawberry vines and it'll ketch the ground moles that's eatin' the roots of the strawberry plants."

Mammie raised up from pickin' strawberries and stood with one hand in her apron pocket. Draps of sweat the size of white soup-beans stood all over her sun-tanned face and shined like dewdrops on the sun. Mammie looked hard at Pappie but it didn't do any good.

"Kill that snake," Pappie shouted. "It must a thought my knuckle was a mole. It ain't goin' to rain nohow unless

I kill a few more black snakes and hang 'em on the fence."

Pappie stood over the black snake. It was quiled and a-gettin' ready to strike at 'im again. It looked like the twisted root of a black-oak tree rolled-up among the half-dead strawberry plants. It must a knowed Pappie was goin' to kill it the way it was fightin' him back. It kept drawin' its long black-oak-root body up tighter so it could strike harder at Pappie. It stuck its forked tongue out at him.

"You would fight me back," Pappie shouted as he raised a big flat rock above his head high as his arms would reach. "You would get me foul and bite me. That's just what you've done. Now I'm goin' to kill you and hang you on the fence and make it rain."

Pappie let the big rock fall on the black snake. The rock's sharp edge cut the snake in two in many places. Its tail quivered against the ground and rattled the dried-up leaves on the strawberry plants. Its red blood oozed out on the dry-as-gunpowder dust. Mammie stood and looked at the pieces of snake writhin' on the ground.

"Old Adam fit with rocks," Pappie said. "They air still good things to fight with."

Pappie stood with his big hands on his hips. He looked at the dyin' black snake and laughed.

"That black snake didn't hurt your hand when it bit you," Mammie said. "Sweeter, you air a hardhearted man. You've kilt a lot of snakes and hung 'em on the fence to make it rain. They air still hangin' there. I aint heard a rain-crow croakin' yet ner felt a drap of rain. The corn is burnt up. You know it has. The corn aint goin' to git no taller. It's tasselin' and it's bumblebee corn. If you's to drap any ashes from your cigar on this strawberry patch it would set the plants on fire. They look green but they air dry as powder. Where is your rain?"

"I don't know, Lizzie," Pappie said. "You tell me where the rain is."

"It's in the sky," Mammie said, "and you won't get it unless you pray fer it to fall. It's about too late fer prayer too. And the Lord wouldn't listen to a prayer from you."

When Mammie said this she looked hard at Pappie. Pappie stood there and looked at Mammie. What she said to him about the Lord not listenin' to his prayer made Pappie wilt. His blue eyes looked down at Mammie. The hot dry wind that moved across the strawberry patch and rustled the strawberry plants, moved the beard on Pappie's face as he stood in the strawberry patch with his big brogan shoes planted like two gray stumps. His long lean body looked like a dead snag where the birds come to light and the beard on his face and the long hair that stuck down below the rim of his gone-to-seed straw hat looked like sour-vines wrapped around the snag.

"Don't stand there, Sweeter, like a skeery-crow and look at me with your cold blue-water eyes," Mammie said. "You know you air a hardhearted man and the Lord won't listen to your prayer. Look at the harmless black snakes you've kilt and have hangin' on the fence and you aint got rain yet. Sweeter, I'm lettin' the rest of these strawberries dry on the stems. I'm leavin' the strawberry patch."

Mammie slammed her bucket against the ground. She pulled her pipe from her pocket. She dipped the light-burley terbacker crumbs from her apron pocket as she walked toward the ridgetop rustlin' the dyin' strawberry plants with her long peaked-toed shoes. By the time Mammie reached the dead white-oak snag that stood on the ridgetop and marked our strawberry patch for all the crows in the country, Mammie had her pipe lit and there was a cloud of smoke followin' her as she went over the hill toward the house.

"Tracey, your Mammie talked awful pert to me."

"Yep, she did, Pappie."

"She talked like the Lord couldn't hear my prayer."

When Pappie talked about what Mammie said about the Lord not payin' any attention to his prayers, his beardy lips quivered. I could tell Pappie didn't like it. He felt insulted. He thought if the Lord listened to prayers, he ought to listen to one of his prayers.

"I'm just hard on snakes, Tracey," Pappie said. "I don't like snakes. My knuckle burned like a hornet stung me when that dad-durned black snake hid among the strawberry plants and bit me. It didn't come out in the open and bite me. Your Mammie got mad because I kilt that snake. I know the baby-handed moles air bad to nose under the roots of the strawberry plants and eat their white-hair roots and the black snakes eat the moles. But that aint no excuse fer a black snake's bitin' me on the knuckle."

"I don't blame you, Pappie," I said.

When I said this, Pappie looked at me and his face lost the cloud that was hangin' over it. The light on Pappie's face was like the mornin' sunshine on the land.

"It's a dry time, Tracey," Pappie said as he kicked the dry strawberry plants with his big brogan shoe. The leaves that looked green fell from the stems and broke into tiny pieces. Little clouds of dust rose from among the strawberry plants where Pappie kicked.

"We don't have half a strawberry crop," I said. "And if we don't get rain we won't have a third of a corn crop."

"You air right, Tracey," Pappie answered. "We'll get rain. If it takes prayers we'll get rain. Why won't the Lord listen to me same as he will listen to Lizzie? Why won't the Lord answer my prayer same as he will answer any other man's prayer in Tanyard Hollow?"

When Pappie said this he fell to his knees among the scorched strawberry plants. Pappie come down against the dry plants with his big fire-shovel hands and at the same time he turned his face toward the high heat-glimmerin' sky. Dust flew up in tiny clouds as Pappie beat the ground.

"Lord, will you listen to my prayer?" Pappie shouted. "I don't keer who hears me astin' you fer rain. We need it, Lord! The strawberries have shriveled on the vines and the corn is turnin' yaller. It's bumblebee corn, Lord. Give us rain, Lord. I've kilt the black snakes and hung 'em on the fence and the rain don't fall. Never a croak from the rain-crow ner a drap of rain. The black snake on the fence is a false image, Lord."

Pappie beat his hands harder on the ground. He jerked up strawberry plants with his hands and tossed them back on the ground. He dug up the hard dry ground and sifted it among the strawberry plants around him. He never looked at the ground. His face was turned toward the high clouds. The sun was beamin' down on Pappie and he couldn't look at the sun with his eyes open.

"Send rain, Lord, that will wash gully-ditches in this strawberry patch big enough to bury a mule in," Pappie shouted. "Let it fall in great sheets. Wash Tanyard Hollow clean."

I didn't bother with Pappie's prayer but I thought that was too much rain. Better to let the strawberry plants burn to death than to wash them out by the roots and take all the topsoil down Tanyard Hollow too. Can't grow strawberry in Tanyard Hollow unless you've got good topsoil of dead-leaf loam on the south hill slopes.

"Give us enough rain, Lord," Pappie shouted, "to make the weak have fears and the strong tremble. Wash rocks from these hillsides that four span of mules can't pull on a jolt-wagon. Wash trees out by the roots that five yoke of cattle can't pull. Skeer everybody nearly to death. Show them Your might, Lord. Put water up in the houses—a mighty river! Put a river of yaller water out'n Tanyard Hollow that is flowin' faster than a hound dog can run. Make the people take to the high hill slopes and let their feet sink into the mud instead of specklin' their shoes and bare feet with dust!"

Pappie prayed so hard that white foam fell from his lips. It was dry foam the kind that comes from the work cattle's mouths when I feed them corn nubbins. The big flakes of white foam fell upon the green-withered strawberry plants.

"Send the thunder rollin' like tater wagons across the sky over Tanyard Hollow," Pappie prayed. "Let the Hollow grow dark. Let the chicken think that night has come and fly up in the apple trees to roost. Let the people think the end of time has come. Make the Hollow so dark a body can't see his hand before him. Let long tongues of lightnin' cut through the darkness across the Hollow and split the biggest oaks in Tanyard Hollow from the tip-tops to their butts like you'd split them with a big clapboard fro. Let pieces of hail fall big enough if ten pieces hit a man on the head they'll knock 'im cuckoo. Let him be knocked cold in one of the biggest rains that Tanyard Hollow ever had. Let the rain wash the dead-leaf loam from around the roots of the trees and let the twisted black-oak roots lie like ten million black snakes quiled at the butts of the big oaks. Lord, give us a rain in Tanyard Hollow to end this drouth! Give us a rain that we'll long remember! I'm through with the brazen images of black snakes! Amen."

Pappie got up and wiped the dry foam from his lips with his big hand.

"I ast the Lord fer a lot," Pappie said. "I meant every word I prayed to Him. I want to see one of the awfulest storms hit Tanyard Hollow that ever hit it since the beginnin' of Time. That goes way back yander. I ast fer an awful lot, and I hope by askin' fer a lot, I'll get a few things."

"Pappie, I don't want to wish you any bad luck," I said, "but I hope you don't get all you ast fer. If you get all you ast fer, there won't be anythin' left in Tanyard Hollow. We'll just haf to move out. The topsoil will all be washed away, the dirt washed from around the roots of the trees and they'll look like bundles of black snakes. The big oaks will split from their tiptops to their butts—right down through the hearts with forked tongues of lightnin'. Trees will be rooted up and rocks washed from the hillsides that a jolt-wagon can't hold up. There won't be any corn left on the hillsides and the strawberry patch will be ruint."

"Tracey, I've ast the Lord fer it," Pappie answered, "and if the Lord is good enough to give it to me, I'll abide by what He sends. I won't be low-lifed enough to grumble about somethin' I've prayed fer. I meant every word I said. I hope I can get part of all I ast fer."

"It's time fer beans," I said. "I can step on the head of my shadder."

Pappie left the strawberry patch. I followed him as he went down the hill. He pulled a cigar from his shirt pocket and took a match from his hatband where he kept his matches so he could keep them dry. He put the cigar in his mouth . . . struck a match on a big rock beside the path and lit his cigar.

"When I was prayin' fer the rain to wash the rocks

from the hillsides," Pappie said, "this is one of the rocks I had in mind. It's allus been in my way when I plowed here."

"If we get a rain that will wash this rock from this hillside," I said, "there won't be any of us left and not much of Tanyard Hollow left."

"You'd be surprised at what can happen," Pappie said. "You can turn a double-barrel shotgun loose into a covey of quails and it's a sight at 'em that'll come out alive."

Sweat run off at the ends of Pappie's beard. It dripped on the dusty path. Sweat got in my eyes and dripped from my nose. It was so hot it just seemed that I was roastin' before a big wood fire. It looked like fall-time the way the grass was dyin'. Trees were dyin' in the woods. Oak leaves were turnin' brown.

Pappie took the lead down the hill. It was so steep that we had to hold to sassafras sprouts and let ourselves down the hill. The footpath wound down the hill like a long crooked snake crawlin' on the sand. When we got to the bottom of the hill, Pappie was wet with sweat as if he'd a swum the river. I was as wet as sweat could make me and my eyes were smartin' with sweat like I had a dozen sour-gnats in my eyes.

"Whooie," Pappie sighed as he reached the foot of the mountain and he rubbed his big hand over his beard and slung a stream of sweat on the sandy path. "It's too hot fer a body to want to live. I hope the Lord will answer my prayer."

"I hope Mammie has dinner ready."

Mammie didn't have dinner ready. She was cookin' over the hot kitchen stove. Aunt Rett and Aunt Beadie were helpin' Mammie.

"Lord, I hope we'll soon get rain," Mammie said to Aunt Rett. She stood beside the stove and slung sweat from her forehead with her index finger. Where Mammie slung the sweat in the floor was a long wet streak with little wet spots from the middle of the floor to the wall.

"It's goin' to rain," I said.

"Why is it goin' to rain?" Mammie ast.

"Because Pappie got down in the strawberry patch and prayed fer the Lord to send rain and wash this Hollow out," I said.

Mammie started laughin'. Aunt Rett and Aunt Beadie laughed. They stopped cookin' and all laughed together like three women standin' at the organ singin'.

"We'll get rain," Mammie said, "because Sweeter has prayed for rain. We'll have a washout in Tanyard Hollow fer Sweeter prayed fer a washout in Tanyard Hollow. We'll get what Sweeter prayed fer."

They begin to sing, "We'll get rain in Tanyard Hollow fer Sweeter prayed fer it."

"Just about like his hangin' the snakes over the rail fence to get rain," Mammie cackled like a pullet. "That's the way we'll get rain."

Uncle Mort Shepherd and Uncle Luster Hix sat in the front room and laughed at Pappie's prayin' fer rain. They thought it was very funny. They'd come down out'n the mountains and were livin' with us until they could find farms to rent. Uncle Mort and Aunt Rett had seven children stayin' with us and Uncle Luster and Aunt Beadie had eight children. We had a big houseful. They's Mammie's people and they didn't think Pappie had any faith. They didn't think the Lord would answer his prayer. I felt like the Lord would answer his prayer, fer Pappie was a man of much misery. Seemed like all of Mammie's people worked against 'im. They'd sit in the house and eat at Pappie's table and talk about gettin' a house and movin' out but they never done it. They'd nearly et us out'n house and home. When they come to our house it was like locust year. Just so much noise when all their youngins got to fightin' you couldn't hear your ears pop.

"It's goin' to rain this afternoon," Pappie said. "There's comin' a cloudbust. If you aint got the Faith you'd better get it."

Uncle Luster got up from the rockin' chear and went to the door. He looked at the yaller-of-an-egg sun in the clear sky. Uncle Luster started laughin'. Uncle Mort got up from his chear and knocked out his pipe on the jamrock. He looked at the sun in the clear sky and he started laughin'.

Uncle Mort and Uncle Luster hadn't more than got back to the two rockin' chears and started restin' easy until dinner was ready, when all at once there was a jar of thunder across the sky over Tanyard Hollow. It was like a big tater wagon rollin' across the sky. Mammie drapped her fork on the kitchen floor when she heard it. Aunt Rett nearly fell to her knees. Aunt Beadie set a skillet of fried taters back on the stove. Her face got white. She acted like she was skeered.

"Thunderin' when the sky is clear," Aunt Beadie said.

Then the thunder started. Pappie was pleased but his face got white. I could tell he was skeered. He thought he was goin' to get what he'd ast the Lord to send. The thunder got so loud and it was so close that it jarred the house. 'Peared like Tanyard Hollow was a big pocket filled with hot air down among the hills and the thunder started roarin' in this pocket. It started gettin' dark. Chickens flew up in the apple trees to roost.

When Mammie saw the chickens goin' to roost at noon, she fell to her knees on the hard kitchen floor and started prayin'. Mammie thought the end of time had come. The chickens hadn't more than got on the roost until the long tongues of lightnin' started lappin' across the Hollow. When the lightnin' started splittin' the giant oak trees from their tip-tops to their butts it sounded louder than both barrels of a double-barreled shotgun.

"Just what I ast the Lord to send," Pappie shouted. Mammie jumped up and lit the lamps with a pine torch that she lit from the kitchen stove. I looked at Pappie's face. His eyes were big and they looked pleased. All Aunt Beadie's youngins were gathered around her and Uncle Luster. They were screamin'. They were screamin' louder than the chickens were cacklin' at the splittin' oak trees on the high hillsides. Uncle Mort and Aunt Rett got their youngins around them and Uncle Mort started to pray. All six of us got close to Mammie. I didn't. I stuck to

Pappie. I thought about how hard he'd prayed fer a good rain to break the long spring drouth. Now the rain would soon be delivered.

Mammie, Aunt Rett and Aunt Beadie let the dinner burn on the stove. I was hungry and I could smell the bread burnin'. I didn't try to get to the kitchen. I saw the yaller water comin' from the kitchen to the front room. The front room was big and we had a big bed in each corner. When I looked through the winder and saw the big sycamores in the yard end up like you'd pull up horse-weeds by the roots and throw 'em down, I turned around and saw Aunt Beadie and Uncle Luster make fer one of the beds in the corner of the room. Their youngins followed them. They were screamin' and prayin'. Uncle Mort and Aunt Rett and all their youngins made fer the bed in the other corner of the room. Mammie and my sisters and brothers made for the stairs. Mammie was prayin' as she run. I stayed at the foot of the stairs with Pappie. When he prayed in the strawberry patch, I thought he was astin' the Lord fer too much rain but I didn't say anythin'. I didn't interfere with his prayer.

The water got higher in our house. A rock too big fer a jolt-wagon to haul smashed through the door and rolled across the floor and stopped. If it had rolled another time it would have knocked the big log wall out'n our house. Uncle Mort waded the water from the bed to the stairs and carried Aunt Rett and their youngins to the stairs. When he turned one loose on the stairs he run up the stairs like a drownded chicken. Uncle Luster ferried Aunt

Beadie and their youngins to the stairs and turned them loose. Pappie had to take to the stairs. I followed Pappie.

"If we get out'n this house alive," Uncle Mort prayed, "we'll stay out'n it, Lord."

Uncle Luster prayed a long prayer and ast the Lord to save his wife and family. He promised the Lord if He would save them that he would leave Tanyard forever. I never heard so much prayin' in a churchhouse at any of the big revivals at Plum Grove as I heard up our upstairs. Sometimes you couldn't hear the prayers fer the lightnin' strikin' the big oaks. You could hear trees fallin' every place.

"The Lord has answered my prayers," Pappie shouted.

"Pray for the cloudbust to stop," Mammie shouted. "Get down on your knees, Sweeter, and pray."

"Listen, Lizzie," Pappie shouted above the roar of the water and the thunder and the splittin' of the big oaks on the high slopes, "I aint two-faced enough to ast the Lord fer somethin' like a lot of people and atter I git it—turn around and ast the Lord to take it away. You said the Lord wouldn't answer my prayer. You've been prayin'! Why aint the Lord answered your prayers? You aint got the Faith. You just think you have."

When the lightnin' flashed in at our upstairs scuttlehole we had fer a winder, I could see Uncle Mort huddled with his family and Uncle Luster holdin' his family in a little circle. Mammie had all of us, but Pappie and me, over in the upstairs corner. I looked out at the scuttlehole and saw the water surgin' down Left Fork of Tanyard

Hollow and down the Right Fork of Tanyard Hollow and meetin' right at our house. That's the only reason our house had stood. One swift river had kilt the other one when they met on this spot. I thought about what Pappie said.

I could see cornfields comin' off'n the slopes. I could see trees with limbs and roots on them bobbin' up and down and goin' down Tanyard Hollow faster than a hound dog could run. It was a sight to see. From my scuttlehole I told 'em what I saw until I saw a blue sky comin' over the high rim of rock cliffs in the head of Tanyard Hollow. That was the end of the storm. I never saw so many happy people when I told them about the patch of blue sky that I saw.

"This is like a dream," Uncle Mort said.

"It's more like a nightmare to me," Uncle Luster said.

"It's neither," Pappie said. "It's the fulfillment of a prayer."

"Why do you pray fer destruction, Sweeter?" Mammie ast.

"To show you the Lord will answer my prayer after the way you talked to me in the strawberry patch," Pappie said. "And I want your brother Mort and your brother-in-law Luster to remember their promises to the Lord."

The storm was over. It was light again. The chickens flew down from the apple trees. The big yard sycamore shade trees went with the storm but the apple trees stood. There was mud two feet deep on our floor. It was all over the bedclothes. There were five big rocks on our house we couldn't move. We'd haf to take the floor up and dig holes and bury the rocks under the floor. Trees were split all over Tanyard Hollow hillside slopes. Great oak trees were splintered clean to the tops. Our corn had washed from the hill slopes. There wasn't much left but mud, washed-out trees, rocks and waste. Roots of the black-oak trees where the dead-leaf loam had washed away, looked like bundles of clean washed black snakes. The big rock upon the steep hillside that bothered Pappie when he was plowin' had washed in front of our door.

"I promised the Lord," Uncle Mort said, "if we got through this storm alive, I'd take my family and get out'n here and I meant it."

"Amen," Pappie shouted.

"Sorry we can't stay and hep you clean the place up," Uncle Luster said, "But I'm takin' my wife and youngins and gettin' out'n this Hollow."

They didn't stay and hep us bury the rocks under the floor. They got their belongin's and started wadin' the mud barefooted down Tanyard Hollow. They's glad to get goin'. Pappie looked pleased when he saw them pullin' their bare feet out'n the mud and puttin' 'em down again. Pappie didn't grumble about what he had lost. The fence where he had the black snakes hangin' washed down Tanyard Hollow. There wasn't a fence rail 'r a black snake left. The strawberry patch was gutted with gully-ditches big enough to bury a mule. Half of the plants had washed away.

"It wasn't the brazen images of snakes," Pappie said,

"that done all of this. Tanyard Hollow is washed clean of most of its topsoil and lost a lot of its trees. But it got rid of a lot of its rubbish and it's a more fitten place to live."

RAIN ON TANYARD HOLLOW

1. Note the many words of dialect in this story. What do the following words mean: *quiled, air, pert, jolt-wagon, skeer, tater, low-lifed, chear*?
2. What one superstition runs through the first part of the story?
3. Why are the moles spoken of as *baby-handed*?
4. Why was Pappie so upset when Mammie said God wouldn't listen to his prayers?
5. Why does Pappie refer to the black snake hanging on the fence as a false or brazen image? From where does this reference come?
6. Why does Pappie pray for a rain which he must know will be destructive?
7. What did Pappie mean by the last sentence?
8. Why is this story told by the boy narrator?
9. The author calls this ". . . a very serious story involving nature and superstition and man's winning against both." Do you agree that this is a serious story? Do you think it is a humorous story? Why?

MAURICE WALSH

1879–

The Quiet Man

COUNTY KERRY, IRELAND, *is the birthplace of Maurice Walsh who published his first short stories while still in his teens. He attended college in Ireland, and then served in the Customs and Excise Service. He has traveled extensively throughout the British Isles.*

Maurice Walsh first came to the attention of many Americans with the publication of a series of his humorous stories in The Saturday Evening Post. *He still resides in Ireland and continues his active, outdoor life there.*

Shawn Kelvin, a blithe young lad of twenty, went to the States to seek his fortune. And fifteen years thereafter he returned to his native Kerry, his blitheness sobered and his youth dried to the core, and whether he had made his fortune or whether he had not, no one could be knowing for certain. For he was a quiet man, not given to talking about himself and the things he had done. A quiet man, under middle size, with strong shoulders and deep-set blue eyes below brows darker than his dark hair—that was Shawn Kelvin. One shoulder had a trick of hunching slightly higher than the other, and some folks said that came from a habit he had of shielding his eyes in the glare of an open-hearth furnace in a place called Pittsburgh, while others said it used to be a way he had of guarding his chin that time he was a sort of sparring-partner punching bag at a boxing camp.

Shawn Kelvin came home and found that he was the last of the Kelvins, and that the farm of his forefathers had added its few acres to the ranch of Big Liam O'Grady, of Moyvalla. Shawn took no action to recover his land, though O'Grady had got it meanly. He had had enough of fighting, and all he wanted now was peace. He quietly went amongst the old and kindly friends and quietly looked about him for the place and peace he wanted; and when the time came, quietly produced the money for a neat, handy, small farm on the first warm shoulder of Knockanore Hill below the rolling curves of heather. It was not a big place but it was in good heart, and it got all the sun that was going; and, best of all, it suited Shawn to the tiptop notch of contentment; for it held the peace that tuned to his quietness, and it commanded the widest view in all Ireland—vale and mountain and the lifting green plain of the Atlantic Sea.

There, in a four-roomed, lime-washed, thatched cottage, Shawn made his life, and, though his friends hinted his needs and obligations, no thought came to him of bringing a wife into the place. Yet Fate had the thought and the dream in her loom for him. One middling imitation of a man he had to do chores for him, an ex-navy pensioner handy enough about house and byre, but with no relish for the sustained work of the field—and, indeed, as long as he kept house and byre shipshape, he found Shawn an easy master.

Shawn himself was no drudge toiler. He knew all about drudgery and the way it wears out a man's soul. He plowed a little and sowed a little, and at the end of a furrow he would lean on the handles of the cultivator, wipe his brow, if it needed wiping, and lose himself for whole minutes in the great green curve of the sea out there beyond the high black portals of Shannon mouth. And sometimes of an evening he would see, under the glory of the sky, the faint smoke smudge of an American liner. Then he would smile to himself—a pitying smile—thinking of the poor devils, devils with dreams of fortune luring them, going out to sweat in Ironville, or to bootleg bad whisky down the hidden way, or to stand in a breadline. All these things were behind Shawn forever.

Market days he would go down and cross to Listowel town, seven miles, to do his bartering; and in the long evenings, slowly slipping into the endless summer gloaming, his friends used to climb the winding lane to see him. Only the real friends came that long road, and they were welcome—fighting men who had been out in the "Sixteen"; Matt Tobin the thresher, the schoolmaster, the young curate—men like that. A stone jar of malt whisky would appear on the table, and there would be a haze of smoke and a maze of warm, friendly disagreements.

"Shawn, old son," one of them might hint, "aren't you sometimes terrible lonely?"

"Like hell I am!" might retort Shawn derisively. "Why?"

"Nothing but the daylight and the wind and the sun setting with the wrath o' God."

"Just that! Well?"

"But after the stirring times beyond in the States—"

"Ay! Tell me, fine man, have you ever seen a furnace in full blast?"

"A great sight."

"Great surely! But if I could jump you into a steel foundry this minute, you would be sure that God had judged you faithfully into the very hob of hell."

And then they would laugh and have another small one from the stone jar.

And on Sundays Shawn used to go to church, three miles down to the gray chapel above the black cliffs of Doon Bay. There Fate laid her lure for him.

Sitting quietly on his wooden bench or kneeling on the dusty footboard, he would fix his steadfast, deep-set eyes on the vestmented celebrant and say his prayers slowly, or go into that strange trance, beyond dreams and visions, where the soul is almost at one with the unknowable.

But after a time, Shawn's eyes no longer fixed themselves on the celebrant. They went no farther than two seats ahead. A girl sat there, Sunday after Sunday she sat in front of him, and Sunday after Sunday his first casual admiration grew warmer.

She had a white nape to her neck and short red hair above it, and Shawn liked the color and wave of that flame. And he liked the set of her shoulders and the way the white neck had of leaning a little forward and she at her prayers —or her dreams. And the service over, Shawn used to stay in his seat so that he might get one quick but sure look at her face as she passed out. And he liked her face, too—the wide-set gray eyes, cheekbones firmly curved, clean-molded lips, austere yet sensitive. And he smiled pityingly at himself that one of her name should make his pulses stir—for she was an O'Grady.

One person, only, in the crowded chapel noted Shawn's look and the thought behind the look. Not the girl. Her brother, Big Liam O'Grady of Moyvalla, the very man who as good as stole the Kelvin acres. And that man smiled to himself, too—the ugly, contemptuous smile that was his by nature—and, after another habit he had, he tucked away his bit of knowledge in mind corner against a day when it might come in useful for his own purposes.

The girl's name was Ellen—Ellen O'Grady. But in truth she was no longer a girl. She was past her first youth into the second one that has no definite ending. She might be thirty—she was no less—but there was not a lad in the countryside would say she was past her prime. The poise of her and the firm set of her bones below clean skin saved her from the fading of mere prettiness. Though she had been sought in marriage more than once, she had accepted no one, or rather, had not been allowed to encourage anyone. Her brother saw to that.

Big Liam O'Grady was a great raw-boned, sandy-haired man, with the strength of an ox and a heart no bigger than a sour apple. An overbearing man given to berserk rages. Though he was a churchgoer by habit, the true god of that man was Money—red gold, shining silver, dull copper—the trinity that he worshipped in degree. He and his sister Ellen lived on the big ranch farm of Moyvalla, and Ellen was his housekeeper and maid of all work. She was a careful housekeeper, a good cook, a notable baker, and she demanded no wage. All that suited Big Liam splendidly, and so she remained single—a wasted woman.

Big Liam himself was not a marrying man. There were not many spinsters with a dowry big enough to tempt him, and the few there were had acquired expensive tastes—a convent education, the deplorable art of hitting jazz out of a piano, the damnable vice of cigarette smoking, the purse-emptying craze for motor cars—such things.

But in due time, the dowry and the place—with a woman tied to them—came under his nose, and Big Liam was no longer tardy. His neighbor, James Carey, died in March and left his fine farm and all on it to his widow, a youngish woman without children, a woman with a hard name for saving pennies. Big Liam looked once at Kathy Carey and looked many times at her broad acres. Both pleased him. He took the steps required by tradition. In the very first week of the following Shrovetide, he sent an accredited emissary to open formal negotiations, and that emissary came back within the hour.

"My soul," said he, "but she is the quick one! I hadn't ten words out of me when she was down my throat. 'I am in no hurry,' says she, 'to come wife to a house with another woman at the fire corner. When Ellen is in a place of her own, I will listen to what Liam O'Grady has to say.' "

"She will, by Jacus!" Big Liam stopped him. "She will so."

There, now, was the right time to recall Shawn Kelvin and the look in his eyes. Big Liam's mind corner promptly delivered up its memory. He smiled knowingly and contemptuously. Shawn Kelvin daring to cast sheep's eyes at an O'Grady! The undersized chicken heart, who took the loss of the Kelvin acres lying down! The little Yankee runt hidden away on the shelf of Knockanore! But what of it? The required dowry would be conveniently small, and the girl would never go hungry, anyway. There was Big Liam O'Grady, far descended from many chieftains.

The very next market day at Listowel he sought out Shawn Kelvin and placed a huge, sandy-haired hand on the shoulder that hunched to meet it.

"Shawn Kelvin, a word with you! Come and have a drink."

Shawn hesitated. "Very well," he said then. He did not care for O'Grady, but he would hurt no man's feelings.

They went across to Sullivan's bar and had a drink, and Shawn paid for it. And Big Liam came directly to his subject—almost patronizingly, as if he were conferring a favor.

"I want to see Ellen settled in a place of her own," said he.

Shawn's heart lifted into his throat and stayed there. But that steadfast face with the steadfast eyes gave no sign and, moreover, he could not say a word with his heart where it was.

"Your place is small," went on the big man, "but it is handy, and no load of debt on it, as I hear. Not much of a dowry ever came to Knockanore, and not much of a dowry can I be giving with Ellen. Say two hundred pounds at the end of harvest, if prices improve. What do you say, Shawn Kelvin?"

Shawn swallowed his heart, and his voice came slow and cool: "What does Ellen say?"

"I haven't asked her," said Big Liam. "But what would she say, blast it?"

"Whatever she says, she will say it herself, not you, Big Liam."

But what could Ellen say? She looked within her own heart and found it empty; she looked at the granite crag of her brother's face and contemplated herself a slowly withering spinster at his fire corner; she looked up at the swell of Knockanore Hill and saw the white cottage among the green small fields below the warm brown of the heather. Oh, but the sun would shine up there in the lengthening spring day and pleasant breezes blow in sultry summer; and finally she looked at Shawn Kelvin, that firmly built, small man with the clean face and the lustrous eyes below steadfast brow. She said a prayer to her God and sank head and shoulders in a resignation more pitiful than tears, more proud than the pride of chieftains. Romance? Welladay!

Shawn was far from satisfied with that resigned acceptance, but then was not the time to press for a warmer one. He knew the brother's wizened soul, guessed at the girl's clean one, and saw that she was doomed beyond hope to a fireside sordidly bought for her. Let it be his own fireside then. There were many worse ones—and God was good.

Ellen O'Grady married Shawn Kelvin. One small statement; and it holds the risk of tragedy, the chance of happiness, the probability of mere endurance—choices wide as the world.

But Big Liam O'Grady, for all his resolute promptness, did not win Kathy Carey to wife. She, foolishly enough, took to husband her own cattleman, a gay night rambler, who gave her the devil's own time and a share of happiness in the bygoing. For the first time, Big Liam discovered how mordant the wit of his neighbors could be, and to contempt for Shawn Kelvin he now added an unreasoning dislike.

II

Shawn Kelvin had got his precious, red-haired woman under his own roof now. He had no illusions about her feelings for him. On himself, and on himself only, lay the task of molding her into a wife and lover. Darkly, deeply, subtly, away out of sight, with gentleness, with restraint, with a consideration beyond kenning, that molding must be done, and she that was being molded must never know. He hardly knew, himself.

First he turned his attention to material things. He hired a small servant maid to help her with the housework. Then he acquired a rubber-tired tub cart and a half-bred gelding with a reaching knee action. And on market days, husband and wife used to bowl down to Listowel, do their selling and their buying, and bowl smoothly home again, their groceries in the well of the cart and a bundle of second-hand American magazines on the seat at Ellen's side. And in the nights, before the year turned, with the wind from the plains of the Atlantic keening above the chimney, they would sit at either side of the flaming peat fire, and he would read aloud strange and almost unbelievable things out of the high-colored magazines. Stories, sometimes, wholly unbelievable.

Ellen would sit and listen and smile, and go on with her knitting or her sewing; and after a time it was sewing she was at mostly—small things. And when the reading was done, they would sit and talk quietly in their own quiet way. For they were both quiet. Woman though she was, she got Shawn to do most of the talking. It could be that she, too, was probing and seeking, unwrapping the man's soul to feel the texture thereof, surveying the marvel of his life as he spread it diffidently before her. He had a patient, slow, vivid way of picturing for her the things he had seen and felt. He made her see the glare of molten metal, lambent yet searing, made her feel the sucking heat, made her hear the clang; she could see the roped square under the dazzle of the hooded arcs with the curling smoke layer above it, understand the explosive restraint of the game, thrill when he showed her how to stiffen wrist for the final devastating right hook. And often enough the stories were humorous, and Ellen would chuckle, or stare, or throw back her red, lovely curls in laughter. It was grand to make her laugh.

Shawn's friends, in some hesitation at first, came in ones and twos up the slope to see them. But Ellen welcomed them with her smile that was shy and, at the same time, frank, and her table was loaded for them with scones and crumpets and cream cakes and heather honey; and at the right time it was she herself that brought forth the decanter of whisky—no longer the half-empty stone jar—and the polished glasses. Shawn was proud as sin of her. She would sit then and listen to their discussions and be forever surprised at the knowledgeable man her husband was—the way he would discuss war and politics and the making of songs, the turn of speech that summed up a man or a situation. And sometimes she would put in a word or two and be listened to, and they would look to see if her smile commended them, and be a little chastened by the wisdom of that smile—the age-old smile of the matriarch from whom they were all descended. In no time at all, Matt Tobin the thresher, who used to think, "Poor old Shawn! Lucky she was to get him," would whisper to the schoolmaster: "Herrin's alive! That fellow's luck would astonish nations."

Women, in the outside world, begin by loving their husbands; and then, if Fate is kind, they grow to admire them; and, if Fate is not unkind, may descend no lower than liking and enduring. And there is the end of lawful romance. Look now at Ellen O'Grady. She came up to the shelf of Knockanore and in her heart was only a nucleus of fear in a great emptiness, and that nucleus might grow into horror and disgust. But, glory of God, she, for reason piled on reason, presently found herself admiring Shawn Kelvin; and with or without reason, a quiet liking came to her for this quiet man who was so gentle and considerate; and then, one great heart-stirring dark o'night, she found herself fallen head and heels in love with her own husband. There is the sort of love that endures, but the road to it is a mighty chancy one.

A woman, loving her husband, may or may not be proud of him, but she will fight like a tiger if anyone, barring herself, belittles him. And there was one man that belittled Shawn Kelvin. Her brother, Big Liam O'Grady. At fair or market or chapel that dour giant deigned not to hide his contempt and dislike. Ellen knew why. He had lost a wife and farm; he had lost in herself a frugally cheap housekeeper; he had been made the butt of a sly humor; and for these mishaps, in some twisted way, he blamed Shawn. But—and there came in the contempt—the little Yankee runt, who dared say nothing about the lost Kelvin acres, would not now have the gall or guts to demand the dowry that was due. Lucky the hound to stean an O'Grady to hungry Knockanore! Let him be satisfied with that luck!

One evening before a market day, Ellen spoke to her husband: "Has Big Liam paid you my dowry yet, Shawn?"

"Sure there's no hurry, girl," said Shawn.

"Have you ever asked him?"

"I have not. I am not looking for your dowry, Ellen."

"And Big Liam could never understand that." Her voice firmed. "You will ask him tomorrow."

"Very well so, *agrah*," agreed Shawn easily.

And the next day, in that quiet diffident way of his, he asked Big Liam. But Big Liam was brusque and blunt. He had no loose money and Kelvin would have to wait till he had. "Ask me again, Shawneen," he finished, his face in a mocking smile, and turning on his heel, he plowed his great shoulders through the crowded market.

His voice had been carelessly loud and people had heard. They laughed and talked amongst themselves. "Begogs! The devil's own boy, Big Liam! What a pup to sell! Stealing the land and keeping a grip on the fortune! Ay, and a dangerous fellow, mind you, the same Big Liam! He would smash little Shawn at the wind of a word. And devil the bit his Yankee sparring tricks would help him!"

A friend of Shawn's, Matt Tobin the thresher, heard that and lifted his voice: "I would like to be there the day Shawn Kelvin loses his temper."

"A bad day for poor Shawn!"

"It might then," said Matt Tobin, "but I would come from the other end of Kerry to see the badness that would be in it for someone."

Shawn had moved away with his wife, not heeding or not hearing.

"You see, Ellen?" he said in some discomfort. "The times are hard on the big ranchers, and we don't need the money, anyway."

"Do you think that Big Liam does?" Her voice had a cut in it. He could buy you and all Knockanore and be only on the fringe of his hoard. You will ask him again."

"But, girl dear, I never wanted a dowry with you."

She liked him to say that, but far better would she like to win for him the respect and admiration that was his due. She must do that now at all costs. Shawn, drawing back now, would be the butt of his fellowmen.

"You foolish lad! Big Liam would never understand your feelings, with money at stake." She smiled and a pang went through Shawn's breast. For the smile was the smile of an O'Grady, and he could not be sure whether the contempt in it was for himself or for her brother.

Shawn asked Big Liam again, unhappy in his asking, but also dimly comprehending his woman's object. And Shawn asked again a third time. The issue was become a famous one now. Men talked about it, and women too. Bets were made on it. At fair or market, if Shawn was seen approaching Big Liam, men edged closer and women edged away. Some day the big fellow would grow tired of being asked, and in one of his terrible rages half kill the little lad as he had half killed other men. A great shame! Here and there, a man advised Shawn to give up asking and put the matter in a lawyer's hands. "I couldn't do that," was Shawn's only answer. Strangely enough, none of these prudent advisers were amongst Shawn's close friends. His friends frowned and said little, but they were always about, and always amongst them was Matt Tobin.

The day at last came when Big Liam grew tired of being asked. That was the big October cattle fair at Listowel, and he had sold twenty head of fat, Polled Angus beeves at a good price. He was a hard dealer and it was late in the day before he settled at his own figure, so that the banks were closed and he was not able to make a lodgment. He had, then, a great roll of bills in an inner vest pocket when he saw Shawn and Ellen coming across to where he was bargaining with Matt Tobin for a week's threshing. Besides, the day being dank, he had had a drink or two more than was good for him and the whisky had loosened his tongue and whatever he had of discretion. By the powers!—it was time and past time to deal once and for all with this little gadfly of a fellow, to show him up before the whole market. He strode to meet Shawn, and people got out of his savage way and edged in behind to lose nothing of this dangerous game.

He caught Shawn by the hunched shoulder—a rending grip—and bent down to grin in his face.

"What is it, little fellow? Don't be ashamed to ask!"

Matt Tobin was probably the only one there to notice the ease with which Shawn wrenched his shoulder free, and Matt Tobin's eyes brightened. But Shawn did nothing further and said no word. His deep-set eyes gazed steadily at the big man.

The big man showed his teeth mockingly. "Go on, you whelp! What do you want?"

"You know, O'Grady."

"I do. Listen, Shawneen!" Again he brought his hand clap on the little man's shoulder. "Listen, Shawneen! If I had a dowry to give my sister, 'tis not a little shrimp like you would get her. Go to hell out o' that!"

His great hand gripped and he flung Shawn backwards as if he were only the image of a man filled with chaff.

Shawn went backwards, but he did not fall. He gathered

himself like a spring, feet under him, arms half-raised, head forward into hunched shoulder. But as quickly as the spring coiled, as quickly it slackened, and he turned away to his wife. She was there facing him, tense and keen, her face pale and set, and a gleam of the race in her eyes.

"Woman, woman!" he said in his deep voice. "Why would you and I shame ourselves like this?"

"Shame!" she cried. "Will you let him shame you now?"

"But your own brother, Ellen—before them all?"

"And he cheating you—"

"Glory of God!" His voice ewas distressed. "What is his dirty money to me? Are you an O'Grady, after all?"

That stung her and she stung him back in one final effort. She placed a hand below her breast and looked *close* into his face. Her voice was low and bitter, and only he heard: "I am an O'Grady. It is a great pity that the father of this my son is a Kelvin and a coward."

The bosses of Shawn Kelvin's cheekbones were like hard marble, but his voice was as soft as a dove's.

"Is that the way of it? Let us be going home then, in the name of God!"

He took her arm, but she shook his hand off; nevertheless, she walked at his side, head up, through the people that made way for them. Her brother mocked them with his great, laughing bellow.

"That fixes the pair of them!" he cried, brushed a man who laughed with him out of his way, and strode off through the fair.

There was talk then—plenty of it. "Murder, but Shawn

had a narrow squeak that time! Did you see the way he flung him? I wager he'll give Big Liam a wide road after this. And he by way of being a boxer! That's a pound you owe me, Matt Tobin."

"I'll pay it," said Matt Tobin, and that is all he said. He stood wide-legged, looking at the ground, his hand ruefully rubbing the back of his head and dismay and gloom on his face. His friend had failed him in the face of the people.

III

Shawn and Ellen went home in their tub cart and had not a single word or glance for each other on the road. And all that evening, at table or fireside, a heart-sickening silence held them in its grip. And all that night they lay side by side, still and mute. There was only one subject that possessed them and on that they dared speak no longer. They slept little. Ellen, her heart desolate, lay on her side, staring into the dark, grieving for what she had said and unable to unsay it. Shawn, on his back, contemplated things with a cold clarity. He realized that he was at the fork of life and that a finger pointed unmistakably. He must risk the very shattering of all happiness, he must do a thing so final and decisive that, once done, it could never again be questioned. Before morning, he came to his decision, and it was bitter as gall. He cursed himself. "Oh, you fool! You might have known that you should never have taken an O'Grady without breaking the O'Gradys."

He got up early in the morning at his usual hour and went out, as usual, to his morning chores—rebedding and foddering the cattle, rubbing down the half-bred, helping the servant maid with the milk in the creaming pans—and, as usual, he came in to his breakfast, and ate it hungrily and silently, which was not usual. But, thereafter he again went out to the stable, harnessed his gelding and hitched him to the tub cart. Then he returned to the kitchen and spoke for the first time.

"Ellen, will you come with me down to see your brother?"

She hesitated, her hands thrown wide in a helpless, hopeless gesture. "Little use you going to see my brother, Shawn. 'Tis I should go and—and not come back."

"Don't blame me now or later, Ellen. It has been put on me and the thing I am going to do is the only thing to be done. Will you come?"

"Very well," she agreed tonelessly. "I will be ready in a minute."

And they went the four miles down into the vale to the big farmhouse of Moyvalla. They drove into the great square of cobbled yard and found it empty.

On one side of the square was the long, low, lime-washed dwelling house, on the other, fifty yards away, the two-storied line of steadings with a wide arch in the middle; and through the arch came the purr and zoom of a threshing machine. Shawn tied the half-bred to the wheel of a farm cart and, with Ellen, approached the house.

A slattern servant girl leaned over the kitchen half-door and pointed through the arch. The master was out beyond in the haggard—the rickyard—and would she run across for him?

"Never mind, *achara,*" said Shawn, "I'll get him. . . . Ellen, will you go in and wait?"

"No," said Ellen, "I'll come with you." She knew her brother.

As they went through the arch, the purr and zoom grew louder and, turning the corner, they walked into the midst of activity. A long double row of cone-pointed cornstacks stretched across the yard and, between them, Matt Tobin's portable threshing machine was busy. The smooth-flying, eight-foot driving wheel made a sleepy purr and the black driving belt ran with a sag and heave to the red-painted thresher. Up there on the platform, bare-armed men were feeding the flying drum with loosened sheaves, their hands moving in a rhythmic sway. As the toothed drum bit at the corn sheaves it made an angry snarl that changed and slowed into a satisfied zoom. The wide conveying belt was carrying the golden straw up a steep incline to where other men were building a long rick; still more men were attending to the corn shoots, shoulders bending under the weight of the sacks as they ambled across to the granary. Matt Tobin himself bent at the face of his engine, feeding the fire box with sods of hard black peat. There were not less than two score men about the place, for, as was the custom, all Big Liam's friends and neighbors were giving him a hand with the threshing—"the day in harvest."

Big Liam came round the flank of the engine and swore. He was in his shirt sleeves, and his great forearms were covered with sandy hair.

"Hell and damnation! Look who's here!"

He was in the worst of tempers this morning. The stale dregs of yesterday's whisky were still with him, and he was in the humor that, as they say, would make a dog bite its father. He took two slow strides and halted, feet apart and head truculently forward.

"What is it this time?" he shouted. That was the un-Irish welcome he gave his sister and her husband.

Shawn and Ellen came forward steadily, and, as they came, Matt Tobin slowly throttled down his engine. Big Liam heard the change of pitch and looked angrily over his shoulder.

"What the hell do you mean, Tobin? Get on with the work!"

"To hell with yourself, Big Liam! This is my engine, and if you don't like it, you can leave it!" And at that he drove the throttle shut and the purr of the flywheel slowly sank.

"We will see in a minute," threatened Big Liam, and turned to the two now near at hand.

"What is it?" he growled.

"A private word with you. I won't keep you long." Shawn was calm and cold.

"You will not—on a busy morning," sneered the big man. "There is no need for private words between me and Shawn Kelvin."

"There is need," urged Shawn. "It will be best for us all if you hear what I have to say in your own house."

"Or here on my own land. Out with it! I don't care who hears!"

Shawn looked round him. Up on the thresher, up on the

straw rick, men leaned idle on fork handles and looked down at him; from here and there about the stackyard, men moved in to see, as it might be, what had caused the stoppage, but only really interested in the two brothers-in-law. He was in the midst of Clan O'Grady, for they were mostly O'Grady men—big, strong, blond men, rough, confident, proud of their breed. Matt Tobin was the only man he could call a friend. Many of the others were not unfriendly, but all had contempt in their eyes, or, what was worse, pity. Very well! Since he had to prove himself, it was fitting that he do it here amongst the O'Grady men.

Shawn brought his eyes back to Big Liam—deep, steadfast eyes that did not waver. "O'Grady," said he—and he no longer hid his contempt—"you set a great store by money."

"No harm in that. You do it yourself, Shawneen."

"Take it so! I will play that game with you, till hell freezes. You would bargain your sister and cheat; I will sell my soul. Listen, you big brute! You owe me two hundred pounds. Will you pay it?" There was an iron quality in his voice that was somehow awesome. The big man, about to start forward overbearingly, restrained himself to a brutal playfulness.

"I will pay it when I am ready."

"Today."

"No; nor tomorrow."

"Right. If you break your bargain, I break mine."

"What's that?" shouted Big Liam.

"If you keep your two hundred pounds, you keep your sister."

"What is it?" shouted Big Liam again, his voice breaking in astonishment. "What is that you say?"

"You heard me. Here is your sister Ellen! Keep her!"

"Fires o'hell!" He was completely astounded out of his truculence. "You can't do that!"

"It is done," said Shawn.

Ellen O'Grady had been quiet as a statue at Shawn's side, but now, slow like doom, she faced him. She leaned forward and looked into his eyes and saw the pain behind the strength.

"To the mother of your son, Shawn Kelvin?" she whispered that gently to him.

His voice came cold as a stone out of a stone face: "In the face of God. Let Him judge me."

"I know—I know!" That was all she said, and walked quietly across to where Matt Tobin stood at the face of his engine.

Matt Tobin placed hand on her arm. "Give him time, *acolleen,*" he whispered urgently. "Give him his own time. He's slow but he's deadly as a tiger when he moves."

Big Liam was no fool. He knew exactly how far he could go. There was no use, at this juncture, in crushing the runt under a great fist. There was some force in the little fellow that defied dragooning. Whatever people might think of Kelvin, public opinion would be dead against himself. Worse, his inward vision saw eyes leering in derision, mouths open in laughter. The scandal on his name would not be bounded by the four seas of Erin. He must change his stance while he had time. These thoughts passed through his mind while he thudded the ground three times with iron-shod heel. Now he threw up his head and bellowed his laugh.

"You fool! I was only making fun of you. What are your dirty few pounds to the likes of me? Stay where you are."

He turned, strode furiously away, and disappeared through the arch.

Shawn Kelvin was left alone in that wide ring of men. The hands had come down off the ricks and thresher to see closer. Now they moved back and aside, looked at one another, lifted eyebrows, looked at Shawn Kelvin, frowned and shook their heads. They knew Big Liam. They knew that, yielding up the money, his savagery would break out into something little short of killing. They waited, most of them, to prevent that savagery going too far.

Shawn Kelvin did not look at anyone. He stood still as a rock, his hands deep in his pockets, one shoulder hunched forward, his eyes on the ground and his face strangely calm. He seemed the least perturbed man there. Matt Tobin held Ellen's arm in a steadying grip and whispered in her ear: "God is good, I tell you."

Big Liam was back in two minutes. He strode straight to Shawn and halted within a pace of him.

"Look, Shawneen!" In his raised hand was a crumpled bundle of greasy bank notes. "Here is your money. Take it, and then see what will happen to you. Take it!" He thrust it into Shawn's hand. "Count it. Make sure you have it all—and then I will kick you out of this haggard—and look"—he thrust forward a hairy fist—"if ever I see your face again, I will drive that through it. Count it, you spawn!"

Shawn did not count it. Instead he crumpled it into a ball in his strong fingers. Then he turned on his heel and walked, with surprising slowness, to the face of the engine. He gestured with one hand to Matt Tobin, but it was Ellen, quick as a flash, who obeyed the gesture. Though the hot bar scorched her hand, she jerked open the door of the fire box and the leaping peat flames whispered out at her. And forthwith, Shawn Kelvin, with one easy sweep, threw the crumpled ball of notes into the heart of the flame. The whisper lifted one tone and one scrap of burned paper floated out of the funnel top. That was all the fuss the fire made of its work.

But there was fuss enough outside.

Big Liam O'Grady gave one mighty shout. No, it was more an anguished scream than a shout:

"My money! My good money!"

He gave two furious bounds forward, his great arms raised to crush and kill. But his hands never touched the small man.

"You dumb ox!" said Shawn Kelvin between his teeth. That strong, hunched shoulder moved a little, but no one there could follow the terrific drive of that hooked right arm. The smack of bone on bone was sharp as whip crack, and Big Liam stopped dead, went back on his heel, swayed a moment and staggered back three paces.

"Now and forever! Man of the Kelvins!" roared Matt Tobin.

But Big Liam was a man of Iron. That blow should have laid him on his back—blows like it had tied men to the ground for the full count. But Big Liam only shook his head, grunted like a boar, and drove in at the little man. And the little man, instead of circling away, drove in at him, compact of power.

The men of the O'Gradys saw then an exhibition that they had not knowledge enough to appreciate fully. Thousands had paid as much as ten dollars each to see the great Tiger Kelvin in action, his footwork, his timing, his hitting; and never was his action more devastating than now. He was a thunderbolt on two feet and the big man a glutton.

Big Liam never touched Shawn with clenched fist. He did not know how. Shawn, actually forty pounds lighter, drove him by sheer hitting across the yard.

Men for the first time saw a two-hundred-pound man knocked clean off his feet by a body blow. They saw for the first time the deadly restraint and explosion of skill.

Shawn set out to demolish his enemy in the briefest space of time, and it took him five minutes to do it. Five, six, eight times he knocked the big man down, and the big man came again, staggering, slavering, raving, vainly trying to rend and smash. But at last he stood swaying and clawing helplessly, and Shawn finished him with his terrible double hit—left below the breastbone and right under the jaw.

Big Liam lifted on his toes and fell flat on his back. He did not even kick as he lay.

Shawn did not waste a glance at the fallen giant. He swung full circle on the O'Grady men and his voice of iron challenged them:

"I am Shawn Kelvin, of Knockanore Hill. Is there an O'Grady amongst you thinks himself a better man? Come then."

His face was deep-carved stone, his great chest lifted, the air whistled through his nostrils; his deep-set flashing eyes dared them.

No man came.

He swung around then and walked straight to his wife. He halted before her.

His face was still of stone, but his voice quivered and had in it all the dramatic force of the Celt:

"Mother of my son, will you come home with me?"

She lifted to the appeal, voice and eye:

"Is it so you ask me, Shawn Kelvin?" . .

His face of stone quivered at last. "As my wife only—Ellen Kelvin!"

"Very well, heart's treasure." She caught his arm in both of hers. "Let us be going home."

"In the name of God," he finished for her.

And she went with him, proud as the morning, out of that place. But a woman, she would have the last word.

"Mother of God!" she cried. "The trouble I had to make a man of him!"

"God Almighty did that for him before you were born," said Matt Tobin softly.

THE QUIET MAN

1. Above all other things, what did Shawn long for when he returned to Ireland from the United States?

2. What details does Mr. Walsh use to sketch briefly the character and appearance of Big Liam O'Grady?

3. Why does Ellen agree to marry Shawn?

4. Note the extraordinary introduction in this story. Where does the real conflict begin?

5. How is suspense built up preparatory to the inevitable fight between Shawn and Big Liam O'Grady?

6. How does Ellen's behavior at the Listowel fair complicate the plot?

7. At what point of the story is Shawn forced to make an irrevocable decision?

8. What does Shawn mean when he says to Big Liam, "You would bargain your sister and cheat; I will sell my soul"?

9. What does Ellen understand when "She leaned forward and looked into his eyes and saw the pain behind the strength"?

10. Why must Shawn burn the money?

11. What distinction does Ellen make between Shawn's two requests that she go home with him?

EUDORA WELTY

1909–

Livvie Is Back

ONE OF *the major influences today in short story writing, Eudora Welty was born in Jackson, Mississippi. She attended Mississippi State College for Women and the University of Wisconsin, where she earned the A.B. degree.* "Livvie Is Back" *illustrates Miss Welty's ability to tell a story of increasing intensity with no unnecessary words, a facet of her style for which she is famous.*

Miss Welty, who writes about the South she knows so well, has been the recipient of many prizes including the O. Henry Memorial Prize for the short story and a $1,000 prize from the American Academy of Arts and Letters. In addition to writing short stories, Miss Welty is also a successful novelist.

Solomon carried Livvie twenty-one miles away from her home when he married her. He carried her away up on the old Natchez Trace into the deep country to live in his house. She was sixteen—an only girl, then. Once people said he thought nobody would ever come along there. He told her himself that it had been a long time, and a day she did not know about, since that road was a traveled road with *people* coming and going. He was good to her, but he kept her in the house. She had not thought that she could not get back. Where she came from, people said an old man did not want anybody in the world to ever find his wife, for fear they would steal her back from him. Solomon asked her before he took her, "Would she be happy?"—very dignified, for he was a colored man that owned his land and had it written down in the courthouse; and she said, "Yes, sir," since he was an old man and she was young and just listened and answered. He asked her, if she was choosing winter, would she pine for spring, and she said, "No indeed." Whatever she said, always, was because he was an old man . . . while nine years went by. All the time, he got old, and he got so old he gave out. At last he slept the whole day in bed, and she was young still.

It was a nice house, inside and outside both. In the first place, it had three rooms. The front room was papered in holly paper, with green palmettos from the swamp spaced at careful intervals over the walls. There was fresh newspaper cut with fancy borders on the mantel-shelf, on which were propped photographs of old or very young men printed in faint yellow—Solomon's people. Solomon had a houseful of furniture. There was a double settee, a tall scrolled rocker and an organ in the front room, all around a three-legged table with a pink marble top, on which was set a lamp with three gold feet, besides a jelly glass with pretty hen feathers in it. Behind the front room, the other room had the bright iron bed with the polished knobs like a throne, in which Solomon slept all day. There were snow-white curtains of wiry lace at the window, and a lace bed-spread belonged on the bed. But what old Solomon slept so sound under was a big feather-stitched piecequilt in the pattern "Trip Around the World," which had twenty-one different colors, four hundred and forty pieces, and a thousand yards of thread, and that was what Solomon's mother made in her life and old age. There was a table holding the Bible, and a trunk with a key. On the wall were two calendars, and a diploma from somewhere in Solomon's family, and under that Livvie's one possession was nailed, a picture of the little white baby of the family she worked for, back in Natchez before she was married. Going through that room and on to the kitchen, there was a big wood stove and a big round table always with a wet top and with the knives and forks in one jelly glass and the spoons in another, and a cut-glass vinegar bottle between, and going out from those, many shallow dishes of pickled peaches, fig preserves, watermelon pickles and blackberry jam always sitting there. The churn sat in the sun, the doors of the safe were always both shut, and there were four baited mouse-traps in the kitchen, one in every corner.

The outside of Solomon's house looked nice. It was not painted, but across the porch was an even balance. On each side there was one easy chair with high springs, looking out, and a fern basket hanging over it from the ceiling, and a dishpan of zinnia seedlings growing at its foot on the floor. By the door was a plow-wheel, just a pretty iron circle, nailed up on one wall and a square mirror on the other, a turquoise-blue comb stuck up in the frame, with the wash stand beneath it. On the door was a wooden knob with a pearl in the end, and Solomon's black hat hung on that, if he was in the house.

Out front was a clean dirt yard with every vestige of grass patiently uprooted and the ground scarred in deep whorls from the strike of Livvie's broom. Rose bushes with tiny blood-red roses blooming every month grew in threes on either side of the steps. On one side was a peach tree, on the other a pomegranate. Then coming around up the path from the deep cut of the Natchez Trace below was a line of bare crape-myrtle trees with every branch of them ending in a colored bottle, green or blue. There was no word that fell from Solomon's lips to say what they were for, but Livvie knew that there could be a spell put in trees, and she was familiar from the time she was born with the way bottle trees kept evil spirits from coming into the house—by luring them inside the colored bottles, where they cannot get out again. Solomon had made the bottle trees with his own hands over the nine years, in labor amounting to about a tree a year, and without a sign that he had any uneasiness in his heart, for he took as much pride in his precautions against spirits coming in the house as he took in the house, and sometimes in the sun the bottle trees looked prettier than the house did.

It was a nice house. It was in a place where the days would go by and surprise anyone that they were over. The lamplight and the firelight would shine out the door after dark, over the still and breathing country, lighting the roses and the bottle trees, and all was quiet there.

But there was nobody, nobody at all, not even a white person. And if there had been anybody, Solomon would not have let Livvie look at them, just as he would not let her look at a field hand, or a field hand look at her. There was no house near, except for the cabins of the tenants that were forbidden to her, and there was no house as far as she had been, stealing away down the still, deep Trace. She felt as if she waded a river when she went, for the dead leaves on the ground reached as high as her knees, and when she was all scratched and bleeding she said it was not like a road that went anywhere. One day, climbing up the high bank, she had found a graveyard without a church, with ribbon-grass growing about the foot of an angel (she had climbed up because she thought she saw angel wings), and in the sun, trees shining like burning flames through the great caterpillar nets which enclosed them. Scarey thistles stood looking like the prophets in the Bible in Solomon's house. Indian paint brushes grew over her head, and the mourning dove made the only sound in the world. Oh for a stirring of the leaves, and a breaking of the nets! But not by a ghost, prayed Livvie, jumping down the bank. After Solomon took to his bed, she never went out, except one more time.

Livvie knew she made a nice girl to wait on anybody. She fixed things to eat on a tray like a surprise. She could keep from singing when she ironed, and to sit by a bed and fan away the flies, she could be so still she could not hear herself breathe. She could clean up the house and never drop a thing, and wash the dishes without a sound, and she would step outside to churn, for churning sounded too sad to her, like sobbing, and if it made her home-sick and not Solomon, she did not think of that.

But Solomon scarcely opened his eyes to see her, and

scarcely tasted his food. He was not sick or paralyzed or in any pain that he mentioned, but he was surely wearing out in the body, and no matter what nice hot thing Livvie would bring him to taste, he would only look at it now, as if he were past seeing how he could add anything more to himself. Before she could beg him, he would go fast asleep. She could not surprise him any more, if he would not taste, and she was afraid that he was never in the world going to taste another thing she brought him—and so how could he last?

But one morning it was breakfast time and she cooked his eggs and grits, carried them in on a tray, and called his name. He was sound asleep. He lay in a dignified way with his watch beside him, on his back in the middle of the bed. One hand drew the quilt up high, though it was the first day of spring. Through the white lace curtains a little puffy wind was blowing as if it came from round cheeks. All night the frogs had sung out in the swamp, like a commotion in the room, and he had not stirred, though she lay wide awake and saying "Shh, frogs!" for fear he would mind them.

He looked as if he would like to sleep a little longer, and so she put back the tray and waited a little. When she tiptoed and stayed so quiet, she surrounded herself with a little reverie, and sometimes it seemed to her when she was so stealthy that the quiet she kept was for a sleeping baby, and that she had a baby and was its mother. When she stood at Solomon's bed and looked down at him, she would be thinking, "He sleeps so well," and she would hate to wake him up. And in some other ways, too, she was afraid to wake him up because even in his sleep he seemed to be such a strict man.

Of course, nailed to the wall over the bed—only she would forget who it was—there was a picture of him when he was young. Then he had a fan of hair over his forehead like a king's crown. Now his hair lay down on his head, the spring had gone out of it. Solomon had a lightish face, with eyebrows scattered but rugged, the way privet grows, strong eyes, with second sight, a strict mouth, and a little gold smile. This was the way he looked in his clothes, but in bed in the daytime he looked like a different and smaller man, even when he was wide awake, and holding the Bible. He looked like somebody kin to himself. And then sometimes when he lay in sleep and she stood fanning the flies away, and the light came in, his face was like new, so smooth and clear that it was like a glass of jelly held to the window, and she could almost look through his forehead and see what he thought.

She fanned him and at length he opened his eyes and spoke her name, but he would not taste the nice eggs she had kept warm under a pan.

Back in the kitchen she ate heartily, his breakfast and hers, and looked out the open door at what went on. The whole day, and the whole night before, she had felt the stir of spring close to her. It was as present in the house as a young man would be. The moon was in the last quarter and outside they were turning the sod and planting peas and beans. Up and down the red fields, over which smoke from the brush-burning hung showing like a little skirt of sky, a white horse and a white mule pulled the plow. At intervals hoarse shouts came through the air and roused her as if she dozed neglectfully in the shade, and they were telling her, "Jump up!" She could see how over each ribbon of field were moving men and girls, on foot and mounted on mules, with hats set on their heads and bright with tall hoes and forks as if they carried streamers on them and were going to some place on a journey—and how as if at a signal now and then they would all start at once shouting, hollering, cajoling, calling and answering back, running, being leaped on and breaking away, flinging to earth with a shout and lying motionless in the trance of twelve o'clock. The old women came out of the cabins and brought them the food they had ready for them, and then all worked together, spread evenly out. The little children came too, like a bouncing stream overflowing the fields, and set upon the men, the women, the dogs, the rushing birds, and the wave-like rows of earth, their little voices almost too high to be heard. In the middle distance like some white and gold towers were the haystacks, with black cows coming around to eat their edges. High above everything, the wheel of fields, house, and cabins, and the deep road surrounding like a moat to keep them in, was the turning sky, blue with long, far-flung white mare's-tail clouds, serene and still as high flames. And sound asleep while all this went around him that was his, Solomon was like a little still spot in the middle.

Even in the house the earth was sweet to breathe. Solomon had never let Livvie go any farther than the chicken house and the well. But what if she would walk now into the heart of the fields and take a hoe and work until she fell stretched out and drenched with her efforts, like other girls, and laid her cheek against the laid-open earth, and shamed the old man with her humbleness and delight? To shame him! A cruel wish could come in uninvited and so fast while she looked out the back door. She washed the dishes and scrubbed the table. She could hear the cries of the little lambs. Her mother, that she had not seen since her wedding day, had said one time, "I rather a man be anything, than a woman be mean."

So all morning she kept tasting the chicken broth on the stove, and when it was right she poured off a nice cup-ful. She carried it in to Solomon, and there he lay having a dream. Now what did he dream about? For she saw him sigh gently as if not to disturb some whole thing he held round in his mind, like a fresh egg. So even an old man dreamed about something pretty. Did he dream of her, while his eyes were shut and sunken, and his small hand with the wedding ring curled close in sleep around the quilt? He might be dreaming of what time it was, for even through his sleep he kept track of it like a clock, and knew how much of it went by, and waked up knowing where the hands were even before he consulted the silver watch that he never let go. He would sleep with the watch in his palm, and even holding it to his cheek like a child that loves a plaything. Or he might dream of journeys and travels on a steamboat to Natchez. Yet she thought he dreamed of her; but even while she scrutinized him, the rods of the foot of the bed seemed to rise up like a rail fence between them, and she could see that people never could be sure of anything as long as one of them was asleep and the other awake. To look at him dreaming of her when he might be going to die frightened her a little, as if he might carry her with him that way, and she wanted to run out of the room. She took hold of the bed and held on, and Solomon opened his eyes and called her name, but he did not want anything. He would not taste the good broth.

Just a little after that, as she was taking up the ashes in the front room for the last time in the year, she heard a sound. It was somebody coming. She pulled the curtains together and looked through the slit.

Coming up the path under the bottle trees was a white lady. At first she looked young, but then she looked old. Marvelous to see, a little car stood steaming like a kettle out in the field-track—it had come without a road.

Livvie stood listening to the long, repeated knockings at the door, and after a while she opened it just a little. The lady came in through the crack, though she was more than middle-sized and wore a big hat.

"My name is Miss Baby Marie," she said.

Livvie gazed respectfully at the lady and at the little suitcase she was holding close to her by the handle until the proper moment. The lady's eyes were running over the room, from palmetto to palmetto, but she was saying, "I live at home . . . out from Natchez . . . and get out and show these pretty cosmetic things to the white people and the colored people both . . . all around . . . years and years.

. . . Both shades of powder and rouge. . . . It's the kind of work a girl can do and not go clear 'way from home . . ." And the harder she looked, the more she talked. Suddenly she turned up her nose and said, "It is not Christian or sanitary to put feathers in a vase," and then she took a gold key out of the front of her dress and began unlocking the locks on her suitcase. Her face drew the light, the way it was covered with intense white and red, with a little patty-cake of white between the wrinkles by her upper lip. Little red tassels of hair bobbed under the rusty wires of her picture-hat, as with an air of triumph and secrecy she now drew open her little suitcase and brought out bottle after bottle and jar after jar, which she put down on the table, the mantel-piece, the settee, and the organ.

"Did you ever see so many cosmetics in your life?" cried Miss Baby Marie.

"No'm," Livvie tried to say, but the cat had her tongue.

"Have you ever applied cosmetics?" asked Miss Baby Marie next.

"No'm," Livvie tried to say.

"Then look!" she said, and pulling out the last thing of all, "Try this!" she said. And in her hand was unclenched a golden lipstick which popped open like magic. A fragrance came out of it like incense, and Livvie cried out suddenly, "Chinaberry flowers!"

Her hand took the lipstick, and in an instant she was carried away in the air through the spring, and looking down with a half-drowsy smile from a purple cloud she saw from above a chinaberry tree, dark and smooth and neatly leaved, neat as a guinea hen in the dooryard, and there was her home that she had left. On one side of the tree was her mama holding up her heavy apron, and she could see it was loaded with ripe figs, and on the other side was her papa holding a fish-pole over the pond, and she could see it transparently, the little clear fishes swimming up to the brim.

"Oh, no, not chinaberry flowers—secret ingredients," said Miss Baby Marie. "My cosmetics have secret ingredients—not chinaberry flowers."

"It's purple," Livvie breathed, and Miss Baby Marie said, "Use it freely. Rub it on."

Livvie tiptoed out to the wash stand on the front porch and before the mirror put the paint on her mouth. In the wavery surface her face danced before her like a flame. Miss Baby Marie followed her out, took a look at what she had done, and said, "That's it."

Livvie tried to say "Thank you" without moving her parted lips where the paint lay so new.

By now Miss Baby Marie stood behind Livvie and looked in the mirror over her shoulder, twisting up the tassels of her hair. "The lipstick I can let you have for only two dollars," she said, close to her neck.

"Lady, but I don't have no money, never did have," said Livvie.

"Oh, but you don't pay the first time. I make another trip, that's the way I do. I come back again—later."

"Oh," said Livvie, pretending she understood everything so as to please the lady.

"But if you don't take it now, this may be the last time I'll call at your house," said Miss Baby Marie sharply. "It's far away from anywhere, I'll tell you that. You don't live close to anywhere."

"Yes'm. My husband, he keep the *money,*" said Livvie, trembling. "He is strict as he can be. He don't know *you* walk in here—Miss Baby Marie!"

"Where is he?"

"Right now, he in yonder asleep, an old man. I wouldn't ever ask him for anything."

Miss Baby Marie took back the lipstick and packed it up. She gathered up the jars for both black and white and got them all inside the suitcase, with the same little fuss of triumph with which she had brought them out. She started away.

"Goodbye," she said, making herself look grand from the back, but at the last minute she turned around in the door. Her old hat wobbled as she whispered, "Let me see your husband."

Livvie obediently went on tiptoe and opened the door to the other room. Miss Baby Marie came behind her and rose on her toes and looked in.

"My, what a little tiny old, old man!" she whispered, clasping her hands and shaking her head over them. "What a beautiful quilt! What a tiny old, old man!"

"He can sleep like that all day," whispered Livvie proudly.

They looked at him awhile so fast asleep, and then all at

once they looked at each other. Somehow that was as if they had a secret, for he had never stirred. Livvie then politely, but all at once, closed the door.

"Well! I'd certainly like to leave you with a lipstick!" said Miss Baby Marie vivaciously. She smiled in the door.

"Lady, but I told you I don't have no money, and never did have."

"And never will?" In the air and all around, like a bright halo around the white lady's nodding head, it was a true spring day.

"Would you take eggs, lady?" asked Livvie softly.

"No, I have plenty of eggs—plenty," said Miss Baby Marie.

"I still don't have no money," said Livvie, and Miss Baby Marie took her suitcase and went on somewhere else.

Livvie stood watching her go, and all the time she felt her heart beating in her left side. She touched the place with her hand. It seemed as if her heart beat and her whole face flamed from the pulsing color of her lips. She went to sit by Solomon and when he opened his eyes he could not see a change in her. "He's fixin' to die," she said inside. That was the secret. That was when she went out of the house for a little breath of air.

She went down the path and down the Natchez Trace a way, and she did not know how far she had gone, but it was not far, when she saw a sight. It was a man, looking like a vision—she standing on one side of the Old Natchez Trace and he standing on the other.

As soon as this man caught sight of her, he began to look

himself over. Starting at the bottom with his pointed shoes, he began to look up, lifting his peg-top pants the higher to see fully his bright socks. His coat long and wide and leaf-green he opened like doors to see his high-up tawny pants and his pants he smoothed downward from the points of his collar, and he wore a luminous baby-pink satin shirt. At the end, he reached gently above his wide platter-shaped round hat, the color of a plum, and one finger touched at the feather, emerald green, blowing in the spring winds.

No matter how she looked, she could never look so fine as he did, and she was not sorry for that, she was pleased.

He took three jumps, one down and two up, and was by her side.

"My name is Cash," he said.

He had a guinea pig in his pocket. They began to walk along. She stared on and on at him, as if he were doing some daring spectacular thing, instead of just walking beside her. It was not simply the city way he was dressed that made her look at him and see hope in its insolence looking back. It was not only the way he moved along kicking the flowers as if he could break through everything in the way and destroy anything in the world, that made her eyes grow bright. It might be, if he had not appeared the way he did appear that day she would never have looked so closely at him, but the time people come makes a difference.

They walked through the still leaves of the Natchez Trace, the light and the shade falling through trees about them, the white irises shining like candles on the banks and the new ferns shining like green stars up in the oak branches.

They came out at Solomon's house, bottle trees and all. Livvie stopped and hung her head.

Cash began whistling a little tune. She did not know what it was, but she had heard it before from a distance, and she had a revelation. Cash was a field hand. He was a transformed field hand. Cash belonged to Solomon. But he had stepped out of his overalls into this. There in front of Solomon's house he laughed. He had a round head, a round face, all of him was young, and he flung his head up, rolled it against the mare's-tail sky in his round hat, and he could laugh just to see Solomon's house sitting there. Livvie looked at it, and there was Solomon's black hat hanging on the peg on the front door, the blackest thing in the world.

"I been to Natchez," Cash said, wagging his head around against the sky. "*I* taken a trip, *I* ready for Easter!"

How was it possible to look so fine before the harvest? Cash must have stolen the money, stolen it from Solomon. He stood in the path and lifted his spread hand high and brought it down again and again in his laughter. He kicked up his heels. A little chill went through her. It was as if Cash was bringing that strong hand down to beat a drum or to rain blows upon a man, such an abandon and menace were in his laugh. Frowning, she went closer to him and his swinging arm drew her in at once and the fright was crushed from her body, as a little match-flame might be smothered out by what it lighted. She gathered the folds of his coat behind him and fastened her red lips to his mouth, and she was dazzled by herself then, the way he had been dazzled at himself to begin with.

In that instant she felt something that could not be told —that Solomon's death was at hand, that he was the same to her as if he were dead now. She cried out, and uttering little cries turned and ran for the house.

At once Cash was coming, following after, he was running behind her. He came close, and half-way up the path he laughed and passed her. He even picked up a stone and sailed it into the bottle trees. She put her hands over her head, and sounds clattered through the bottle trees like cries of outrage. Cash stamped and plunged zigzag up the front steps and in at the door.

When she got there, he had stuck his hands in his pockets and was turning slowly about in the front room. The little guinea pig peeped out. Around Cash, the pinned-up palmettos looked as if a lazy green monkey had walked up and down and around the walls leaving green prints of his hands and feet.

She got through the room and his hands were still in his pockets, and she fell upon the closed door to the other room and pushed it open. She ran to Solomon's bed, calling "Solomon! Solomon!" The little shape of the old man never moved at all, wrapped under the quilt as if it were winter still.

"Solomon!" She pulled the quilt away, but there was another one under that, and she fell on her knees beside him. He made no sound except a sigh, and then she could hear in the silence the light springy steps of Cash walking and walking in the front room, and the ticking of Solomon's silver watch, which came from the bed. Old Solomon was far away in his sleep, his face looked small, relentless, and devout, as if he were walking somewhere where she could imagine the snow falling.

Then there was a noise like a hoof pawing the floor, and the door gave a creak, and Cash appeared beside her. When she looked up, Cash's face was so black it was bright, and so bright and bare of pity that it looked sweet to her. She stood up and held up her head. Cash was so powerful that his presence gave her strength even when she did not need any.

Under their eyes Solomon slept. People's faces tell of things and places not known to the one who looks at them while they sleep, and while Solomon slept under the eyes of Livvie and Cash his face told them like a mythical story that all his life he had built, little scrap by little scrap, respect. A beetle could not have been more laborious or more ingenious in the task of its destiny. When Solomon was young, as he was in his picture overhead, it was the infinite thing with him, and he could see no end to the respect he would contrive and keep in a house. He had built a lonely house, the way he would make a cage, but it grew to be the same with him as a great monumental pyramid and sometimes in his absorption of getting it erected he was like the builder-slaves of Egypt who forgot or never knew the origin and meaning of the thing to which they gave all the strength of their bodies and used up all their days. Livvie and Cash could see that as a man might rest from a life-labor he lay in his bed, and they could hear how, wrapped in his quilt, he sighed to himself comfortably in sleep, while in his dreams he might have been an ant, a beetle, a bird, an Egyptian, assembling and carrying on his back and building with his hands, or he might have been an old man of India or a swaddled baby, about to smile and brush all away.

Then without warning old Solomon's eyes flew wide open under the hedge-like brows. He was wide awake.

And instantly Cash raised his quick arm. A radiant sweat stood on his temples. But he did not bring his arm down—it stayed in the air, as if something might have taken hold.

It was not Livvie—she did not move. As if something said "Wait," she stood waiting. Even while her eyes burned under motionless lids, her lips parted in a stiff grimace, and with her arms stiff at her sides she stood above the prone old man and the panting young one, erect and apart.

Movement when it came came in Solomon's face. It was an old and strict face, a frail face, but behind it, like a covered light, came an animation that could play hide and seek, that would dart and escape, had always escaped. The mystery flickered in him, and invited from his eyes. It was that very mystery that Cash with his quick arm would have to strike, and that Livvie could not weep for. But Cash only stood holding his arm in the air, when the gentlest flick of his great strength, almost a puff of his breath, would have been enough, if he had known how to give it, to send the old man over the obstruction that kept him away from death.

If it could not be that the tiny illumination in the fragile and ancient face caused a crisis, a mystery in the room that would not permit a blow to fall, at least it was certain that

Cash, throbbing in his Easter clothes, felt a pang of shame that the vigor of a man would come to such an end that he could not be struck without warning. He took down his hand and stepped back behind Livvie, like a round-eyed schoolboy on whose unsuspecting head the dunce cap has been set.

"Young ones can't wait," said Solomon.

Livvie shuddered violently, and then in a gush of tears she stooped for a glass of water and handed it to him, but he did not see her.

"So here come the young man Livvie wait for. Was no prevention. No prevention. Now I lay eyes on young man and it come to be somebody I know all the time, and been knowing since he were born in a cotton patch, and watched grow up year to year, Cash McCord, growed to size, growed up to come in my house in the end—ragged and barefoot."

Solomon gave a cough of distaste. Then he shut his eyes vigorously, and his lips began to move like a chanter's.

"When Livvie married, her husband were already somebody. He had paid great cost for his land. He spread sycamore leaves over the ground from wagon to door, day he brought her home, so her foot would not have to touch ground. He carried her through his door. Then he growed old and could not lift her, and she were still young."

Livvie's sobs followed his words like a soft melody repeating each thing as he stated it. His lips moved for a little without sound, or she cried too fervently, and unheard he might have been telling his whole life, and then he said,

"God forgive Solomon for sins great and small. God forgive Solomon for carrying away too young girl for wife and keeping her away from her people and from all the young people would clamor for her back."

Then he lifted up his right hand toward Livvie where she stood by the bed and offered her his silver watch. He dangled it before her eyes, and she hushed crying; her tears stopped. For a moment the watch could be heard ticking as it always did, precisely in his proud hand. She lifted it away. Then he took hold of the quilt; then he was dead.

Livvie left Solomon dead and went out of the room. Stealthily, nearly without noise, Cash went beside her. He was like a shadow, but his shiny shoes moved over the floor in spangles, and the green downy feather shone like a light in his hat. As they reached the front room, he seized her deftly as a long black cat and dragged her hanging by the waist round and round him, while he turned in a circle, his face bent down to hers. The first moment, she kept one arm and its hand stiff and still, the one that held Solomon's watch. Then the fingers softly let go, all of her was limp, and the watch fell somewhere on the floor. It ticked away in the still room, and all at once there began outside the full song of a bird.

They moved around and around the room and into the brightness of the open door, then he stopped and shook her once. She rested in silence in his trembling arms, unprotesting as a bird on a nest. Outside the redbirds were flying and crisscrossing, the sun was in all the bottles on the prisoned trees, and the young peach was shining in the middle of them with the bursting light of spring.

LIVVIE IS BACK

1. What essentials are established in the first paragraph?
2. How does Miss Welty make it clear that Solomon's home was an alien world to Livvie? Which one possession of her own makes dramatic this life in an alien world?
3. What symbolic meaning does the coming of spring have in this story? What is the purpose of the scene of the men and women, boys and girls at work? Of the last paragraph?
4. How does the incident with Miss Baby Marie and the chinaberry lipstick help prepare for the end of the story? Of what was Livvie reminded?
5. ". . . but the time people come makes a difference." How does this apply to Cash's initial appearance and its consequences?
6. Cash was ". . . a transformed field hand" of Solomon's. Why did he have such an instant appeal to Livvie? What one particular detail makes this clear?
7. What is the significance of Cash's sailing the stone into Solomon's bottle trees?
8. What quality of Solomon's arrested Cash's arm in mid-air?

9. What did Solomon mean by "Young ones can't wait"? Why did he describe Cash as coming ". . . in my house in the end —ragged and barefoot"?
10. What mistake did Solomon realize he had made? How did he try to atone for it?
11. Why, in almost the very presence of the dead man, are we satisfied with the concluding incident?
12. "Livvie Is Back"—to what?

JESSAMYN WEST

1907–

Learn to Say Good-by

BORN IN INDIANA *of Quaker parents, Miss West attended a Quaker college in California and wrote her first successful book,* The Friendly Persuasion, *about the life of a Quaker family of the nineteenth century. She also attended the University of California and later adopted the state for her home.*

Much of her work was published originally in the New Yorker *magazine. In addition to* The Friendly Persuasion, *Miss West has written* The Witch Diggers, *a novel, and* Cress Delahanty, *a series of charming stories about an adolescent girl. During the summers Miss West frequently appears as a lecturer at writing conferences.*

"Learn to Say Good-by" originally appeared in the New Yorker *under the title "The Lesson."*

John Thomas had awakened thinking of Curly—or, rather, when he woke up, he did not stop thinking of Curly, for all night he had been with the young steer, encouraging him, patting him on his curling forelock, leading him before the admiring judges. The boy was wide awake now, yet Curly's image was still as strongly with him as in the dream—the heavy shoulders, the great barrel, the short legs, the red coat shining with health and with the many brushings John

Thomas had given it. And Curly's face! The boy's own face crinkled happily as he thought of it, and then turned scornful as he thought of the people who said one baby beef was just like another. Curly looked at you with intelligence. His eyes weren't just hairless spots on his head, like the eyes of most baby beeves. They showed that Curly knew when eating time had come and that he understood the difference between being told he was a lazy old cuss and a prize-winning baby beef. You had only to say to him, "You poor old steer," and he put his head down and looked at you as much as to say he knew it was true and not to kid him about it. John Thomas remembered a hundred humors and shrewdnesses of Curly's, and lay in bed smiling about them —the way he had of getting the last bite of mash out of his feed pail, and his cleverness in evading the vet, and how he would lunge at Wolf when the collie barked at him.

"This is the day!" John Thomas said aloud. "This is the day!"

Across the hall came a girl's sleepy voice. "Johnny, you promised to be quiet."

John Thomas didn't answer. No use arguing with Jo when she was sleepy. He sat up and slipped his arms into the sleeve of his bathrobe, and then stepped onto the floor boards, which were so much cooler than the air, and walked slowly, because he wanted so much to walk fast, to the window.

There Curly was, standing with his nose over the corral fence looking up toward John Thomas's window. Curly acts as if he knows, the boy thought. I bet he does know.

"Hey, Curly!" he called softly. "How you feel this morning? Feel like a prize baby beef? Feel like the best steer in California? First prize for Curly?" Curly swished his tail. "Don't you worry, Curly. You *are* the best."

John Thomas knew he was going to have to go in and talk to Jo, even though she'd be mad at being waked so early. If he stood another minute looking at Curly—so beautiful in his clean corral, with the long blue early-morning shadows of the eucalyptus falling across it—and listening to the meadow larks off in the alfalfa and remembering that this was the day, he'd give a whoop, and that would make both Jo and Pop mad. He tiptoed across the hall, opened his sister's door, and looked at her room with distaste. Grown-up girls like Jo, almost twenty, ought to be neater. All girls ought to be neater. The clothes Jo had taken off before she went to sleep made a path from her door to her bed, starting with her shoes and hat and ending with her underwear. Curly's corral's neater, he thought, and said, "It's time to get up, Jo!"

Jo rolled over on her face and groaned. John Thomas stepped over Jo's clothes and sat down on the edge of the bed.

Jo groaned again. "*Please* don't wake me up yet, Johnny," she said.

"You're already awake. You're talking."

"I'm talking in my sleep."

"I don't care if you don't wake up, if you'll talk. I've seen Curly already. He looks pretty good. He looks like he knows it's the day."

"He's dead wrong, then. It's still the night."

John Thomas laughed. If he got Jo to arguing, she'd wake up. "It's six o'clock," he said.

Jo, still face down, raised herself on one elbow and looked at her wrist watch. Then she whirled onto her back, stuck one leg out from under the sheet, and gave her brother a kick that set him down on the floor with a thud. "Why, John Thomas Hobhouse!" she said indignantly. "It's only five-fifteen and Nicky didn't get me home until two. You're so kind to that damned old steer of yours, but you don't care whether your own sister gets any sleep or not."

John Thomas bounced back onto the bed. Jo looked at him sharply and he knew what was to come.

"What have you got on under that bathrobe, John Thomas Hobhouse?" she demanded. "Did you sleep in your underwear last night?"

"I slept in my shorts."

"That's a filthy thing to do."

"You say it's filthy if I don't wear them in the daytime and filthy if I do wear them at night. What's daylight or dark got to do with it? Now, if I—"

"Look, Johnny, let's not get started on that. There are some things you're going to have to do that aren't reasonable. Once school starts, you'll be spending some nights with the other boys, and their mothers will be saying I don't look after you, and let you sleep in your underwear."

"I don't do it away from home, Jo, but it was so hot last night. You tell Mrs. Henny to do my ducks up special for today? Boy, wait till you see me and Curly go by the grandstand! Wait till you see us in the ring when Curly wins!"

"When Curly wins! Maybe he won't win, Johnny."

"Maybe the judges *won't* see he's best—but they will if they're any good."

John Thomas lay on his stomach, hanging his head over the edge of the bed until his long pompadour spread out on the floor like a dust mop and his face was out of Jo's sight. "I prayed about today," he said.

"Did you, Johnny?"

"Yep, but I didn't think it was fair to pray for Curly to win." He heaved himself up and down, so that his hair flicked back and forth across the floor. "A lot of kids probably did pray they'd win, though."

Jo regarded him with tenderness and amazement. "I never would have thought most of the kids who go to the fair had ever heard of praying," she said.

"Oh, sure, they all heard of it," Johnny said. "And when it comes to something important like this, they all think you ought to try everything. But I didn't ask for Curly to win. I just prayed the judges would be good and know their stuff. If they do, Curly will get the blue ribbon, all right. With everyone else asking to win, I thought maybe that would kind of make an impression on God."

It made an impression on Jo. Lord, she thought, I'm a heathen. "What do you care whether or not Curly wins, if you know he's best?" she asked.

John Thomas heaved his head and shoulders up onto the bed and lay on his stomach with his face near Jo's. "How can you wear those tin things in your hair?" he asked. Then he answered her question. "I know for sure Curly's best, but *he* don't. He knows he's good, but he don't know he's that good. I want him to win so he can have the blue ribbon on his halter and walk up in front of the people while all the other baby beeves watch him."

"You going to walk with him, kid?" Jo asked.

"Yep, I got to."

"Kinda nice to have the other kids watch, too."

This slyness tickled John Thomas and he laughed. No use trying to fool Jo about anything. "Anyway, it's mostly Curly," he said.

Jo started taking the curlers out of her hair. She tucked them, one by one, into Johnny's bush of hair as she took them out. "Remember when Curly got bloated?" she asked. "You weren't much help then. You cried and didn't want the vet to stick him."

"Yeah, but, Jo, it looked so awful. To take a knife and stick it inside him. And Curly was so darned scared." He spoke dreamily, with the satisfaction and relief of dangers past. "He looked like he was going to have a calf, didn't he? And I guess it hurt more."

"Yep, Johnny. A cow's made to have a calf, but a steer isn't made to have gas. Hand me my comb. Top left-hand drawer."

John Thomas got up and stood looking at himself in the mirror. His hair was thick enough to keep the curlers from dropping out.

"You look like an African Bushman," Jo said. "Come on, get that comb."

When John Thomas handed it to her, she began loosening her sausagelike curls. He watched her turn the fat little sausages into big frankfurters.

"Time to get dressed, kid," she said. "Jump into your ducks. They're all done up fresh and hanging in your closet."

"Do you think I've been giving him too much mash, Jo?" Johnny asked. "Does he look kind of soft to you? Too fat?"

"He looks just right to me. But it's all over now. No use worrying any more. This time tomorrow, he'll be someone else's problem."

John Thomas sat down on the window sill and looked out at the tank house. The sunlight lay on it in a slab as heavy and yellow as a bar of naphtha soap. There was already a dance of heat out across the alfalfa fields. White clouds were boiling up from behind purple Tahquitz. The morning-glories were beginning to shut themselves against the sun. This was the day all right, but he could not think ahead until tomorrow, when Curly would have been sold.

The boy made the width of the room in three jack-rabbit hops, and banged the door behind him.

Jo swung herself out of her bed and her nightgown in a single looping movement and stood before her mirror. I guess it's hell to be thirteen and not have a mother, and to love a steer that's going to be beefsteak in forty-eight hours, she thought somberly. I ought to take better care of Johnny, and Dad ought to wake up from remembering Mother. He's been that way ever since she died.

But the air flowed like liquid silk about her naked body,

and she lifted her arms and tautened her body, thinking no longer of John Thomas but of Nicky. She regarded her image with affection and pride. I don't know where I would change it, she thought. The sound of Johnny's leaps down the stairs—four house-shuddering thuds—and his cracked voice calling out to Mrs. Henny made her look at her watch. Almost six. Jo grabbed fresh underwear from the drawer and ran for the bathroom.

When Jo came downstairs, ten minutes later, all dressed except for putting on the scarf and belt that were hanging over her shoulders, she saw her father seated at the table on the screened porch where they ate breakfast in summer and reading the morning paper. She was fond of her father, but in one respect he was unsatisfactory: She didn't like his appearance. He didn't look fatherly to her. There wasn't any gray in his black hair or any stoop to his shoulders, and her girl friends exasperated her by saying, "I could go for your old man."

He called to her now, "Tell Mrs. Henny we're ready to eat."

Jo went through the porch door into the sunny kitchen, where Mrs. Henny was slicing peaches for breakfast. She was already dressed for the fair, in a lavender dotted swiss with a lavender ribbon through her bobbed gray hair. "Hello, Mrs. Henny," Jo said. "Dad says let's eat. Gee, you look swell!"

"I thought I'd better wear something light," Mrs. Henny

said. "It's going to be hot as a little red wagon today. Take these peaches out with you. Time you've finished them, everything else will be ready."

Jo stopped to buckle on her belt and tie her scarf. Then she took the peaches out to the porch. Her father put the Los Angeles *Times* under his chair and took his dish of peaches out of her hand. "Well, Josephine," he said, "considering you only had three hours' sleep last night, you don't look so bad."

"You hear me come in?"

"Nope, but I heard that fellow drive away. He ran into everything loose and bangable on the place. What's wrong with him?"

"Blind with love, I guess," Jo said lightly.

Her father held his third spoonful of sugar poised over his peaches. "I take it that you have no impairment in your eyesight," he said.

"Things look a little rosy, but the outline's still plain, I think."

Mrs. Henny came in with the eggs and bacon and muffins. "I don't want to hurry you," she said, pausing, on her way out, at the kitchen door, "but it's not getting any earlier."

"Where did Johnny go?" Jo asked. "He ought to be eating. He'll be sick this afternoon if he doesn't eat." She took two muffins, buttered them, and put them on Johnny's plate.

"He's out talking to Curly. You'd better call him."

"Dad, what's Johnny going to do about not having Curly

any more after today?" Jo asked. "You know he acts as if Curly were a dog—or a brother."

"Oh, Johnny's all right. He knows what the score is," her father said, with his mouth full of muffin and scrambled eggs. "But call him, call him. We've less than an hour to eat and load the steer. I ought to have taken him down last night, but John Thomas was afraid Curly would look peaked today if he spent a night away from home."

"Remember John Thomas's kitten?"

"Kitten?" said her father grumpily. "He's had a dozen."

"This was the one he had when he broke his leg. Don't you remember? He said, 'Let's never let her see herself in a mirror, and then she'll think she's just like us, only smaller.' He's that way about Curly now, you know. He never lets Curly know there's any other difference than size between them."

"Doesn't he know where Curly'll be tomorrow?"

"He *must* know it, but he hasn't felt it yet."

"Well, call him, call him," her father said. He got up from the table and stood with his back to her. "He can't learn to say good-by any earlier."

He's thinking of Mama, Jo thought, and walked slowly out through the screen door and down the steps into the sunshine, eating a muffin-and-bacon sandwich as she went. She stopped at the foot of the steps to pick up the cat, and balanced him, heavy and purring, on her shoulder, and let him lick the last of the muffin crumbs from her fingers. "Oh, Nicky, Nicky," she murmured, pressing her face close against the cat's soft, furry side. Then she saw Johnny, sitting hunched up on the top rail of the corral, looking at Curly. "Well, Bud," she called out, "he looks like silk!"

"He's kind of rough on the left flank," Johnny said as she came and stood beside him. "Been rubbing against something. Can you notice it? I been working on it."

"Can't see a thing," Jo said. "Now, look here, John Thomas, you're going to make him nervous, sitting there staring at him—give him the jitters before he ever gets to the fair. You'll spoil his morale. Dad let you keep him here till this morning when he didn't want to, so don't you gum things up now."

John Thomas slid to the ground. "So long, Curly," he said. "I got to eat now." And he ran for the house.

A little before eight, they all drove into Verdant, the county seat—Mr. Hobhouse and Mrs. Henny and Jo and Johnny in the car, and Curly in the trailer behind them. "Awnings up early this morning," said Mr. Hobhouse as they moved slowly forward in the already long line of cars. "Going to be a scorcher, I guess. Flags look dead when there isn't any wind, don't they?"

Jo, who was riding beside her father in the front seat, nodded, but nothing looked dead to her. She loved the beginning-again look of a town in the morning—the sidewalks sluiced down, the vegetables fresh and shining, the storekeepers in clean shirts, the feeling that nothing that had been spilled or broken or hurt or wronged the day before need be carried over into the new day. The heat made her sleepy, and because she wouldn't be seeing Nicky until evening, the day seemed dreamlike, unimportant. She would move through it, be kind to Johnny, and wait for evening and Nicky again. Her father swerved sharply to avoid hitting a car that had swung, without signaling, out of the line of cars heading for the fair.

"Hey, Pop, take it easy!" John Thomas yelled anxiously from the back seat, where he sat with Mrs. Henny. "You almost busted Curly's ribs then."

"John Thomas ought to be riding back there with that steer," declared Mrs. Henny. "Or else I wish I could have rid in the trailer and the steer could have set here with John Thomas. The boy hasn't done a thing since we started but put his feet in my lunch basket and squirm, till I've got a rash watching him."

"Hold out five minutes longer, both of you, and we'll be there," Mr. Hobhouse said.

Jo roused herself, lifted her eyelids, which seemed weighted down with the heat, and turned around. "Hi ya, Johnny," she murmured.

As soon as they were well inside the fairgrounds, her father maneuvered out of the line of cars and stopped. "Jo, you and Mrs. Henny had better get out here," he said. "It'll take me and Johnny some time to get Curly unloaded."

As Jo climbed out, John Thomas touched her arm. "You'll sure be there, won't you, Sis?" he asked.

"Where?"

"In the grandstand for the parade at ten-thirty. All the baby beeves."

"Johnny, where'd you think I'd be then? Looking at the

pickle exhibit, maybe? Of course I'll be there. Just you and Curly listen when you go by the stand. You'll hear me roar."

"Hurry up, you two," said her father. "It's getting late."

"When's the judging, Johnny?" Jo asked.

"Two-thirty. Front of the Agriculture Pavilion," he replied.

"I'll see you then. Don't worry. I think the judges are going to know their business." She poked a finger through the trailer's bars and touched Curly. "So long, Curly. You do your stuff!"

Her father edged the car and trailer back into the line of traffic. Mrs. Henny lumbered off, with a campstool on one arm and the lunch basket on the other, and Jo was left alone. The day was already blistering and she was glad. She took no pleasure in a moderately warm day, but a record breaker, one that challenged her ability to survive, elated her. She went into one of the exhibition buildings and walked through acres of handiwork, wondering if she would ever find life so empty that she would need to fill it with the making of such ugly and useless articles. Children whimpered as mothers jerked them doggedly through the heat. Oh, Nicky, I promise you never to be like them, Jo thought.

She was in the grandstand at ten-thirty when a voice from the loudspeaker announced, "Ladies and gentlemen! The Future Farmers of Riverbank County and their baby beeves will now pass in front of the grandstand for your inspection. At two-thirty, the final judging will take place in front of the Agriculture Pavilion, and after that the steers will be auctioned to the highest bidders. I'm proud to announce that there isn't a first-rate hotel in Los Angeles that hasn't a representative here to bid in one or more of these famous Riverbank beeves. There they come now, ladies and gentlemen, through the west gate. Let's give them a big hand—the Future Farmers of Riverbank County!"

Jo craned forward to watch the long line of steers and boys move proudly in review before the grandstand. The steers were mostly Herefords, shining like bright-russet leather in the blazing sun. Jo had not realized how thoroughly John Thomas had convinced her of Curly's superiority. She looked down the long line, expecting Curly, by some virtue of size or spirit, to be distinct from all the others.

A woman leaned heavily against her to nudge a friend in the row below them. "There they are!" she said excitedly.

Jo followed their glances before it occurred to her that they were not talking about John Thomas and Curly. Finally, she saw them, well along toward the end of the line, the steer like the other red steers, the boy like the other white-clothed boys. But unlike, too, for surely no other boy walked with the sensitive, loving pride of her brother. Then she saw that Johnny was the only boy who did not lead his animal by a halter or rope. He walked beside Curly, with only a hand on his neck. Idiot, thought Jo, he's put something over on somebody; he ought not to be doing that.

She stood up and, to fulfill her promise, shouted, over

and over, "Hi, Johnny! Hi, Curly!," until a man behind her jerked her skirt and said, "Sit down, Sis, you're not made of cellophane."

After the boys and the steers had circled the grandstand and passed through the west gate again and out of sight, Jo closed her eyes and half slept, hearing as in a dream the announcement of the next event. She fully awakened, though, when someone wedged himself into the narrow space that separated her from the stair railing on her right.

"Dad! Where did you come from?" she exclaimed.

"I was up above you," her father said. "Well, the boy's having his day. You're half asleep, Jo."

"More than half. Where's the car? I think I'll go and sleep in it until the judging. I've seen all the Yo-yo pillows and canned apricots I can take in one day."

"I don't know whether you can find the car or not," her father said. "It's over in the first nine or ten rows of cars back of the dining tents. Here's the key, and don't forget to lock it when you leave."

Jo slept for a long time, doubled up on the back seat of the car, and then awakened with a sudden sick start. She seemed to be drowning in heat, and the velours of the seat she was sleeping on was a quicksand that held her down. She looked at her watch and saw with consternation that it was after four o'clock.

She had a long way to go to reach the Agriculture Pavilion, and because she was so angry with herself and still so sleepy, she ran clumsily, bumping into people. I'm so full of fair promises, she accused herself bitterly, and now I've let poor Johnny down. She wanted to hurt herself running—punish herself—and she finally reached the Pavilion with a sick, cutting pain in her side and a taste of sulphur in her throat. A deep circle of onlookers stood around the judging ring, laughing and talking quietly. At last, she saw Johnny and her father in the front line of the circle, a little to her left. Paying no heed to the sour looks she got, she pushed her way to them. John Thomas saw what she had done and frowned. "You oughtn't to do that, Jo," he said. "People'll think we can get away with anything just because we own the winner."

"Has Curly won already?" Jo asked.

"No, not yet," Johnny said. "Couldn't you see the judging where you were?"

"Not very well," Jo said. "No, I couldn't see a thing."

She looked now at the animals that were still in the ring, and saw that Curly was there with three other Herefords and an enormous Black Angus. He was wearing a halter now, and one of the judge's assistants was leading him. Unless one of the five steers had a cast in his eye or a tick in his ear, Jo did not see how any man living could say that one was an iota better than another. She knew the points in judging as well as Johnny himself; she had stood by the corral many half-hours after breakfast while Johnny recounted them for her, but while she knew them well, her eye could not limn them out in the living beasts.

"Why're you so sure Curly will win?" she asked Johnny.

"Higgins said he would."

"Who's Higgins?"

Johnny shook his head, too absorbed to answer her question. The judge, an old, bowlegged fellow in a pale-blue sweater, had stopped examining the animals and was reading over some notes he had taken on the back of a dirty envelope. He walked over for another look at the Ayrshire. Seemingly satisfied by what he saw, he took off his gray felt hat and with the back of his hand, wiped away the sweat that had accumulated under the sweatband. He set his hat on the back of his head, stuffed his envelope in a hip pocket, stepped to the edge of the ring, and began to speak.

"Ladies and gentlemen, it gives me great pleasure to be able to announce to you the winner of the Eighteenth Annual Riverbank Baby Beef Contest."

There was a hush as the spectators stopped talking, and Jo tried to find in her father's face some hint of what he thought the decision would be. She saw nothing there but concern. Johnny, though, had a broad and assured smile. His eyes were sparkling; the hour of Curly's recognition had come.

"And I may say," continued the judge, enjoying the suspense he was creating, "that in a lifetime of cattle judging I have never seen an animal that compares with today's winner."

The fool, thought Jo, the damn fool orator! What's got into him? They never do this. Why can't he speak out?

But Johnny looked as if he enjoyed it, as if he knew whose name would be announced when people's ears had become so strained to hear it that it would seem to be articulated not by another's lips but by their own heartbeats.

"The winner, ladies and gentlemen, is that very fine animal, John Thomas Hobhouse's Hereford, Curly!" said the judge.

There was a lot of good-natured hand clapping. A few boys yelled "Nerts!," but the choice was popular with the crowd, most of whom knew and liked the Hobhouses. The judge went on to name the second- and third-prize winners and the honorable mentions. Then he called out, "I would like to present to you Curly's owner, John Thomas Hobhouse himself. Come take a bow, Johnny!"

Jo was proud of the easy, happy way Johnny ran over to his side. The judge put out a hand intended for the boy's shoulder, but before it could settle there, Johnny was pressing his cheek against Curly's big, flat jowl. The steer seemed actually to lower his head for the caress and to move his cheek against Johnny's in loving recognition. This delighted the spectators, who laughed and cheered again.

"Now, ladies and gentlemen, the show's almost over," said the judge. "Only one thing left—the auctioning of these animals—and, believe you me, the enjoyment you've had here is nothing to the enjoyment you're going to have when you bite into one of these big, juicy baby beefsteaks. Now if you'll all just clear the ring. Ladies and gentlemen, may I present that silver-tongued Irish auctioneer, Terence O'Flynn. Terence, the show is all yours."

The non-prize winners were disposed of first and in short

order. They fetched fancy prices, but nothing like what would be paid for the prize winners. The big Los Angeles hotels and the Riverbank Inn liked to be able to advertise "Steaks from Riverbank's Prize Baby Beeves." Jo felt sick at her stomach during the auction. This talk of club steaks and top sirloins seemed indecent to her, in front of animals of whom these cuts were still integral parts. But Johnny seemed unaffected by the auction. "Bet you Curly will get more than that," he said whenever a high price was bid.

"He'll fetch top price," his father answered him shortly. "You'll have a big check tonight, besides your blue ribbon, Johnny." The prize winners were auctioned last. All of them except Curly went to Los Angeles hotels, but the Riverbank Inn, determined not to let outside counties get all the prize winners, bid Curly in for itself.

"I'm not a Riverbank citizen," boomed O'Flynn, but I don't mind admitting, folks, that I'm going to come back the day my good friend Chef Rossi of the Riverbank Inn serves steak from Curly. I know that baby beef is going to yield juices that haven't been equaled since Abel broiled the first steak. If *I* was young Hobhouse, I'd never sell that animal. I'd barbecue it and pick its bones myself."

Most of the animals had already been led into slaughter-house vans and trucks, and the rest were being quickly loaded. A van belonging to Mack's Market, the Riverbank Inn's butchers, backed up to the ring, which now held only Curly and the Ayrshire. As O'Flynn finished speaking, two young fellows in jumpers marked "Mack's" leaped out and came over to give Curly a congratulatory pat before sending him up the runway.

"Well, kid," one said pleasantly to John Thomas, "you got a fine animal here."

Johnny didn't hear him. He was looking at O'Flynn, hearing those last words of his.

Now it's come, thought Jo. Now he's really taken in what he's been preparing Curly for. Now he knows for the first time. Don't look that way, Johnny, she pleaded silently. Oh Johnny, you *must* know you can't keep Curly—you can't keep a fat pet steer.

But Johnny didn't smile. He walked over and stood with one arm about Curly's neck, staring incredulously at O'Flynn. "Nobody's going to pick Curly's bones," he said to the auctioneer. Then he turned to the steer. "Don't you worry, Curly. That guy hasn't got anything to do with you."

There was a sympathetic murmur among the bystanders. "The poor kid's made a pet of him," one man said. "Too bad. Well, he can't learn any earlier."

The men from Mack's Market tried to take the matter rightly. "Look here, Bud," said one of them. "Get yourself a canary. This steer don't want to be nobody's pet. He wants to be beefsteaks." And he put a hand on Curly's halter.

Johnny struck it down. "Don't touch Curly!" he shouted. "He's going home, where he belongs! He's won the prize! That's all he came here to do!"

The circle of onlookers came closer, augmented by passers-by whose ears had caught in Johnny's voice the sound of passion and hurt. The buzzards, Jo thought. She saw Johnny press himself still more closely against Curly, keeping his eyes all the time on O'Flynn. She gripped her father's arm. "Dad, do something!" she cried. "Let Johnny take Curly home. There's plenty of food and room. Johnny wouldn't feel this way about him except for you and me. It's our fault!" She was half crying.

"Yes, this nonsense can't go on," her father agreed, and went quickly over to Johnny.

Jo couldn't hear what he said or see his face, for he stood with his back to her, but she could see Johnny's face, and its anguish and disbelief. At last, the boy turned and threw both arms around Curly's neck and buried his face against the steer's heavy muscles. Jo saw his thin shoulder blades shaking.

When her father turned and came toward her, eyes to the ground, she found she could not say to him any of the bitter things that had been on her tongue's tip.

"Dad," she said, and put her hand out to him.

"There's no use, Jo."

"But he loves Curly so."

"Oh, love!" her father said, and then added more quietly, "It's better to learn to say good-by early than late, Jo."

"I'm going to the car," Jo said, and she turned and ran blindly through the crowd. Because Dad's had to learn, why must Johnny, she thought bitterly.

She got into the front seat and leaned across the wheel, without any attempt to stop crying. Then, as the sobs let up, she pounded the wheel. "No, sir!" she said aloud. "I *won't* learn! I refuse to learn! I'll be an exception."

LEARN TO SAY GOOD-BY

1. Why does Miss West spend most of the first two pages describing the steer? Isn't this the boy's story?
2. Jo is Johnny's sister, but she is also what else to him? What does this relationship foreshadow, established early in the story as it is?
3. Why does Jo say, "Maybe he [Curly] won't win, Johnny"?
4. What sentence of Johnny's reveals his real anxiety? Why could he "not think ahead until tomorrow, when Curly would have been sold"?
5. What is there in Johnny's prayer which enlists our sympathies with Johnny and his problems?
6. Note Miss West's skill in the use of figurative language in the bedroom scene. How does she describe the following: (*a*) Johnny's hair as he lies on his stomach, (*b*) Jo's loosening of her curls, (*c*) Johnny's progress across the bedroom floor, and (*d*) the flow of air around Jo's body?
7. Why does the father say at breakfast, "He can't learn to say good-by any earlier"?

8. Is Jo really concerned about Johnny's making Curly nervous by watching him? Why does she say it?

9. Jo will ". . . be kind to Johnny," but what is her real interest in life at this time?

10. What artistically is gained by showing Johnny's confidence and the father's concern?

11. What words of the auctioneer make Johnny finally realize the true situation?

12. What is the purpose of having one of the men in the crowd repeat the words of the theme of the story?

13. Why does Jo refer to the onlookers and passers-by as buzzards? Why does Miss West speak of these people as onlookers and passers-by?

14. Why does Jo run off when her father says, "Oh, love! . . . It's better to learn to say good-by early than late, Jo"?

THOMAS WOLFE

1900–1938

One of the Girls in Our Party

From Death to Morning, *the volume of fourteen short stories from which "One of the Girls in Our Party" is taken, was said by Wolfe to contain "as good writing as I've done."*

Generally thought of as one of America's most promising novelists, Thomas Wolfe is remembered mainly for Look Homeward, Angel. *Publication of this autobiographical novel made it almost impossible for him to go home to his native Asheville, North Carolina. Two other excellent novels by Wolfe are* You Can't Go Home Again *and* The Web and the Rock.

The mid-day meal was ended and "the tour"—a group of thirty women, all of them teachers from the public schools of the American Middle West—had got up from their tables and left the dining-room of the sedate little Swiss hotel where they were quartered. Now they were gathered in the hall beyond: their voices, shrill, rasping and metallic, were united in a clamor of strident eagerness. In a moment one of the older women, who wore an air of authority, returned to the dining-room, and looking through the door at two young women who were still seated at one of the tables hastily bolting a belated luncheon, called imperatively:

"Miss Turner! Miss Blake! Aren't you coming? The bus is here."

"All right!" Miss Turner, the smaller of the two women, was the one who answered. "In a moment."

"Well, you hurry then," the woman said in an admonishing tone as she turned to go. "Everyone else is ready: we're waiting on you."

"Come on," Miss Turner said quickly, in a lowered tone, as she turned to Miss Blake, "I guess we'd better go. You know how cranky they get if you keep them waiting."

"Well, you go on then," said Miss Blake calmly. "I'm not coming." Miss Turner looked at her with some surprise. "I've decided to pass this one up. I've got some letters to answer, and if I don't do it now, they just won't get answered."

"I know," said Miss Turner. "I haven't written a word to any one in two weeks. The way they keep you on the go there's no time to write." The two women got up from the table, moved toward the door, and there faced each other in a gesture of instinctive farewell. Then for a moment each stood in a constrained and awkward silence, as if waiting for the other one to speak. It was Miss Turner who first broke the pause:

"Well," she said, "I guess that means I won't see you again, will I?"

"Why?" Miss Blake said. "You'll come back here before you get your train, won't you?"

"No," said Miss Turner, "I don't think so. They've taken our baggage to the station and I think we're going to get out there on the way back—I mean, all the girls in *my* party."

"Well," Miss Blake said, in her curiously flat and toneless way, "I guess I won't see you, then—not until we get to Vienna, anyway. I'll see you there."

"Yes," Miss Turner agreed, "and I want to hear all about it, too. I almost wish I were going along with you—I've always wanted to see Italy—I'd almost rather go there than where we're going, but then you can't take in everything at one time, can you?"

"No," Miss Blake agreed, "you certainly can't."

"But I think it's just wonderful how much you do see!" Miss Turner went on with considerable enthusiasm. "I mean, when you consider that the whole tour only lasts six weeks from the time you leave home, it's wonderful how much you do take in, isn't it?"

"Yes," Miss Blake said, "it certainly is."

"Well, good-bye. I guess I'd better go."

"Yes, you'd better," Miss Blake answered. "I wouldn't want you to miss the bus. Good-bye."

"Good-bye," Miss Turner answered, "I'll see you in Vienna. Have a good time, and take care of yourself, now."

"All right," Miss Blake said flatly. "You do the same."

Miss Blake watched the bus go, then turned and went quickly upstairs to her room and set to work on her unfinished letters. She wrote:

England was the first place we went to when we left the ship. We were in England a whole week, but it rained all the time we were in London. The coffee that they drink is awful. All the traffic goes to the left in London, and none of the girls could get used to this. Miss Cramer, who is one of the girls in our party, came within an inch of being run over one day because she was looking in the wrong direction; I know they have a lot of accidents. London was also the place where Miss Jordan slipped and fell and sprained her ankle when getting out of the bus. She is one of the girls in our party. She didn't get to see anything of London because she was in bed all the time we were there and has been walking on a cane with her ankle taped ever since. But we took two bus-tours while we were in London that covered the whole city. In the morning we saw the Bank of England and the Tower of London and the Crown Jewels and came back for lunch to an old inn where Doctor Johnson, who was a good friend of Shakespeare's, used to eat. Miss Barrett was especially interested in this as she teaches English literature in the Senior High at Moline. She is one of the girls in our party. After lunch we saw Trafalgar Square with Nelson's Monument and the National Gallery. We didn't stay long at the National Gallery, we just stopped long enough to say we'd seen it. Then we visited the Houses of Parliament, Westminster Abbey with the Poet's Corner, and Buckingham Palace with the sentinels on duty walking up and down. We got there just as the King and Queen were driving out; we got a good look at her but you could hardly see the King because of the big hat she was wearing. You couldn't help feeling sorry for the poor man. As Miss Webster said, he did look so small and henpecked peeking out from behind the edges of that big hat. Miss Webster is one of the girls in our party.

We also spent a day at Oxford. We had good weather there, it didn't rain at all the day we were there. Then we spent a day at Stratford-on-Avon where Shakespeare was born. But as Miss Webster said, they've fixed that house up a lot since he lived in it. It didn't rain the morning of the day we went to Stratford-on-Avon but it started in again as we were coming back. It rained most of the time we were in England. No wonder everything is so green.

The next country that we visited was Holland. Of all the countries we have been to I like Holland best. Everything was so clean in Holland. We spent three days in Holland, and it didn't rain the whole time we were there. We were in Amsterdam for a day, and we went out to the Island of Marken where all the people were dressed up in their quaint costumes and even the children wore wooden shoes just the same as they have done for hundreds of years. Miss Turner took some pictures of some children. She is making a collection to show to her classes when she gets back home. It is a very interesting collection, and most of the pictures came out very well. Miss Turner is one of the girls in our party.

We spent another whole day at Haarlem and The Hague. We saw the Palace of Peace and some pictures by Rembrandt, including "The Anatomy Lesson," which of course was interesting to me and some more "grist for the mill" as I will be able to make use of all this material in my drawing class when school takes up again.

In Holland we had the nicest guide we met on the whole trip. Every one was crazy about him, we have thought so often of him, and laughed so much about him, since. He was an old man named Singvogel, and when Miss Watson, who is one of the girls in our party asked him what that name meant, he said the name meant Song-Bird, so after that we called him our Song-Bird. You couldn't get the best of Mr. Singvogel, no matter what you said. He always had an answer ready for you. We have laughed so much about it since whenever we thought of Mr. Singvogel.

Singvogel iss my name unt dat means Sonk-birt. Sonk-birt by name, sonk-birt by nature; if you are nice to me perhaps I sink for you. Now ve are comink to de olt shot-tower. It vas conshtructed in de year uff sixteen hundert unt t'venty-nine mit contribushions mait by all de burghers uff de town. De roof is uff golt unt silfer conshtructed vich vas gifen by de laities from deir chewells, ornaments unt odder brecious bossessions. De two fickures dat you see on top uff de olt glock iss subbosed to represent de burgermeister uff dat beriod, Pieter Van Hondercoetter, unt his vife Matilda. Upon de shtroke uff t'ree o'glock you vill see dem come out on de blatform, turn unt shtrike mit golten mallets on de bell—so! it comes now, vatch it!—so! *vun!* de burgermeister shtrikes upon his seit vun time—you see?—so! now! *two!* —de laity shtrikes upon her seit vun time—so! now! *t'ree*— de burgermeister shtrikes upon his seit—now it iss t'ree o'glock— all iss ofer for anodder hour—unt laities, dat's de only time dat a man has effer been known to haf de last vort mit a vooman.

Oh, you couldn't get the best of Mr. Singvogel, we used to tease him but he always had an answer ready for you.

Now, laities, dis tower vas erected at a cost of t'welluf million guilders vich iss fife million dollars in real money. It took ofer sixteen years to built it, de golt, chewells unt odder brecious metals in de roof alone is vort ofer vun million two hundert unt fifty t'ousand dollars. De tower is two hundert unt sixty-t'ree feet tall from top to bottom unt dere iss tree hundert sixty-fife shtone steps in de shtair-case, vun for effery day in de year, engrafed mit de name uff a citizen who gafe money for de tower. If you vould like to gount de shteps yourself you gan now glimb to de top but ass for me I t'ink I shtay here. For ald'ough my name iss Sonk-birt, I am now too olt to fly.

Mr. Singvogel always had a joke for everything. Well, we all climbed up to the top of the tower then and when we got back down Miss Powers said that Mr. Singvogel was wrong because she had counted three hundred and sixty-seven steps both ways, and Miss Turner swore that he was right, that she had made it three hundred and sixty-five both up and down. And then Mr. Singvogel said: "Vell, laities, I tell you how it iss. You are both wronk because I liet to you. I forgot to tell you dis iss leap year, unt ven leap year gomes dere is alvays vun shtep more. Dis year you find dat dere is t'ree hundert sixty-six if you gount again."

Well, we had to laugh then because you couldn't get the best of Mr. Singvogel. But Miss Powers was awfully mad and swore that she was right, that she had counted three hundred and sixty-seven both ways. She and Miss Turner had an argument about it and that's why they've hardly spoken to each other since. But we all liked Holland, it didn't rain there, and every one was crazy about Mr. Singvogel.

We were in Paris for four days, and it only rained once. We were really only there three days, we got there late at night, and we were all so tired that we went to bed as soon as we got to the hotel. But we didn't get much sleep, it was the noisiest place you ever saw, and those little taxi horns they have kept tooting all night long right under your window until it almost drove you crazy. Some of the girls thought they'd lost their baggage, it failed to arrive when we did, they almost had a fit. It didn't get there until the day we left for Switzerland and Miss Bradley said her whole stay in Paris was ruined by worrying about it. Miss Bradley is one of the girls in our party.

We took a bus tour the first day and saw Notre Dame and the Latin Quarter, the Eiffel Tower and the Arch de Triumph, and came back and had lunch at the hotel. After lunch some of the girls went shopping, but the rest of us went to the Louvre. We didn't stay long, just long enough to see what it was like, and to see the Mona Lisa. One night we all had tickets for the Opera, where we saw Faust. The next night we went to the Folies Bergère and the last night we went up to Montmartre in busses to see the night life there.

Today we are in Montreux: this is the place where the tour splits up, some of the party leaving us to take the trip along the Rhine, and then to Munich, Salzburg, and the Bavarian Alps, while the rest of us are seeing Switzerland and Italy. After visiting Milan, Venice, Florence, Rome, and the Austrian Tyrol, we will join up with the other group in Vienna two weeks from now.

All of us were sorry to say good-bye to most of the girls, but we know it will only be for two weeks' time, and we are all looking forward eagerly to our meeting in Vienna and relating our experiences to one another. But, frankly, there are one or two of the girls we wouldn't miss if we never saw them again. There are always one or two on a party like this who can't adjust themselves to the group, and do their best to spoil the trip for every one. That Miss Powers was one of them. She was always losing her baggage, or forgetting something, and leaving it behind; we got so tired of having her yapping all the time that there were three hundred and sixty-seven steps in that old shot tower, that she was right and Miss Turner wrong, until Miss Turner finally said: "All right, have it your own way—there were three hundred and sixty-seven—who cares about it? Only, for heaven's sake, forget about it, and give the rest of us some peace."

Of course, that only made Miss Powers madder than ever, she was furious about it. She was certainly a pest, if I ever saw one. She was forever coming up to one of the girls and asking her to write something in her memory book. She carried that memory book with her wherever she went; I believe she slept with it under her pillow.

Now when one of the girls wants to be funny, she says, "Won't you please write something in my memory book?"—It's become a regular joke with us. But Miss Powers was certainly a nuisance, and none of the girls are sorry to say good-bye to her.

We have been spending the day in Switzerland. We all visited the League of Nations in Geneva and the famous castle of Chillon this morning. This afternoon, while I am writing this letter, every one has gone for a bus tour through the Alps. We are leaving for Rome tonight.

Well, it has been a wonderful trip and a wonderful experience, as well as being very educational. I can hardly wait now until I get home and have time to think over the many beautiful things I have seen.

The tour has been well run and well conducted from start to finish. And on the whole the girls are enthusiastic about the way the trips have been managed. Of course when you have to cover so many countries—we will have covered nine countries—England, Holland, Belgium, France, Switzerland, Italy, Austria, Czechoslovakia, and Germany—by the time we set sail for home again, just thirty-one days after we disembarked—it is wonderful to think of all you do take in in such a short space of time.

I get a little confused sometimes when I try to remember all the places we have been to and all the wonderful things we've seen, and if I come back again I think I will take it a little more slowly and travel in a smaller party, with just a friend or two. But

I'm certainly glad I took this tour, it gives you a chance to look around and pick out the high spots, so you will know what you want to see when you come back a second time. And it has certainly been very educational. Still, I won't be sorry to see home again. I am looking forward to it already.

I'm dying to see you and have a good long talk with you as soon as I get back. I'm starved for news. What has happened? Is Ted still going with the Trumbull girl, or has he found himself a new "inamorata"? ("Ain't love grand?" Especially when you are seventeen—hah! hah!) Have you been out to the lodge this summer, and were Bill and Lola there? Couldn't we get them to take us out the first week-end after I get back? It will be good to get a cup of real coffee for a change. Summer has come and gone before I knew it, and soon autumn will be here again.

. . . and the smell of the woodsmoke in Ohio and the flaming maples, the nights of the frosty stars, the blazing moons that hang the same way in a thousand streets, slanting to silence on the steeple's slope; nights of the wheel, the rail, the bell, the wailing cry along the river's edge, and of the summer's ending, nights of the frost and silence and the barking of a dog, of people listening, and of words unspoken and the quiet heart, and nights of the old October that must come again, must come again, while we are waiting, waiting, waiting in the darkness for all of our friends and brothers who will not return.

I'll see you in September.

ONE OF THE GIRLS IN OUR PARTY

1. The author introduces his characters in the first paragraph. How does he characterize the women? Is there any special reason for describing the hotel as sedate?
2. Note how Wolfe prepares the reader in the paragraph beginning, "'But I think it's just wonderful how much you do see!'" for the irony of the entire story.
3. Who was the one person the girls took time to get to know? What was their interest in that person?
4. What do we learn about Miss Powers and Miss Turner from their stair-climbing experience?
5. Did Miss Blake get to know the girls of her own party?
6. What did she gain from her trip abroad?
7. What is the purpose of the last paragraph?

JESSE STUART

How I Write My Short Stories

Often when you read a story and look at the printed page, you feel that something wonderful has been created. It is an art to be able to make the characters in a story seem like real people to the reader.

It takes a skilled author to make a fictional story seem to be true. As you read such a story, your mind eagerly follows the pictures his words have painted. He describes a rising cloud of dust, a cloud in the sky, a tree beside a road, a highway, or a mountain path so that his reader is able to visualize it.

The people the author is writing about may be similar to your neighbors or to your own family. He is writing about people like those you have seen and those you know. This makes the story so real you might even believe that the author has slipped into your neighborhood to obtain his story. Yet, you have the feeling that you could never write anything as good as this story, which is so funny, so sad, so romantic, or so frightening.

You might say writing a short story is not for you. Well, perhaps it isn't, but you'll never know until after you have tried to write one. Forget about all the stories you have read when you try to write a story of your own. Just sit down, start writing, and be your natural self. Of course when you sit down to write it on a typewriter or with a pen or pencil, you should have some idea about what you are going to write. Write the story as if you were telling it to a friend who is sitting across the table from you.

How can you find a story, and how do you know whether your material is the stuff a story should be made of? There are hundreds of impressions that flash through your mind and some of these you think will make short stories. First let us think of themes we might call eternal. How many of your impressions fit into the category of eternal themes? Love is one of the great themes, but it is not necessarily boy meeting girl. Love is a great word; love your neighbor, love wild animals and wildlife, love your home, your country . . . and most of all, love people.

Then there are stories that can be written about families and family life—your family, or a family that lives close to you. Families are a constant source of stories. There is the man who tries to build his neighborhood to a higher level while one of his neighbors is a man who is trying to tear it down. This creates a conflict and a story with an eternal theme. We have these themes now; our ancestors had them five thousand years ago, and future generations will have them two thousand years hence.

You might overlook these themes because you think they are small ones and no one will want to read about them. But, because they are eternal, people will read them, depending on how well you write the story, hundreds of years from now. For example, read the play *Antigone* by Sophocles, written about twenty-four hundred years ago. Why has *Antigone* survived all these centuries? Sophocles tells of a sister's love for her brother, of the complications that arise, and the tragedy that results. There is both love and hate in this short play, and in the end those who caused the trouble pay for their sins. This is an eternal plot and it will never grow old from overuse. So, find out what is good and durable, something that has lasted for the ages, and it will still be a good theme to use.

When I was a small boy, my parents had a falling out and my mother planned to leave my father. She had packed my sister's, my brother's, and my clothes and had planned to go to her father's, taking us with her. But a rainstorm came up from nowhere, one of the hardest rains I have ever seen fall. While it was raining so hard, we couldn't leave; my mother's and father's tempers cooled, they ironed out their differences, and lived together for forty-nine years. Many years later, in 1937, during a tempest as I was crossing the English Channel for the first time, I wrote this story and called it "The Storm." After World War II, when so many families were torn apart as a result of the war, this story was published all over Europe. It was liked because it had universal appeal.

There are stories in your family and in the family next door to you for you to write about. To people in all countries of the world, family is an important unit. There is love, but not enough, throughout the world. There is hate, too, among people in our country and people in countries over the earth. In every country there is the struggle of man to achieve, and in every country there are those who want to destroy. These are themes of universal appeal for you to use for stories in your high school, or in college, or when you have finished school. Write on the universal themes, and if you weave them through your stories they will have meaning for all people.

Today I am most grateful to my gray-haired English teacher, Mrs. R. E. Hatton, who taught in Greenup High School, because she made me aware of creative expression on paper. She encouraged me and helped me to become a writer and teacher. She told the members of our little English class back in 1923: "Write what you know most about." Out of my English class in Greenup High School came my first short story, "Nest Egg," about my pet rooster. It was written as a theme and published twenty years later in the *Atlantic Monthly;* since then it has been reprinted in college and high school textbooks. Years later, the associate editor of one of America's best magazines said to me: "The finest material sent to us is written by people from the country. Usually this material comes from a journalist who is writing about agricultural products or something about the land. Unfortunately we can only use a small portion of this writing since our magazine must have a balance for readers from all walks of life." Then I said to him, "Why do you think the best writing is coming from writers who live and work on the land?" He replied quickly, "Because they know what they are writing about." This very same thing had been told to me twenty years before by my English teacher, Mrs. Hatton.

It stands to reason, doesn't it, that you can write more and better about something you know well than something you know little about? I am speaking only of creative writing. This principle doesn't apply to research work for which writers must study and read all they can about a person who lived long ago to do a biography of him, or to create an atmosphere of an ancient country, like Greece or Egypt for a play or a novel. It often takes an author years to get the material for such books.

When you write a short story, it is not difficult to know what the first paragraph should include. When you write or speak a simple sentence, such as "John Smith went to town," you know that John Smith is your subject, that he is the one you are talking about, that he is your main interest. So it is with the short story.

You should manage to mention the principal character in the first paragraph, even in the first sentence if you can. There is no need to say: "The road is a winding one from here to Blakesburg. It is five miles long. John Smith went to Blakesburg this morning over this road." This would change the whole setting and make the road the subject instead of John Smith.

If you reverse the order and say that John Smith went to Blakesburg, he went in his car, or he rode horseback, or he walked five miles over a winding road, then you are on your way to the interesting beginning of a short story. Your reader will want to know why he went, and he will want to know what is going to take place when John Smith gets to Blakesburg. You will have the beginning of a story in a few simple sentences.

The procedure is simple if you will think of your story

line instead of thinking about how to write it, for your words will fall into place. If some of the words and sentences are not right, you can revise the story later. What you want to do first is tell your story.

Along with establishing the main character in the first paragraph, mention a few of the minor characters, too, if possible. Once when I was young, I received a bit of advice along this line from Elizabeth Maddox Roberts, who was at that time one of the best known novelists and short story writers in America. She knew that I was from the Hill country of Eastern Kentucky, and she gave me an illustration about using a main character and minor characters. "Let the backbone of the mountain be your main character," she said. "Let the small ridges that extend from the backbone of the mountain be your minor characters."

While handling your characters you can drop in, with one word, with a sentence, or with a paragraph, the background of your story. If you mention the name of a town or city, whether real or fictitious, the reader knows immediately that the story has something to do with village, town, or city life. If you should write a story with a Western setting, you should mention desert or plain, and for a Southern setting, you could mention a cotton field. And it doesn't hurt to mention the name of the state where the story takes place. I have mentioned "hills" or "mountains" and "Kentucky" in the majority of my stories.

It should be very easy for you, the young would-be short story writer, to write in simple, communicative language. Do not feel you must use words so difficult that your readers will have to look them up in a dictionary. When you read the stories that have been carefully selected for this volume, note the simplicity of the language that the authors have used.

Although each author considers his ideas first, his language is important, too, for it is the author's means of conveying the story to the reader. There are few words in the stories in this book for which you will have to use a dictionary to understand their meaning. The ancient Greeks, who have given more cultural heritage to the world than any other country, said simple art is great art. Ernest Hemingway's *The Old Man and the Sea* is an outstanding example of powerful, but simple, writing.

Try to listen to the ordinary conversation of people. You certainly won't want to reproduce all the trivia of the usual conversation, but you can get the feel of the right language for your story. After you get it down on paper, remove all the excess words when you revise your story.

Where did Hemingway get his true-to-life language in *The Old Man and the Sea?* Remember, he was a great fisherman and he absorbed this language from other fishermen who were his friends. Hemingway is noted for his ability to use simple words and weave them into powerful sentences. And it didn't matter if he wrote a story with a setting in Spain, Africa, Cuba, or the United States; he became acquainted with the people he wrote about and listened carefully to their language. When he wrote about war, as he did in two powerful novels, *A Farewell to Arms* and *For Whom the Bell Tolls,* he used the ordinary language of soldiers in combat.

Once I had a college professor who taught creative writing. He said to the class: "Make your language simple. Stop trying to use big words. If you write using big words and stilted language, no one will read what you have written. Try using nouns as verbs and verbs as nouns. And for fast action in a story, use short, simple sentences." I didn't think he knew what he was talking about, but I followed his instruction and at least twenty short stories I wrote for his class in college have sold to large circulation magazines in America. His pupils from that small class, up to the present time, have published over one hundred books.

There is also the *feeling* for words that one who writes should have. This sensitivity must be a part of your physical make-up; nobody can give it to you, nor can it be taught to you by your teachers. Since you as the writer must project yourself into your characters, you must feel the joy a character feels when he is happy about something, and you must be able to weep with a character you are writing about who has lost his best friend. You have to project yourself into every character you put down on paper and tell your story with feeling, in simple, communicative language. You might, by writing many short stories, tell one of the more powerful stories that will become a classic in American literature.

After the story is down on paper comes the job I am most reluctant to perform—the revising or rewriting, the drudgery of the process of story writing. But it must be done. In the process of revising, remove the repetitious lines; change verbs and modifiers. Switch nouns to verbs and verbs to nouns. Play with the language, remembering always to keep it simple. A simple adjective may have to be changed half a dozen times. In paragraphs of action, shorten the sentences. In rewriting paragraphs you may want to switch their order. Nearly all of my stories are revised twice, and very often three times. I have revised a few stories seven and eight times. As a rule, don't do all of your revising at a single sitting. If it isn't quite right, and by being quite right I mean if it doesn't suit you, if it doesn't excite and communicate, lay it aside for another revision at another time.

All around you, wherever you live, are stories that are going to waste every day. This world is full of unwritten stories. It is up to you to utilize this raw material, to select the important from the unimportant, and to weave it into the fabric of polished short stories to be added to America's literary heritage.

Now that you have read Jesse Stuart's chapter on "How I Write My Short Stories," you noted that he gets his ideas for stories from the commonplace, the day-to-day occurrences that many of us might overlook. Every day we come into contact with people, we observe human and animal behavior, we watch man battle against the rain, the heat, or the drought. What are his problems? How does he meet the challenges? What does he learn from his experiences? The answers to these questions make for short story (and short short story) plots.

You who have read the stories in this book may want to try your hand at story writing; perhaps you may want to try first to write a short short story. You may remember that in our Introductory Notes we defined the short short story as one of about one thousand words. It is frequently printed on a single page in a magazine. In the section that follows you will find three short short stories of different types.

A short short story looks remarkably easy, but do not be misled; because of its very brevity it is difficult. The basic features of all short stories are essential in the short short ones, but, in addition, the very concise nature makes it imperative that character, incident, and plot contain no extraneous material. More than ever, the story must be restricted to a single incident, to a few characters who must be made real in a few words, and to a plot that, despite its brevity, has a beginning, a middle, and an end.

The stories that follow were written by a brilliant young college student whose work has appeared in many literary magazines, by a high-school student, and by a professional writer.

JESSICA JANE STUART

1942–

Bright Moment

MISS STUART *is the daughter of Jesse Stuart and grew up in Greenup County, Kentucky, where her father makes his home. She has traveled extensively, has attended schools in foreign lands, graduated from Western Reserve University in 1964, and is now married and living in Cleveland, Ohio.*

Miss Stuart has had her poetry and short stories published in many literary magazines.

When I was a child, I lay snugly in my feather bed, beneath a patchwork quilt, waiting for the sugar snow to melt into warm white syrup in the moonglow, listening to the crackle of crisp cinnamon gold stars against December ice-winds, wondering . . . will it come back again this Christmas?

Often I would cry, my face buried beneath the pillow, so my mother would not hear. I would cry softly, but in a few minutes I would hear the creak of the staircase and she would be standing there, a pale shadow-spectre wavering in the mid-moon shadows.

"Do you weep again?" she would whisper, coming toward me, her hands stretched forth to comb through the tangles in my hair.

"Yes, Momma."

"Why, my child?"

Down, down deeper beneath the cover I would burrow until I could hear only the ticking of the grandfather's clock in the corner and the sharp intake of my mother's breath.

"Why?"

"For no reason, Momma."

Then she would sit down on the edge of my trundle bed, and lift up the covers, to stroke me.

"Perhaps," she would say, "perhaps you are waiting for it to come back . . ."

"Perhaps, Momma."

"Ah, I thought so . . ."

"Do you think it will?"

Slowly, slowly came her breath now, and she replied with a voice as sweet as the sound of the wind in the moon-flowers we often gather on the other side of the mountain,"I do not know, my daughter. I do not know."

"We shall wait for it, Momma."

"Yes, we shall wait."

"And hope for it?"

"Yes, we shall hope."

The days passed quickly before Christmas. There was more snow on the mountain, burying the footpaths under hard white drifts, glossing the green tips of fir trees with white diamond polish, cracking the wind with wedges of cold, cold, ever-falling flakes . . .

The cabin was not warm, so we sat by the fire, staring into the glow of the ruby flames, our eyes glazed, our thoughts far-away as our hands went through the motions of work—cutting, stitching, piecing. Sometimes a gust of wind brought soot down the chimney, and we must dust off our work before we could continue.

When there were only three days left, I went with Momma on horseback to town for the small bits of wrapping paper, ribbons, and Christmas trinkets we could afford. Sometimes, if we had saved enough pennies, there were oranges and even tiny bags of hard candy. Momma walked beside me through the narrow streets, and we told each other the things we would have some year. She chose white china with a narrow silver band, and I, letting my fancy run wilder than a snow-dredged river, chose bolts and bolts of red velvet for a coat, and a piece of rabbit fur for a muffler.

Before we left, we stopped at the church to ask what we could bring to the Supper. The parson always said, "Strawberry jelly." I asked myself, does he like the jelly or does he know we can bring no more, because there is no money? Momma says he likes the jelly, but I wonder . . .

At last it was Christmas Eve, and our neighbors, the farmer and his wife, stopped for us. I could hear the horses stomping impatiently in the snow as I was bundled into heavy blankets and placed carefully in the wagon. The hay was heavy, giving me warmth, and I wondered, if I opened my tightly squeezed-together eyes, would that hay be golden?

"Momma," I would whisper.

"Not yet, my child . . . wait until you have prayed."

It was an hour before I heard the ringing of the church bells. The clapper must be old and rusty now, but still, the sounds of the bells were silver, silver sifting through snowflakes, silver shimmering through the dull grey metal of the souls of these simple country people.

Soon I was seated on a wooden bench, between Momma and the farmer's wife. My head was bowed, my hands pressed tightly together beneath my coat, my mind struggling to shut out the thoughts of warm green pine boughs and candles dripping bayberry-scented wax.

"Dear Christ Child," I prayed, "send back the miracle."

I heard the low whisperings of my mother, the cold lip muttering of the farmer's wife. I heard the deep rich tones of the pastor, and the high sweet caroling of the choir. I felt the moment was coming closer, closer, and my own prayer became louder, more intent. "Dear Christ Child," I prayed, "send back the miracle."

I groped for my mother's arm, and I felt her fingers tighten about my arm. Slowly, slowly, for this is the moment, said the sweet voices of the choir and the silver song of the bells. I opened my eyes, my sightless eyes, and there before me I could see the snow swept hills, the stars so near to earth that they could tumble into my lap if I held up my skirts. I saw the shepherds, the manger, and the baby Jesus smiling at me . . . I saw the tears in the eyes of my mother, and the smile on her face said, "It is the Gift of the Christ Child; be thankful for the moment."

Then I would grow tired and close my eyes. The darkness was there, but it was a darkness of comfort, not despair —for the brightness of the Christmas miracle would remain, giving me sight throughout the year. I would not see the Valley, or the blackberry blossoms, or the white hay blowing in the summer wind, but I would see truth and beauty and love, gentleness in the hands of others, happiness in their laughter, faith in their words. "For we walk by faith, not by sight."

EMILY LEWIS (MRS. HIRAM NORCROSS)

1908–

Little Boy Blue

EMILY LEWIS NORCROSS *attended the John Burroughs School in her native St. Louis, Missouri. It was while a student in that school that she wrote* "Little Boy Blue." *Later she attended the Ethel Walker School and Bryn Mawr College. She served for a time on the staff of the St. Louis* Post-Dispatch *and does book reviewing and free-lance writing. She has traveled widely and is an amateur ornithologist.*

The tide was going out. In fact, it had all gone, leaving stretches of smooth sand on the shore and thousands of barnacles clinging to the fully exposed piles of the pier and to the slippery, slimy rocks. It was noontime, and the summer sun shone down upon the sea and the sand and heated the paved walks of the very fashionable summer resort.

Many of the resorters were from New York; there were a few from Washington, and a whole colony from Boston. There was one family from Chicago—the Remingtons. This was the Remingtons' first summer on the Island. They were very young—Mr. and Mrs.—and Mrs. Remington was exquisitely beautiful and attractive. The resorters were very fond of them. They stayed at the best hotel; they had a very sporty car and a large sailboat; they were enthusiastic and game for anything. Now they were off with a crowd of friends, sailing in their yacht. They had taken their lunch with them and would not be back till late that night, for they were going to the mainland in the evening to an inn to dine and dance.

Meanwhile they had left *him* in his cozy bed at the hotel. He was sound asleep when they had left. He had been put to bed for his nap before they had even awakened—the night before there had been a dance at the club and so, most likely, they had not seen him that morning. Oh, well! Jane was carefully supervising his pastimes and would see that he ate and slept properly, that his little suits were fresh, and that he looked clean and bright and adorable. Jane was an excellent nurse.

They called him Boy Blue; he was just five. They dressed him in little blue suits, sky blue in color, china blue—well, boy blue. He looked sweetest thus, for his cheeks were so red—so provokingly red—that the blue contrasted adorably, as well as matching his huge, pensive, deep eyes. Sometimes he wore pink or even pale green or white; but he had no yellow suits, for Mrs. Remington didn't care for yellow, and besides, yellow was not becoming to him. Yes, blue was really his color. His portrait was painted in a blue suit. It was a lovely portrait! Boy Blue looked entrancingly sweet in it.

Soon Boy Blue woke up. He had been dreaming of a field—"A great big field," he told Jane, "with flowers everywhere." It was a very pretty field, which smelled of all the fragrant flowers. But he walked and walked and walked, and he could not leave the meadow nor find anyone at all. He was lost! Then all the sweet things faded away as they are apt to do in dreams; a cloud floated down and he clambered upon it.

"Clouds are awfully comfy, Jane!"

"I imagine." She buttoned his small white shoe.

"I sank and sank!" He was very thoughtful.

"Does it hurt?" she questioned, combing his hair.

"To sink in a cloud?"

"No! No! Wake up, child!"

"Ouch!"

She pulled the hair a little more, accidentally, and then kissed his forehead and lifted him to a chair.

"I liked the cloud. I wish I knew what had happened when I started to sink. It felt awfully nice, Jane."

"Yes, dear. Do eat this spinach. It's very good for little boys."

He ate the spinach.

"Jane, may I have a cookie?"

"Not today. Perhaps tomorrow. You mustn't have cookies very often. They are not good for you."

"A piece of candy?"

"No! No! I gave you one this morning. That's plenty."

"Why, my mother gave me a cookie and two great big pieces of candy yesterday."

"She doesn't know that they are not good for you!"

A pause.

"Where is my mother?"

"I don't know, child. Out sailing, I suppose."

"Yesterday she took me riding, Jane, when you were

busy. It was such fun. Do you think she will take me again?"

"Perhaps. Drink your milk."

"Jane, do you know Agnes has a kind mother?"

"Agnes has no nurse."

"Why not?"

"Don't be silly. I don't know."

Agnes lived across the hall—Agnes and her mother together.

"She has no daddy, Jane."

"No."

"Her mother is very queer."

"Why?"

"She always plays with her and walks with her as you do with me."

"Agnes has no nurse."

"I'm glad I have a nurse—at least a nice nurse."

"Now, that's a sweet boy."

"But Agnes' mother is so nice. She plays with me, too. I like her."

"Are you through, dear?"

"She's a nurse-mother, isn't she?"

"Yes."

"Ha, ha! A nurse-mother. How funny!"

"Come on, Boy Blue. Hold up your head and let me put your hat on."

"I don't like hats."

"Shame on you!"

"Agnes doesn't always wear a hat."

"Boy Blue, put your head up." She spoke almost sternly.

Boy Blue and Jane went down in the elevator and out onto the broad porch.

"Hello, there, Boy Blue!" someone exclaimed.

"Say 'How do you do?' " prompted Jane.

"How do you do?" He bowed politely.

"Isn't he too sweet!"—"The image of Grace Remington" —"Bowing like a true gallant"—"Too cute," etc.

Jane and her small charge walked along a paved walk by the shore.

"Jane, may we play on the beach?"

"Soon, dear."

"May we walk on the beach?"

"Well, yes."

They walked along the beach.

"Jane, I'm so tired."

"Why, you little baby! Tired?"

"Just a little, Jane."

They walked on. "Jane, look at that great big man. He's bigger than my daddy."

"Where?"

"Up there." He pointed.

"Oh, yes. Why, if it isn't Jim! Hello, Jim!"

The big man turned around and came running back to Jane.

"If I wasn't looking for you, myself!"

"How are you?" Jane smiled.

"Just fine. Hello, kid."

"How do you do?" Boy Blue bowed politely.

There was much laughter and smiling and nodding. Then chattering proceeded.

Finally Jim departed. "You walk on slowly, and I'll be back in no time. Shall I get some for the kid, too?"

"No, he can't have candy. Just for us two." He went; and Jane laughed joyfully.

"Come on, Boy Blue, we'll walk on a little further."

"Jane, what is this water?"

"That's the ocean."

"Great, big, blue ocean. Look! the waves keep moving—moving—rocking. I wonder—what makes the waves do that?"

"What?" Jane is lost in happy thoughts.

"Do you know what makes the water always change?"

"Oh, God, I guess."

"God?"

"Yes," impatiently.

"What is God?"

"He's a Man, I suppose." She hummed a little tune.

"A man! Where does He live?"

"In the sky, Boy Blue. My heavens!"

"Can He really make the waters move?"

"Yes."

"Is that all He does?"

"My lands, no. He makes the clouds move. He makes everything move, even you."

"But, Jane, I make me move. See?" He took a step.

"Um-hum."

"Then, how can He?"

"Well, He lets you do it."

"Oh."

"He's *very, very* great! He can do anything He wishes. He can see everything you do. So be good!"

"Yes, Jane. Is He good?"

"Of course. Do you see the man coming again?"

"No. But look Jane—"

"What!"

"Well—then God is a Man. Do you know Him, Jane?"

"What are you talking about? God is the Person to Whom you say your prayers."

"Is He?"

A pause.

"Jane, how far does the sky go?"

"Ye gods, ask the Lord!"

"Lord, how far does the sky go?"

"Boy Blue, don't be silly."

"You said to ask the Lord."

"Have you no sense?"

After a while—"The sky must be awfully big. I wonder how far it goes. Would my mother know?"

"I doubt it."

"Doesn't my mother know everything?"

"Of course not."

"Agnes' mother does."

"Oh, well."

"Jane, I don't like my mother."

"Of course you do. Everyone likes his mother."

"Really?"

"Yes. And she likes you."

"I like mother, then, but I wish she knew how far the sky goes."

"Boy Blue, I've never known a child so young to think so much and ask so many questions. What matter is it how far the sky goes?"

"Then I'll ask Agnes' mother. She'll know, and she won't think I'm silly. Once I asked mother where the ships go and she said, 'Don't be silly.' "

"No wonder."

"Then I asked Agnes' mother. She told me."

"Do you see the man coming?"

"No, Jane."

"I wish he'd hurry."

"Do you like him?"

"Boy Blue!"

"Jane, do you like me?"

"Oh—of course."

"Really truly, Jane?"

"I'd almost have to—living with you day and night."

"Then, please don't say I'm silly when I ask you something."

"But you *are* silly."

"Please Jane, please like me. I want someone to like me."

"I do like you. And besides, you mother does, too."

"No, Jane, I don't think so."

"Why?"

" 'Cause she always says I'm silly and won't answer my questions."

"But she can still like you."

"No! Agnes' mother likes her. She always answers her."

"But your mother can like you just the same."

"I don't think so, Jane."

"Don't be silly. Why are you crying?"

"I want you to like me."

"I said I did."

"You said, 'Don't be silly.' "

"You little goose!"

There was a long pause. Boy Blue ceased to ask questions. He ceased to smile. He ceased to play. He craved something. He craved it so much! Listlessly he played with sand. Jane was too occupied to notice. She was always too occupied to notice things unusual. She rose, fixed her hair a bit, and went to meet Jim, who was approaching.

"We'll send the kid to play in the cave so we can eat our candy in peace. What do you say?" suggested Jim.

"Yes, anything to get rid of the nuisance," and Jane led Boy Blue around the cliff which reached out into the water in high tide, but now left a passageway; and she told him to stay and not to leave, and to play with pebbles.

She came back and the two talked together, walking to and fro. The wind, however, increased, and the waves beat upon the shore, thundering. They talked on.

"I've got to be going, Jane."

"Yes, and here it is almost the troublesome kid's supper-time."

Jim left and Jane turned about. The tide was coming in. In fact, it was almost at its height now. The hungry waves were leaping up on the sand; and over further, where the cliffs reached into the ocean, were beating furiously against them.

"Where is little Boy Blue?"

Doesn't the Mother Goose rhyme run like that?

Jane couldn't see him. (Had she really heard faint cries when she and Jim were walking?)

Jane couldn't reach the cave.

Jane couldn't find him.

Ask the waves where little Boy Blue is! Useless.

Ask his mother! She will sob and will not say.

Ask God! Didn't Jane say He knew everything?

MICHAEL McLAVERTY

1907–

The Wild Duck's Nest

A NATIVE OF IRELAND, *Michael McLaverty attended St. Malachy's College, Belfast. He is the author of several successful novels and is also at home with the short story of Irish life.* The Game Cock, *his collection of short stories, received high praise when it was published in this country.*

Michael McLaverty is now a schoolmaster in Ulster County in his native Ireland.

The sun was setting, spilling gold light on the low western hills of Rathlin Island. A small boy walked jauntily along a hoof-printed path that wriggled between the folds of these hills and opened out into a crater-like valley on the cliff-top. Presently he stopped as if remembering something, then suddenly he left the path, and began running up one of the hills. When he reached the top he was out of breath and stood watching streaks of light radiating from golden-edged clouds, the scene reminding him of a picture he had seen of the Transfiguration. A short distance below him was the cow standing at the edge of a reedy lake. Colm ran down to meet her waving his stick in the air, and the wind rumbling in his ears made him give an exultant whoop which splashed upon the hills in a shower of echoed sound. A flock of gulls lying on the short grass near the lake rose up languidly, drifting like blown snowflakes over the rim of the cliff.

The lake faced west and was fed by a stream, the drainings of the semi-circling hills. One side was open to the winds from the sea and in winter a little outlet trickled over the cliffs making a black vein in their gray sides. The boy lifted stones and began throwing them into the lake, weaving web after web on its calm surface. Then he skimmed the water with flat stones, some of them jumping the surface and coming to rest on the other side. He was delighted with himself and after listening to his echoing shouts of delight he ran to fetch his cow. Gently he tapped her on the side and reluctantly she went towards the brown-mudded path that led out of the valley. The boy was about to throw a final stone into the lake when a bird flew low over his head, its neck a-strain, and its orange-colored legs clear in the soft light. It was a wild duck. It circled the lake twice, thrice, coming lower each time and then with a nervous flapping of wings it skidded along the surface, its legs breaking the water into a series of silvery arcs. Its wings closed, it lit silently, gave a slight shiver, and began pecking indifferently at the water.

Colm, with dilated eyes, eagerly watched it making for the farther end of the lake. It meandered between tall bulrushes, its body black and solid as stone against the graying water. Then as if it had sunk it was gone. The boy ran stealthily along the bank looking away from the lake, pretending indifference. When he came opposite to where he had last seen the bird he stopped and peered through the sighing reeds whose shadows streaked the water in a maze of black strokes. In front of him was a soddy islet guarded by the spears of sedge and separated from the bank by a narrow channel of water. The water wasn't too deep—he could wade across with care.

Rolling up his short trousers he began to wade, his arms outstretched, and his legs brown and stunted in the mountain water. As he drew near the islet, his feet sank in the cold mud and bubbles winked up at him. He went more carefully and nervously. Then one trouser leg fell and dipped into the water; the boy dropped his hands to roll it up, he unbalanced, made a splashing sound, and the bird arose with a squawk and whirred away over the cliffs. For a moment the boy stood frightened. Then he clambered on to the wet-soaked sod of land, which was spattered with sea gulls' feathers and bits of wind-blown rushes.

Into each hummock he looked, pulling back the long grass. At last he came on the nest, facing seawards. Two flat rocks dimpled the face of the water and between them was a neck of land matted with coarse grass containing the nest. It was untidily built of dried rushes, straw and feathers, and in it lay one solitary egg. Colm was delighted. He looked around and saw no one. The nest was his. He lifted the egg, smooth and green as the sky, with a faint tinge of yellow like the reflected light from a buttercup; and then he felt he had done wrong. He put it back. He knew he shouldn't have touched it and he wondered would the bird forsake the nest. A vague sadness stole over him and he felt in his heart he had sinned. Carefully smoothing out his footprints he hurriedly left the islet and ran after his cow. The sun had now set and the cold shiver of evening enveloped him, chilling his body and saddening his mind.

In the morning he was up and away to school. He took the grass rut that edged the road for it was softer on the bare feet. His house was the last on the western headland and after a mile or so he was joined by Paddy McFall; both boys, dressed in similar hand-knitted blue jerseys and gray trousers, carried home-made school bags. Colm was full of the nest and as soon as he joined his companion he said eagerly: "Paddy, I've a nest—a wild duck's with one egg."

"And how do you know it's a wild duck's?" asked Paddy slightly jealous.

"Sure I saw her with my own two eyes, her brown speckled back with a crow's patch on it, and her yellow legs—"

"Where is it?" interrupted Paddy in a challenging tone.

"I'm not going to tell you, for you'd rob it!"

"Aach! I suppose it's a tame duck's you have or maybe an old gull's."

Colm put out his tongue at him. "A lot you know!" he said, "for a gull's egg has spots and this one is greenish-white, for I had it in my hand."

And then the words he didn't want to hear rushed from Paddy in a mocking chant, "You had it in your hand! . . . She'll forsake it! She'll forsake it! She'll forsake it!" he said, skipping along the road before him.

Colm felt as if he would choke or cry with vexation.

His mind told him that Paddy was right, but somehow he

couldn't give in to it and he replied: "She'll not forsake it! She'll not! I know she'll not!"

But in school his faith wavered. Through the windows he could see moving sheets of rain—rain that dribbled down the panes filling his mind with thoughts of the lake creased and chilled by wind; the nest sodden and black with wetness; and the egg cold as a cave stone. He shivered from the thoughts and fidgeted with the inkwell cover, sliding it backwards and forwards mechanically. The mischievous look had gone from his eyes and the school day dragged on interminably. But at last they were out in the rain, Colm rushing home as fast as he could.

He was no time at all at his dinner of potatoes and salted fish until he was out in the valley now smoky with drifts of slanting rain. Opposite the islet he entered the water. The wind was blowing into his face, rustling noisily the rushes heavy with the dust of rain. A moss-cheeper, swaying on a reed like a mouse, filled the air with light cries of loneliness.

The boy reached the islet, his heart thumping with excitement, wondering did the bird forsake. He went slowly, quietly, on to the strip of land that led to the nest. He rose on his toes, looking over the ledge to see if he could see her. And then every muscle tautened. She was on, her shoulders hunched up, and her bill lying on her breast as if she were asleep. Colm's heart hammered wildly in his ears. She hadn't forsaken. He was about to turn stealthily away. Something happened. The bird moved, her neck straightened, twitching nervously from side to side. The boy's head swam with lightness. He stood transfixed. The wild duck with a panicky flapping, rose heavily, and flew off towards the sea. . . . A guilty silence enveloped the boy. . . . He turned to go away, hesitated, and glanced back at the bare nest; it'd be no harm to have a look. Timidly he approached it, standing straight, and gazing over the edge. There in the nest lay two eggs. He drew in his breath with delight, splashed quickly from the island, and ran off whistling in the rain.

GLOSSARY

Glossary

Action The incidents in a story occurring between the original incident and the conclusion contributing to the development of the plot. It may be achieved by the physical acts of the characters, or it may be achieved through conversation. It may be dramatic and explosive, or it may be quiet and unobtrusive.

Allegory A prolonged metaphor which has meaning in itself but which also has a much broader or more important meaning than the story itself. The allegory can seemingly be a story of a struggle between two people, and yet it may imply the struggle of mankind between two forces such as good and evil.

Anticlimax An event of little significance which follows or conflicts with a major development in the story. It may also be a commonplace comment following news of great significance.

Atmosphere The general mood of a piece of literature. It may be gay or sad, light or heavy; it may be influenced by setting, by characters, or by the author's style.

Characters The participants in the story. Characters may be human or animal. At times natural forces such as cold or wind may be characters; in many stories gods become characters.

Climax The turning point of the story, but not to be confused with the point of greatest interest. The climax or turning point occurs when fortunes take a definite turn for the better or worse for the character or characters in whom we are primarily interested. Climax and point of greatest dramatic interest may or may not occur simultaneously.

Complication Events in the plot presenting a problem to the central character and placing obstacles in his solution of it.

Conflict The opposing forces in the story. There can be no story without conflict and there can be no interest if the central character has no problem confronting him.

Denouement A French word meaning "the untying." In fiction the term is used to describe the part of a story that follows the climax or turning point and that tells what happens to the characters at the end of the story. In the short story the denouement may seem to occur at the same moment as the turning point.

Dialect Language peculiar to the people of a particular race, region, or degree of education. It is often used to provide local color or to describe a character.

Dialogue Conversation between two or more characters. It may be used to help establish setting or character, or it may be used to advance plot.

Exposition That part of the story which establishes setting, identifies characters, and introduces the first complicating factor.

Fable A short story frequently employing animals as characters and stressing peculiarities of human nature.

Foreshadowing An indication of something to occur later in the story.

Imagery A figure of speech in which the language used evokes an image conceived by one or more of the five senses.

Irony A type of humor, ridicule, or light sarcasm implying the opposite of the literal sense of the words. A state of affairs or a result opposite to, and as if in mockery of, the appropriate result.

Melodrama A story (usually a play) in which an extreme appeal is made to the sympathies of the reader. Melodrama frequently borders on the maudlin and may result in an excess of emotional response not consistent with reality.

Metaphor An implied comparison between two unlike things. "Her eyes were saucers" is an example of a metaphor. "Her eyes were *like* saucers" is an example of a simile, in which the comparison is *stated*, not implied as in the case of the metaphor.

Pace A term used to suggest the progress of events in the story, slow or fast. The pace of a modern short story is apt to be fast as compared with one by Poe or Hawthorne.

Parable A story told to teach a moral lesson. "The Minister's Black Veil" by Hawthorne is an example.

Pathos A legitimate appeal to the emotions as contrasted with *bathos* which is false or strained.

Personification A figure of speech in which the qualities of a human being are given to inanimate things.

Plot The range of the story from opening situation, through development of conflict, climax or turning point, to denouement, and (perhaps) a separate conclusion.

Point of View The attitude and place of the teller of the story. The author must remain remote from the characters, but the story will reveal his point of view, whether sympathetic or unsympathetic, serious or comic, contemporary or historic.

Propaganda Details or information in a story deliberately introduced by the author to induce thought or action desired by the author.

Protagonist The character of the story who is the center of interest; he is usually the character who keeps the story moving.

Pun A play on words having a similar sound but different meaning, or different applications of a word for comic effect.

Realism A literary style closely following the expected pattern of life as opposed to *romanticism,* which is more imaginative and which allows the author greater freedom in character and plot development.

Rhythm Commonly associated with poetry, rhythm also has its use in prose. Certain prose writers use rhythm in their writing to create specific effects. The pace of reading may be speeded or slowed by the author's use of a rhythmic pattern.

Sentimentality Akin to melodrama, sentiment may be used to excite proper responses, usually sympathy. If overdone, it is called sentimentality.

Setting The place where and the time when the story occurs.

Simile *See* Metaphor.

Surprise Ending A device used by some storytellers to produce an effect. Properly used, the surprise ending adds an additional pleasure to the reading of some stories; improperly used, it leaves the reader feeling cheated. The surprise ending must be logically related to incidents or events mentioned earlier in the story.

Symbol Frequently discussed with imagery, the symbol is the use of a concept or device to stimulate certain emotional responses. Commonly used symbols are the flag for patriotism and the cross for the Christian religion.

Theme Idea which the author wishes to convey to the reader. While not necessarily the same as *moral,* theme may sometimes be understood best in connection with it.

Understatement The making of a point by deliberately playing it down such as saying, "I went to some little effort" for, "I went to a great amount of trouble."

Unity The achievement of the single effect as called for in Poe's definition of the short story. (See Introductory Notes.)

Vignette A brief impression of a person, thing, or event in a form lacking the plot structure of a short story but giving a clear and often a sympathetic picture.